GLIDING

INTO

WAR

The Story of a Territorial Soldier

1930 to 1945

by

Ian and Celia Toler

HORSESHOE PUBLICATIONS . WARRINGTON . CHESHIRE

ISBN 1 899310.20.7

British Library Cataloguing in Publication Data
A catalogue record for this book is available from The British Library

First reprint 1999 by
HORSESHOE PUBLICATIONS
Box 37, Kingsley, Warrington,
Cheshire WA6 8DR

Book cover designed and illustrated
by Stephen Williams

Printed and bound in Great Britain by
Print Express Services Ltd
Frodsham, Cheshire WA6 7HL

Acknowledgements

The authors would like to thank all those who have allowed their personal reminiscences to be drawn on, especially: Arnold Baldwin, John Foxcroft, Jim Hooper, Angus Low, 'Dusty' Millar, Inga Miller, Rosemary Morton, Bert Parsons, Arthur Shackleton, Gordon 'Cheese' Stilton, Joan Toler, Robin Walchli, Peter Wood, and many others who have taken part in informal reminiscences over the years. We would also like to thank: Terry Miller for his introduction and his help in checking the manuscript; Stephen Williams for designing the cover; Richard Barnes for his first reading of the MS and advice; and our family and friends who have helped in this project. Also: Rh. G. Williams, Principal Librarian, Llandudno; Brigadier R. J. T. Kirby CBE, HQ Quartermaster General; Mark Curtoys, Archivist Christ Church, Oxford; Dr Brian Holden Reid FRGS, Staff College Camberley; Don Elliot and Sharon Brown, Curator, Catalyst Museum, Widnes; Adrian Groeneweg, Airborne Museum 'Hartenstein', The Netherlands; and Curtis Brown Ltd. for Churchill's quotation.

Although much, but not all, of this book took place in reality, most names in the text have been changed for the sake of anonymity although well-known names remain for historical authenticity. It is stressed that the content of this book is the result of the imagination and personal opinion of the authors, that it is fiction and no offence is intended to persons living or dead who may also have experienced these events at the time.

This story is dedicated to all those who served in "B" Squadron, No 1 Wing of the Glider Pilot Regiment.

"Still, if you will not fight for the right when you can easily win without bloodshed; if you will not fight when your victory will be sure and not too costly; you may come to the moment when you will have to fight with all the odds against you and only a precarious chance of survival. There may even be a worse case. You may have to fight when there is no hope of victory, because it is better to perish than to live as slaves."

W. Churchill - "The Gathering Storm"

FOREWORD

For a young man of the 'middle class' growing up in the twenties and thirties of this century, the First World War - The Great War, as it was known in those days - was still a powerful folk-memory. The idea that it had truly been "the war to end wars" was still fresh in people's mind. Yet the slide - or glide - into a new war had already begun, in China, in Ethiopia, in Spain. 'Tom Clayton's' father was being unfashionably far-sighted when, in 1930, he urged his son to join the Territorial Army.

The account of these years presented by the Tolers, *père et fille*, - the daily round of Oxford and after, the early jollities and anxieties and first experiences, the technicalities, as well as the alarms and excursions, of industrial life (particularly a succession of notable smells) - are brought alive to the eye (and the nose) of the reader. The flavour is, as one would expect, that of the natural scientist and engineer - characteristically straight-forward, plain, clear, precise.

For the TA too, preparation - of a sort - for the "British way of war" carried on happily through the 30s, pretty much as a continuation of drills established in the last war, or even the last but one. Thus the 'phoney peace' passed, with some surprise but little excitement, into the phoney war, to Tom Clayton's rather uncomfortable introduction to life at the 'sharp end', and the beaches of Dunkirk.

From this turning-point the <u>Glide</u> of the title narrows from the general flavour of an epoch to the particularities of troop-carrying aeroplanes without engines - the glide-historical replaced by the glide-literal. The period of training for the new airborne divisions was one of remarkable intensity. The Commander-in-Chief of Bomber Command is said to have pronounced it impossible to train soldiers to crash-land what was, in effect, a medium-sized passenger aircraft whose engine had failed. This prediction turned out, fortunately for the passengers, to be wrong. The Horsas were put down for the most part perfectly safely, and not just singly, or in twos and threes, or dozens, but in scores, on landing-zones often smaller than the average civilian airfield of the time.

The texture of the narrative also narrows, and the <u>dramatis personae</u>, nearer to us in time, are more easily recognizable, albeit not as individuals, but as compounds of several. The great operations of war, of course, are all themselves - the familiar code-names *Overlord, Market-Garden, Varsity* - and B Squadron, Glider Pilot Regiment takes over from 56 Anti-tank Regiment and 1 Airlanding Anti-tank Battery, Royal Artillery, as the central focus.

Ernest Hemingway, momentarily in transit through RAF Brize Norton in the summer of 1944, used to say to the aspirant novelist - "Tell it like it was". To have been in the thick of the action is an advantage in telling the tale, and Ian Toler, who was very much there, tells it like it was, at Arnhem, and the crossing of the Rhine.

But there comes a point where the reader must look between the lines for some aspects of experience that a plain account cannot convey. The glider pilots of B Squadron, to whom the novel is dedicated, had not grown up under the watchful eye of a long regimental tradition. Yet they had become a family, and the head of the family was the squadron commander. When Ian Toler was demobbed they gave him a silver tankard inscribed "From a happy and grateful squadron to a great leader and a good scout", and they meant it, every word.

A distinguished military historian has described generalship as "possibly the most complete human activity, since [it] involves all the intellectual, physical, and moral power in a man". But these same qualities of command are required as much at the operational level of the fighting units - the batteries, companies, squadrons. B Squadron was lucky in its commander.

There used to be a rule of symmetry in literature, that a story should have a beginning, a middle, and an end. Gliding into War has an additional symmetry, echoing a famous royal motto of the sixteenth century - "In my end is my beginning". Tom Clayton's father, and the river near his old home, which began the story, also end it, and mark the start of a new life.

T. G. (Terry) Miller
ex-3 Flight, B Squadron, Glider Pilot Regiment
Sedgeford
September 1997

CHAPTER 1

It was 1930. I was in the workshop at the back of the country house where we were living and which I had monopolised for my various interests. It was cluttered with bits of wireless sets, bottles of chemicals, broken furniture and bits and pieces which the family had asked me to mend. I was particularly interested in making model steam engines. On the bench in front of me was a half-inch scale stationary steam engine with a separate vertical boiler. I had finished building it and was ready to try it out.

I lit the fire in the tiny firebox of the boiler with some sticks and small lumps of coal and it was getting up steam nicely with smoke coming out of the chimney. I opened the control valve gently and the engine started to move, rotating the steel flywheel which I had turned on my lathe and was very proud of. I opened the valve a little further which made the engine speed up but as it was not fastened down it started to jump about. Just then my father came into the workshop. I hadn't enough hands to hold the engine down and operate the control valve at the same time and so I called out, "Father please hold the engine down."

He held it but it was really wanting to go, the flywheel spinning and the steam hissing and soon he shouted: "Thomas turn it off, I think it's going to explode." Well of course it wasn't going to explode but I closed the valve and the engine became quiet. My father sank thankfully into a rocking chair which was waiting to be repaired as the woodworm had got into it.

"Thomas my boy," he said, his tone serious so that although I was still thinking about the engine, I looked up. "You are now 18," he continued, "and are about to go up to Oxford. I am certain that before very long there will be another war with Germany. I don't want you to be like all those young men in the last war who had to go to the trenches with very little training. I would like you to join the Territorial Army now and learn something about soldiering before it starts."

Suddenly the steam escaping through the safety valve whistled shrilly and then subsided. My father smiled. I tried to concentrate. I had not thought about another war. My memories of the last one were only of the two minutes silence in which I fidgeted, unable, as a small boy, to keep still. I had not thought about joining the army. In fact I had not thought about much at all apart from my hobbies, the summer and that life would go on for ever, just as it was. I asked him if I could think about it and he nodded, got off the chair and left it rocking unevenly, the dust from the woodworm subsiding in drifting motes to the old tiles on the floor.

The summer of 1930 was hot and cloudless as some English summers can be. The River Dane flowed at the bottom of the meadow below our house in Cheshire. It was a narrow winding river. In some places the clear water rippled over stones, and in others, as it turned a corner, there were pools deep enough for swimming. These pools were surrounded by high banks covered with trees, known in Cheshire as a *clough*. Some of the banks were studded with holes, the homes of martins and swallows. Suddenly there was a bright flash of colour signifying a kingfisher skimming the surface in search of food, or a dragonfly would be darting about, the sunshine glinting on its iridescent wings. Little did the river know that many decades later it would be so polluted that my three sisters would not have been able to swim in it as they were doing that day.

Our young brother, David, aged 9, plunged into the water, splashing my sisters and making them shout with indignation. My third eldest sister, Janet, said: "If you splash us again Dave, we'll dunk you." And of course he did and so my sisters launched themselves upon him, splashing and dunking and shouting with laughter.

When I was fourteen I built myself a canvas canoe from some drawings I had found in a book. I painted it green and called it *Cuthbert*. One day, rather foolishly, I took it out on the river when it was in spate. All was well until racing down the stream I hit an overhanging branch. Cuthbert sailed on leaving me hanging half in and half out of the raging waters. Luckily help was at hand as my second eldest sister Nancy had been watching and she rescued me with the help of a rope while Cuthbert was later recovered from lower down the river.

On this sunny day the river was calm. I had launched Cuthbert and was paddling in it up and down the river.

David wanted to join me in Cuthbert but my mother said, "No", and, although she didn't say it we all knew it was because of that previous ignominious incident. David was much younger than us and full of mischief. Even now, unobserved by the women, he was scrambling up an oak tree which grew beside the river. My sisters, after their swim, laid themselves down and were sunbathing, exposing as much of their bodies to the sun as was possible. They had no fear of danger from the Ozone hole which had not even been thought of as yet.

Our mother, a striking lady with white hair, who was sitting on a tartan rug spread out on the bank, turned to the girls and remarked dryly.

"I think the moths must have got into your costumes. There are more holes than fabric."

The girls laughed and my eldest sister Sybil asked, "Mama, did you swim when you were a little girl?"

Our mother who had been brought up in the latter part of the nineteenth century replied, "Yes. Sea bathing was considered a healthy pursuit but you must remember it was in the reign of Queen Victoria and it had to be done with a certain amount of decorum. Bathing machines were provided on the beaches of the popular resorts. They were really mobile changing rooms which could be drawn into the sea by a horse until the water was deep enough to cover you. It may surprise you but in those days men bathed in the nude." All my sisters laughed with disbelief and I, for some reason, blushed.

"What sort of costume did you wear Mama?" asked Nancy who was wearing a pretty blue but somewhat brief swimsuit.

"I wore a voluminous costume covering most of my body and also a skirt. It made swimming rather difficult," she replied smiling. "I wonder if Thomas remembers me taking him to Llandudno when he was quite little?"

"Yes." I replied from the pool, taking my eyes off Dave who had reached an attractive and solid looking branch that grew over the river. "I seem to remember going into one of those machines with you. The water was jolly cold."

"Your father took you to the hot brine baths in the hotel. I think you preferred that."

"Oh yes I enjoyed them," I said closing my eyes and replacing the warmth of the sun with the memory of the hot baths. Suddenly there was loud crack, a shout and a splash and David fell harmlessly, since he was a good swimmer, into the water.

My sisters and mother all got up and rushed to the edge of the river. "Well," said Sybil, "the moral of that is not to go climbing trees over rivers." But we all laughed because she sounded so serious and it was an impossible thing for a young boy not to do. I hauled Dave into Cuthbert so that he got his ride anyway as we paddled back to the bank.

Then, as the sun was going down, we packed up and went back to the house for afternoon tea with scones, bread and butter and cakes with a choice of China or Indian tea.

After tea I went back to my workshop which was next to our electrical generating plant. There was no public electricity supply to houses in the country such as ours, so we had to make our own from a single cylinder engine fuelled by paraffin.

In the house we had lived in previously the only lighting was by oil lamps until my father installed what was very advanced for those times, an acetylene plant. The acetylene gas was made by dripping water on to carbide, a substance like small rocks. It was loaded into wire baskets which were inserted into two metal tubes fixed to either side of the gasometer. The gas was distributed from there to the house.

When the carbide was used up it left a nasty smelling, sticky white substance like limewash. This had to be removed and was an unpleasant job which had to be done by one of us.

The gas is very explosive and looking back it is surprising that we did not have an accident. It was the same gas that was used to provide the light in the headlamps of the early motorcars. We had such a car - a Le Zebre - made in 1912 by a French firm. It was this car which first gave me my interest in mechanical engineering but that evening I couldn't concentrate on my steam engine. I felt restless and went back out to walk by the river.

Water was another thing that we had to supply for ourselves. We got this from a spring and pumped the water up to a tank in the roof of the house by a hydraulic ram. Sewage also had to be disposed of. This was done by means of a septic tank which purified the sewage so that it could be discharged to the river.

The only public service that we did have was the telephone which went through a manual exchange in the local village. The Postmistress who operated it could overhear all our conversations and knew where everyone was. This could at times be useful but at others embarrassing. If, for example, you wanted to speak to your girlfriend and were informed she was out with someone else. This happened to me once when I wanted to speak to a girl who lived in a house a little further down the river. I didn't think she was very interested in me and turning back from my walk rather abruptly, I returned to the house for supper.

In October of my 18th year, as my father had said, I was due to go up to Oxford where I had won a scholarship to study physics.

My father, John Clayton, was born in 1862 and at the start of the First World War was 52 and therefore too old for active service. He had been in the Eton College Volunteers and his Commission, signed by Queen Victoria, was as a Lieutenant in the Volunteer Forces (5th Cheshire Rifle Corps). It was dated 1882.

A few days later he came into the workshop again and sat on the same rocking chair which I had still not mended. He asked if I had thought any more about our last discussion. I replied that I certainly had but would like to learn more about the Territorials before coming to a decision. I asked him if he would tell me something about them.

"Yes I will," he replied and started on a long dissertation on the origins of the Territorial Army.

"As you know I was a Volunteer myself and have watched the Territorial Army since its inception. The history of the Militia, which was the progenitor of the Territorials, goes back to Anglo-Saxon times when it was known as the Fyrd, which was a levy of freemen. They fought with great distinction in many of the battles against the Danes. Much later the Volunteers were formed and took part with the rest of the English Army at the battle of Bannockburn. You remember the story of Robert The Bruce and the spider? However, in spite of their bravery, they were not taken seriously by the authorities and were regarded as the Cinderella of the forces. I'm afraid a lot of fun was poked at them."

"Did they have uniforms?" I asked.

"Yes, but when the Militia was formed the Militiamen had to provide their own uniforms and even ammunition. By the way, did you know that The Cheshire Yeomanry is one of the oldest of our volunteer forces? It was instituted in 1761 and many famous Cheshire names and families are associated with it."

I now wondered if I would have to fight overseas as in the last war, but my father, not to be put off from his chronological account, continued.

"Hmm," he mused, marshalling his thoughts and still sitting carefully on the rocking chair. "At the beginning of the nineteenth century everyone was frightened by the possibility of invasion by Napoleon. The Militia, although originally it was to be used solely for home defence, did have to go overseas and fought at Waterloo. However when the threat of invasion had passed, the volunteers had still not found favour with the War Office. Now, if you have done your history at school, you will remember that at the end of the last century there was a war in South Africa - The Boer War."

"At first the War Office declined to use the volunteer forces. But after some severe reverses in South Africa, Sir Alfred Newton, who was the Lord Mayor of London, raised and equipped 1000 men from the City of London. They were paid for entirely by City banks, Livery Companies and West End firms and were known as the 'City of London Imperial Volunteers'. They took part in the campaign and suffered many casualties."

He paused, looking serious for a moment and then went on.

"It was about 1904 when a Royal Commission, known as the Norfolk Commission, was appointed to look into the volunteer forces. Shortly after that Richard Haldane, who was the Secretary of State for War, introduced a Bill in Parliament which authorised a new Territorial Force to be formed out of both the Militia and The Volunteers. As a result the Territorial Army was created. It was organised into divisions, brigades and battalions just like the regulars and its equipment was provided by the War Office but administration was by Territorial Associations based on County boundaries. Originally it was intended to supply garrisons for fortresses round the coast, in order to repel raids. What was most important, was that it would now be used to supply units for the expansion of the regular army."

"Well I hope that gives you some idea as to how our Territorial Army came into being."

"Were they paid?" I asked, always being interested in the pecuniary aspect.

"No, not at the time. That came later when both officers and men drew their pay on training as well as an annual bounty."

"Another thing I should tell you is that as the original volunteer force had in many cases been raised by local gentry and landlords, this tradition tended to carry through and, even during the first World War, many of the officers including myself had been to school together. As a result we spent much of our off-duty time in our country pursuits of hunting, shooting and fishing. Incidentally, your Godfather was an Assistant Director of the T.A. in 1908. And by the way," he concluded, standing up with one of the arms of the rocking chair still in his hand, "I think it's time you fixed this chair."

I felt I had learned quite a lot of the history of the T.A. but later I asked my father about his own service in the last war.

He told me that he had been at Eton with the Commanding Officer of his unit who was more often than not away fishing. As a result, my father found himself frequently in charge of the battalion. He was stationed first in the Chesterfield district and then on the East coast where the German Zeppelins came over, their raids fortunately doing little damage. As his CO was so often away or sick, my father was put in charge of taking drafts of men to France where he accompanied them up to the front.

It may have been the wounded that he saw on these trips to France which persuaded him to make sure I was not untrained for a war in which he felt sure I would be involved. Yet his description made it seem to have been a rather gentlemanly war. He made no mention of the terrible casualties and suffering on the battlefields of Flanders. Perhaps he left it out on purpose so that I would not be put off or perhaps it was that he did not want to be reminded of it.

After we had finished our talk in the workshop, we returned to the house for a glass of sherry before supper. My father had decided at 18 that I should be allowed a limited amount of alcohol so that I would be acclimatised to it and not become addicted. He was terrified of anyone becoming an alcoholic as had happened to one of his brothers.

On a table in the sitting room there were photographs of my father. They showed him in uniform, looking very smart with belt and crossbelt. I asked him what these were called.

"That's a *Sam Browne* called after a soldier, Sir Samuel J. Browne who lived in the late nineteenth century. The cross belt is to support the sword which is carried in a *frog* at the side."

"Do you have a sword?" I asked. "And what did you use it for?"

"Oh yes. I have a sword but it was only used for ceremonial purposes. You'll have to learn how to salute with one," he replied.

CHAPTER 2

The next day, having thought it over carefully, I decided to take my father's advice and apply for a commission in the Territorial Army.

A few weeks later, after I had made the necessary application and filled in numerous forms, I went off to the Drill Hall in the local market town of Sandbach where I was duly sworn in. Some months later I received my Commission as a Second Lieutenant in the Cheshire Regiment. The *Commission* was an interesting and somewhat impressive document which I read carefully. It told me "...to exercise and well discipline in Arms both the inferior Officers and Men serving under you and use your best endeavours to keep them in good Order and Discipline." I was not sure what my *best endeavours* were supposed to be. It sounded as if the men might be a bit recalcitrant. Further - "And we do hereby Command them to Obey you as their superior Officer and you to observe and follow such Orders and Directions as from time to time you shall receive from Us (The Crown) and your superior Officer, according to the Rules and Discipline of war,...". At the end it stated that the document was - "Given at the Court of St James on the thirtieth day of September 1930 in the twenty first year of our reign" and signed by the Adjutant General. This was by order of - "George the Fifth by the Grace of God of Great Britain, Ireland and the British Dominions beyond the Seas, King, Defender of the Faith, Emperor of India etc." It was certainly a most prestigious document, but I did wonder about the *etc.*

So with these rather weighty instructions in my head, the first thing was to obtain a uniform, for which a benevolent country was prepared to make me a grant. This was just as well as the salary of my father as a country land agent was not very great and only sufficient to give me a small allowance. A visit to a military tailor in Manchester was arranged.

The uniform of a Second Lieutenant (subaltern) consisted of a jacket of khaki barathea and a khaki shirt and tie. The other ranks - O.R.s - wore a khaki jacket with a collar which buttoned round the neck but they did not wear a tie. The Officer's nether regions were clad in what were called Plus Twos. Battle dress had not yet been designed for either Officers or men. Next came brown boots and khaki puttees, the latter having to be wound very carefully round the leg so that a neat overlap was shown. The O.R.s also had puttees but their boots were black. On the head was worn a flat peaked cap carrying the badge of the Cheshire Regiment, an acorn surrounded by two oak leaves.

I was interested to find out the origin of this badge and later enquired about it from one of the officers. I had thought it had something to do with King Charles and a Cheshire Oak but found that this was not so. In 1743 the English and the Hanoverians defeated the French at the battle of Dettingen in Bavaria. George II, who took part in the battle, hid in an oak tree to avoid being captured. A detachment of the 22nd Regiment of Foot (later to become the Cheshire Regiment) surrounded the tree and prevented his capture by the French.

For this the Regiment was given the acorn as its emblem and the right to display an oak leaf on their headdress whenever inspected by Royalty.

After the khaki uniform, I also had to purchase blue patrols - a dress uniform in dark blue with a high collar round the neck which had a detachable white starched collar inside. I found this pretty uncomfortable but then, as my father said rather sharply when I complained, I had not been used to Eton collars having been educated at the local grammar school. Although my father had gone to Eton, I resisted all efforts to send me there, even to running away from a preparatory school, with the result that I became a weekly boarder at the Macclesfield Grammar School. There were times when I regretted I had not got the cachet of Eton, especially at Oxford where I was mixing with men from the public schools. This at first gave me a feeling of inferiority which I gradually overcame.

The trousers of the blue patrols were narrow and tight fitting with a smart scarlet stripe running down the side and a strap which buttoned under the instep of the boot to keep the trousers tight. My feet and lower legs were supposed to be encased in patent leather *Wellingtons*. I was rapidly running out of cash and as the tailor said he could provide ankle boots at a lower price this was agreed. However later I always felt slightly incorrect even though the difference in the boot could not be seen. Finally I purchased detachable dress spurs which fitted into a slot in the heel of the boot. My father had already agreed to lend me his Sam Browne and sword which, with his *swagger* cane, completed my equipment.

So the great day arrived when I donned my khaki uniform for the first time to attend my first drill night at the Drill Hall. I had decided that I would drive there in the family car and a sergeant in the T.A. who lived in the village had promised to go with me to *show me the ropes*, as he called it. I was very nervous. I knew the sergeant would be in uniform and would salute me and I would have to reply. This should not have been difficult for me as I had been in the O.T.C. (Officers Training Corps) at school. As arranged the sergeant arrived at the gate and gave me a very smart salute to which I replied equally smartly but to my horror realised afterwards that I had used my LEFT hand! The sergeant never batted an eyelid and we proceeded on our way.

At the Drill Hall I met some of the other Officers. I was in grave doubt as to whom I should salute or who should salute me. In fact saluting or being saluted became something of a worry to me, partly on account of my innate shyness. That night the training consisted of a small squad of men carrying out foot drill, which involved forming fours, and arms drill with the rifle. I always thought forming fours to be a fascinating piece of drill when, on the word of command, a body of men in two ranks suddenly changed to four. Unfortunately when it came to threes this didn't work.

It seemed that all I was expected to do on that first night was to stand about with my swagger cane under my arm, showing a passive interest in what was going on. I suppose I was being let down lightly as next time I would have to drill the men myself.

A typical drill night lasted one or two hours. The first part was taken up with foot and arms drill and then instruction on how to strip down the Lewis gun and how to clean and maintain your rifle. Although the floor was of timber the noise of the boots and rifles descending on it rang throughout the hall and the smell of dust, sweat and gun oil pervaded the atmosphere. Lectures for the officers on tactics, camouflage and etiquette were carried out in the adjacent lecture rooms. I had already met the Commanding Officer, a rather pompous little man whose lectures were mainly on how to behave as *An Officer and A Gentleman*.

The officers also had to learn how to salute with the sword. This could be quite tricky. You first had to withdraw the sword with your right hand from it's scabbard, which is on your left side. Then hold the sword vertically with the sword's hilt in front of your nose, and with your sword arm horizontal. For the salute you brought the sword down so that it was at an angle, the point no more than 6 to 8 inches from the ground. After the eyes left or right, if you were marching, you brought the sword up again in front of your face and then had to return it to its scabbard. Under no circumstances must you look down during any part of the operations, and finding the opening in the scabbard to insert the point of the sword, without cutting your fingers, was the most difficult. It was the same for the men when returning their bayonets after the command 'Unfix bayonets'.

After the drills were over most of the men visited the bar which was a prominent feature of most drill halls which were also frequently let out for dances and other functions. Attendance at drills didn't seem to be taken too seriously although a certain number had to be attended every year.

There were occasions when, on a Saturday, we would go to the rifle ranges at Altcar near Liverpool for rifle practice. I had been brought up by my father on how to shoot, mostly with a shot gun, at rabbits, partridges, pheasants and other game on the small estate surrounding our house, but I had also used a small bore rifle. In the woods behind the house there was a rookery and as the rooks did considerable damage to the crops, it was necessary to keep their numbers down. Firing at the rooks in the tall trees had made me a passable shot so that I found little difficulty when presented with a service rifle.

Apart from firing at the targets in the butts to get the highest score, the most exciting competition was the *falling plates*. For this the competitors were given five rounds each and split into two teams. Starting at the 300 yard firing point, you got up and ran to the 200 yard point, carrying your rifle. Of course the sooner you got there the better but if you ran too fast and were not very fit, you arrived out of breath, and would have more difficulty in holding your rifle steady. At the 200 yard point, you lay down and started firing at a series of iron plates in the butts. The team which knocked down the most plates in the time allowed, or knocked them all down first, were the winners. It meant careful team work to allocate your rounds so that you did not all fire at the same plate and if your plate fell, to distribute your fire to the others. It was a most realistic exercise and one where I could imagine the plates to be the enemy.

The highlight of the year for the Territorials was the fourteen-day annual camp. Not only was there pay and a bounty, but for the men it was probably their only holiday, generally near the sea, and a chance to get away from the family! It certainly made a good reason for them to join. The year I joined, camps were cancelled, partly owing to Government financial restrictions but also because, at that time, the country had not yet woken up to the fact that another war might break out again sooner than anyone expected. There was also a strong feeling of pacifism and a lot of people considered the Armed Forces to be an expensive and unnecessary requirement. The cancellation was so unpopular with the T.A. and reduced the recruiting to such an extent that the camps were reintroduced the following year and as a result I was able to go to camp the year after I joined.

My first camp, at the end of the summer of 1931, took place in North Wales. On the appointed day I arrived at the Drill Hall where the whole Battalion was paraded. Everyone was in uniform with boots and brasses highly polished, the officers with swagger canes under their arms and brown gloves, the senior officers in breeches and field boots. The men had their rifles which they brought smartly to the slope. On the word of command, out we all marched, company by company, led by the Colonel. In front of him marched the Regimental Band playing a martial tune which assisted the battalion to keep in step. Keeping in step was another thing I found rather troublesome at first, especially when marching in front of my platoon and trying to keep in step with those in front of me. Certainly the band helped.

As it was a Saturday, the population of the town turned out in strength, and waved and cheered as the soldiers passed just as if we were all going off to war instead of to a nearby town on the North Wales coast. We reached the railway station and entrained for the comparatively short journey to Rhyl where we detrained and marched off to the camp.

The camp site was a short distance away on a large flat field not far from the sand dunes and the sea shore. The Welsh mountains were just visible in the distance and the weather was fine. The tents, the weapons which consisted of Lewis and Vickers Machine Guns, and the other items, all of which had been carried in the limited amount of motor transport allotted to the battalion, were already there.

Tents were erected and latrines dug. I found the rather public use of the latter 'conveniences' somewhat embarrassing and pretty uncomfortable. Marquees were put up for the various messes, cookhouse and quartermaster's stores. Our sleeping accommodation was in bell tents. The men slept six to a tent, on palliasses filled with straw and two blankets per man, and the Junior Officers, like myself, slept two to a bell tent and were allowed to have camp beds. I had borrowed a camp bed belonging to my father, and a canvas wash basin and bath (the latter I avoided using as it was only six inches deep and again I felt a bit shy at having to use it in public). I also had a camp table and a canvas chair, and finally a sleeping bag and pillow. Every morning the canvas flap around the bottom circumference had to be raised to air the tent.

Reveille was sounded at an early hour. Shortly afterwards everyone had to be on parade. The Junior Officers checked their men to see that their equipment was blancoed, their boots highly polished and their rifles clean. Breakfast followed after the Orderly Officer had inspected the cookhouse. I don't think he was expected to have any culinary knowledge but his presence was sufficient to ensure that the cooks did their job properly. He then had to see that the food was distributed fairly to the men. When he had completed his task, the Orderly

Sergeant called out in his stentorian tones, "Any Complaints?". If there were any, which was not often, it was the Orderly Officer's job to sort it out.

Then followed a parade of the whole Battalion with the Commanding Officer and Adjutant mounted on horses. The horses were not used to the noise from the loud words of command nor to the clash of weapons as the troops sloped arms, and their riders had a hard time keeping them in check, much to the silent amusement of the troops.

I had been allotted a batman (soldier servant) to look after me and to polish my Sam Browne and boots but I was still apprehensive lest my puttees were not straight or my gloves and cane not in the correct position when the Commanding Officer carried out his inspection which he did during the parade.

The Colonel of the Regiment - not our CO - was an elderly gentleman with iron grey hair, cut very short. He was visiting the Battalion and had been allotted a tent next to mine. Looking out one morning I saw the Colonel, stark naked, standing in his canvas bath whilst his batman poured cold water over him. The very idea made me shiver.

Military training consisted mainly of drill, weapon training, map reading, route marches and occasionally a military exercise.

We were also *taught* to ride, as the horse was still considered an essential part of the Army. Taught was not quite the right word! Subalterns were simply allotted some pretty rough 'remounts' and told to mount and get on with it. The horse decided who was in charge and the rider just held on for dear life. My mount simply took off the moment I got into the saddle and following the others at full gallop, cleared a couple of ditches and a hedge on the way. Much to my surprise and probably the horse's as well, I found I was still on board when we got to the end of the gallop. It happened that some years later when I was on some military exercise, my horse threw up its head and caught me on the mouth, knocking out two teeth. I never saw eye to eye with horses after that!

Around 6 pm each evening, Guard Mounting was a ceremony carried out before dinner by the Orderly Officer. We subalterns had to learn how to do this as our turn as Orderly Officer would come soon enough.

On special evenings (generally *guest nights*) the Officers changed into their blue patrols for dinner. In the Mess the Senior Subaltern's word was law. He was a good fellow but we were much in awe of him. He explained the rules of the Mess - no talking shop, or politics, no discussion of women by name and no smoking until after the port. The drinking of the Loyal Toast was something we had to comply with implicitly. The PMC (President of the Mess Committee) would rise and say "Mr Vice". Mr Vice was a junior subaltern elected for the night who sat at the far end of the table who then rose and, raising his glass, said "Gentlemen, the King". We all stood, raised our glasses and drank the port, while saying firmly "The King". The PMC would then give us permission to smoke.

After dinner there were rough games, no doubt with the intention of toughening us up. There was one game called *Cock Fighting*. The antagonists lay on the floor, shoulder to shoulder but head to tail, and linked arms. Raising one leg in the air and trying to lock it round your opponent's leg, you endeavoured to force him to roll over. Mess spurs had to be removed for this! Another game was to circumnavigate the inside of the mess tent without touching the floor. This called for a good deal of agility especially after a fair amount of liquor had been imbibed.

After the annual camp, training went on at the Drill Hall as before but another event took place which I thought somewhat anachronistic. The Commanding Officer decided that the officers of his Battalion should attend a Levee at St James's Palace and be presented to the King. We travelled to London by train and were put up at the Strand Palace Hotel.

I had been told by the other subalterns that this hotel was renowned for supplying 'ladies of easy virtue' if required. I was approached by one of these in Wardour Street and, not knowing what to do, disappeared rapidly in the opposite direction. However not seeing anyone else who seemed likely to importune me, I returned to my room and donned my service dress, ready for the presentation.

At St James's Palace we waited in a queue along with hundreds of other officers from different regiments. Slowly we passed in front of the Monarch. I have to admit I was left with little impression of what the King looked like. He poor man must have been very bored with hundreds of us passing in front of him, each of us halting for a brief moment only, with a slight bow of the head as our names were called out. I suppose it was all part of tradition but I wondered if it was really necessary. Anyway, I had seen the King under whom I was serving according to my Commission.

CHAPTER 3

Shortly after I had been sworn in at the Drill Hall at Sandbach, it was time for me to start my career at the University. Janet, the youngest of my three elder sisters, drove me to Crewe station. I caught the train to Oxford and changed at Bletchley junction which was the parting of the ways for going either to Oxford or to, what an Oxford man would call *the other place*, which was of course Cambridge. Oxford had two stations, one at Rewley Road where I arrived. The other was for the Great Western Railway carrying the express trains to Paddington by which undergraduates were able to take trips to London, time and finance allowing, which many of the better off ones frequently did.

The University year was split into three terms, still called by their archaic names: Michaelmas, Hilary and Trinity. The names were taken from the nearest saint's day to the beginning of term and were similar to those used in the Law Courts. The winter or Michaelmas term was called after St. Michael's day on the 29th September. The spring or Hilary term after St. Hilary who was the Bishop of Poitiers in the fourth century A.D. and whose saint's day in England is the 13th of January. The summer or Trinity Term reflects Trinity Sunday which is moveable according to the date of Easter. I was *going up* in the Michaelmas term of 1930.

It was raining and as I had a large amount of luggage to last me the term, I decided that, in spite of the expense, I would have to take a taxi if one could be found, which was not very easy as they were few and far between. Having at last hailed one, successfully, the taxi took me via George Street, turning into the *Corn* (Cornmarket Street), across Carfax and down St Aldates where I eventually arrived at Christ Church, at the main gate under Tom Tower. The Head Porter, having made a mental picture of the young undergraduate (which he never forgot - he had a retentive memory for all the young men who passed through his gate), told me the number of my room which was in Meadow Buildings.

Christ Church, also called *The House*, although I never found out the reason, was founded by Cardinal Wolsey in 1525 and the insignia of the college is a Cardinal's hat. It considered itself to be a representative college and as a result there were undergraduates from all walks of life - the rich, the titled, those from well known public schools and from lesser known ones, and those like myself from the Grammar Schools. Some came to work but some still came only to play.

The college was split up into quadrangles known as Quads. The higher echelons of the well-to-do were housed in Canterbury and Tom Quad, having spacious rooms with oak panelling which had not changed for a century or more. There was no plumbing in any of our rooms. Hot water to wash was brought up by the Scout (College Servant). There was a W.C. on each landing and baths in the basement with copious hot water. Peckwater Quad usually catered more for the *Hearties* - the undergraduates concerned with sport - rowing, rugger, athletics, as well as fox hunting and beagling. My father, who had been a running Blue and one-time Master of the beagles, had had rooms in Peck.

Anyone who has visited Christ Church will most likely have entered, as I did, by the same gate under Tom Tower which houses the six and a half-ton bell, *Great Tom*. Every evening at five past nine, the deep harmonious tolling of Tom can be heard throughout the city and in the surrounding countryside. I was to stand many times on Headington Hill, listening to the 101 strokes which signified the original number of students at the college in the seventeenth century and used to announce that the gates would be closed on the last stroke.

Going through the gate the visitor will have seen the spacious quadrangle, Tom Quad, and the small ornamental pond in the centre. In the 17th century it contained a stone statue of the God Mercury standing on a globe with fountain pipes issuing from his head. This was later replaced by a statue of Mercury cast in lead with a head of bronze. Then, in 1817, the Earl of Derby as a result of a riotous party, pulled the statue down and it was not replaced until 1928 when a copy of Giovanni de Bologna's Mercury was erected. This was the one in position when I arrived.

The rain had now lessened and it was almost dusk as I walked into the quad and eyed the new statue with apprehension. My father had warned me that there was a custom at Christ Church which was that an unpopular undergraduate is thrown into the pond after he has been debagged, generally as a result of an uproarious and inebriated party to celebrate some event of athletic prowess. My father had also told me about the devastation to property which had occurred in the past. In 1870, a few years before my father came up, a scout by the name of Timms whose duty it was to report any misdemeanours of his charges had been dismissed for overlooking some of them. To avenge his dismissal, the members of Loders, an exclusive club for noblemen and rich commoners, removed a number of priceless marble busts from the Library and lit bonfires around them causing irreparable damage. Dean Liddell (whose daughter Alice the book *Alice in Wonderland* was based on) was the head of the college and had some difficulty in deciding how to deal with the offenders, two of whom were noble Lords. He pointed out that men of large fortunes had little to fear from such fines as he could impose and their parents looked with sympathy on acts similar to those which they themselves had taken part in, in previous years. His solution was courageous in the face of the influence that some of these wealthy families had. He expelled three of the offenders and rusticated (temporarily expelled) a fourth.

Although some high-spirited japes did take place during my time nothing so serious as the damage to the statues occurred. It was true that during the years of the Second World War, when undergraduates felt their life expectancy to be minimal, a considerable amount of glasses and furniture were damaged in wild drinking sessions.

I walked on through Tom Quad, thinking about these stories and expecting to be attacked by a rabble of students at any moment, but it was deserted. On the far side opposite the gate is the Cathedral. The entrance is not imposing since it is small and appears to be like the rest of the buildings round the quad. To the right of this entrance and in the far corner of the quad is a stone stairway which leads to the Great Hall. The stairway was surmounted by a magnificent fan vaulted roof. Leaving my luggage at the bottom after checking that there was no one about, I went up. Surmounting the four newel posts were lamp standards which no doubt originally held flambeaux but which now housed electric light bulbs spreading a soft light over the stairway. I entered the Great Hall and looked up at the roof which was decorated with over six hundred badges, devices, and coats of arms. It was built by Cardinal Wolsey and is the largest pre-Victorian college hall in Oxford. I was to dine there during my four years at Christ Church and every time I was impressed, as I was now, my eyes wandering on to the wonderful collection of portraits of famous men and women adorning the walls which would look down on the young men, some of whose pictures might one day occupy a space.

Whenever I dined in Hall I was to hear Grace, a rather long one and in Latin, read by a scholar each evening before the meal could begin. I found that protocol such as wearing a gown had to be followed and anyone transgressing was *sconced* which meant he had to buy two quarts of ale in a silver tankard or sconce for the table.

The ale was obtained from the Buttery, which also dispensed wines and spirits and was on the right hand side as you left the Hall. I was to find it the scene of many a lively drinking party after the meal had finished. Fred, who was in charge, knew all of *his young men* and how much they could imbibe with safety.

The High Table at the far end of the hall, under the portrait of Cardinal Wolsey, was for the Dean, the Dons and Professors. At the back there was an entrance to the Senior Common Room where the Dean and his guests retired after dinner to drink port. Port, you must know, is always passed round in a clockwise direction. A problem arises when the drinkers are sitting round a fireplace, none of them having the inclination to get up and pass the port across it. An ingenious contraption had been manufactured and was in use at some of the colleges, in which the decanter was placed in a cradle on a little inclined railway and carried by gravity to the other side of the fireplace. When the decanter was removed the cradle returned to its original position by means of a counterweight. The Dons, who were mostly of a non-mechanical bent, were delighted with this practical device.

Turning back past the Buttery, I went down the stairway and found an undergraduate who told me how to get to Meadow Buildings. It was down a flight of steps at the bottom of the stairway and through the cloisters. Externally Meadow Buildings was very different from the rest of the college and some said it was rather ugly. On the other hand, most of the rooms had the great advantage over those in the other Quads which looked out over the sordid roofs and buildings of the town, in that, from their windows, you could gaze at the beautiful Meadows with the tall trees and green grass, and the *New Walk* leading to the river Isis. In summer you could watch the gaily coloured crowds of men and women flowing down to the river during Eights Week.

I had been allotted rooms on staircase No 3, known as *Meadows Three*. There were nine rooms on this staircase and I found my name painted in white on a black board at the foot of the staircase along with eight others. As the numbers started at the bottom it was obvious that my room would be at the top. The staircase was of stone and on each landing there were two rooms with stout oak doors which had no handles but only a keyhole. One of them was shut and to me it seemed that the occupant had been locked in, as if he were in a dungeon. I learned later that the owner of the room had *sported his oak*. This meant that he was not to be disturbed, no one could enter and he was safe from any rowdy students who might want to beat him up.

When I got to the top landing I found that there was an open wooden staircase leading to a yet higher room which had my name painted over the door. I dragged my cases up the stairs to the rooms which were to be my home for the next three terms. There was a bedroom with a wash basin, no taps of course, and a chamber pot; and a sitting room or study with a coal fire which I later found smoked abominably, in spite of complaints to the Steward. The outlook was not over the Meadows as I had hoped but in the opposite direction over the college buildings and the Cathedral.

I had never been away from home for long without my family. Homesickness is common enough in a child but for a young man of eighteen it can still be painful. I sat and thought of home and my father and mother and what I would have been doing in my workshop and perhaps of a girl who lived not far from my home who I thought I had fallen in love with. However these thoughts passed and I felt that as I was starting out on a new life I had better get on with it.

There was a knock on the door and a man of about forty entered and announced that he was my Scout and his name was Timms. College servants were always known by their surnames and he may well have been a descendant of the Timms mentioned earlier. Timms asked if I wanted anything and when I would like my hot water to wash and when I would like my breakfast brought up. He told me the times of meals in Hall and when I would have to attend Roll Call and times to be back in College at night. I felt better.

After Timms had left I stood at the top of the stairs and looking down saw a completely naked man standing at the foot. I was embarrassed. I was not used to seeing naked men, or women for that matter. I had just been reading *How I found Livingstone in Central Africa* by H.M. Stanley and in a moment of mental aberration I thought I was seeing a native emerging from his hut in darkest Africa and about to attack me. However this one was white and appeared to be friendly enough and went back into his room which was below mine. I found out later that his name was Andrew. He was a second year man and the senior one on the staircase. From subsequent conversation I learned that Andrew had in fact been brought up in Africa and was the son of a famous anthropologist.

The occupant of the room opposite was a tall clean-limbed young man, whose name was Robert. He was a keen Boy Scout and occasionally appeared in scouting uniform for which he was generally ribbed by his contemporaries. He, like me, was in his first year and came from a provincial Grammar School but, being a *scholar*, he wore a special gown and sat at the scholar's table in Hall. I had had a problem over gowns. When I had passed the scholarship examination I was told that I could have either an exhibition or a scholarship. Both were of the same monetary value but for some reason I had opted for the exhibition. On arriving at Oxford I had asked at the outfitters which gown I should wear as an exhibitioner and was told a scholar's. This was incorrect and caused me some embarrassment when I sat at Robert's table and found out that I should have been wearing a commoner's gown and sitting at the other tables. However I soon got over it.

On the next landing were two medical students from one of the smaller public schools. Tony was a good squash player and had a somewhat caustic wit which he used to good effect. William had a rather squeaky voice and spoke very quickly so you couldn't be sure what he was talking about.

Lower down were two rather different types. Philip, destined to become a schoolmaster, was a cheerful character who you could always rely on and played hockey. Bernard, on the other hand, had a rather round face and a slightly affected voice and manner. He didn't play games but had a great liking and capacity for college ale and was very sociable. He was highly intelligent, reading an oriental language, and later became a much respected Professor in the University. Still further down the staircase was Peter. Peter was the son of a Member of Parliament and was rather more affluent than the others but avoided showing it although he was generous in his hospitality. His sherry was more *up market* than the inferior brands purchased by ourselves when throwing parties, and Harvey's Bristol Cream was something to be expected when visiting him. I was never quite sure what Peter was reading but he always seemed just to pass the various terminal examinations which allowed him to remain at Oxford.

We made frequent visits to each others' rooms where beer was consumed and talk and discussions on many subjects took place. Social intercourse is, after all one of the most valuable aspects of university life. As a result I learned much and all of us on the staircase became firm friends.

By now I had learnt the routine at Christ Church. In the first year one had to attend Roll Call (a *roller*) in Hall from 7.55 a.m. to 8.0 a.m. on four week days in each week. Every Sunday one had to attend at least one service in the Cathedral wearing one's surplice. There was also an alternative to the Roll Call known as a *Gate*. If an undergraduate went out of College before 8.45 a.m. on Sundays or 7.45 a.m. on weekdays he would be credited with a roller if he gave his name to the Porter. This meant he could *appear* at the gate before the appointed time in any informal dress, and nominally walk in and out and then, if he wanted, go back to bed. One of my lasting memories is of Peter in brightly coloured silk pyjamas and flowing dressing gown, scurrying across Tom Quad in a snow storm to get to the gate in time.

Undergraduates had to be in college by a certain time on pain of financial penalties. If they continued to infringe the rules they might be rusticated. For all colleges except Christ Church this time was midnight but for the House it was 20 minutes past midnight. The reason for this extra 20 minutes is not clear. It had been in existence for a long time. One explanation was that an unknown benefactor had left a substantial sum to the college with this stipulation. Another suggestion is that originally undergraduates had to be in by 9.05 p.m. but, as Tom struck 101 strokes, they could wait until it had finished striking, which might well take some 15 minutes, before they had to enter the college.

In those days of strict sexual segregation, ladies were allowed to visit undergraduates in their rooms but had to be out of them by 10 p.m. Lunch parties could be arranged with the meal being brought up by the scout. Breakfast was available in one's rooms between 8 and 9 a.m. It could be quite a social meal to which you could invite your friends and breakfast parties proliferated on our staircase.

Academically the system was based on tutorials and lectures.

I was introduced to my tutor who lived in college and whom I visited once a week for a one-to-one session on my work. A great deal depended on the ability of the tutor to impart his knowledge and on the undergraduate being able to understand him. My tutor was a brilliant physicist but not always very easy to follow. I also had to go every day to the laboratories in Parks Road and it was here that I listened to lectures by such eminent scientists as Lindemann, Einstein and others.

In order to get to Meadow Buildings, there was the flight of steps down to the Cloisters through which I went to get to my rooms. Directly opposite, as you went down the steps, was a building above the Cloisters which was the home of one of the Canons of the Cathedral. The far side looked out over the college gardens but on this side at the top was a window which no doubt belonged to a bedroom.

One day, as I descended the steps, I chanced to look up at the window and was met by an entrancing smile from the female occupant. No one else was looking up and I was intrigued and had immediate visions of romance. Having made some discreet enquiries, I discovered there were three *Home Students* who were undergraduettes at the University but not attached to any of the four women's colleges, and who lodged with the Canon and his wife. They were extremely nice girls but were kept on a tight leash by the Canon and his wife as they were living in a college entirely occupied by men. They came to be known as the Nippies as the Canon's initials were N.P. My problem was how to find out the name of the one at the window and how to get to know her. Every time I went down the steps I looked up at the window and nearly tripped up several times. Sometimes she was not there but on the occasions that she was and if she smiled at me my heart missed a beat. Eventually I discovered her name and plucked up enough courage to ring the bell at the Canon's door and ask to see her. Her name was Mary. She was of medium height with light brown hair curling at the back of her neck and brown eyes which glistened mischievously at her admirers. She had high cheek bones and lips which required no embellishment. I fell madly in love with her.

CHAPTER 4

One morning during my first year a letter from my mother arrived. It was short and to the point: "I am coming to Oxford next week, arriving 11.55. I shall be staying with Connie".

My mother, Mrs Marianne Clayton, was the youngest daughter of Sir Josiah Wilkes who had made his fortune by astute investments in the new railway companies which had sprung up in the nineteenth century. My mother was very beautiful and as a young woman her portrait had been painted by a well known portrait painter and had crossed the Atlantic to be exhibited in New York. When her sisters had married and my mother was the youngest unmarried daughter of her family, she had been despatched on a cruise with her elder brother, a handsome captain in the Coldstream Guards, and with an aunt as chaperone. In those days a chaperone was essential for a young unmarried woman travelling abroad on what was known as *fishing trips*. The holiday was ostensibly to find her a husband which frequently occurred on these trips. My father, John Clayton, happened, by chance, to be on the same cruise and with the same purpose, since his first wife had died. It was therefore not surprising that they met and shortly afterwards married.

Connie Ruskin, married to an Oxford Don, lived in North Oxford and was a dear friend of my mother before she married. I had already been to several rather austere parties at her house. The houses along the Banbury Road, where she lived, were built in yellow brick, with narrow Gothic-type windows inset with stained glass panels. Were it not for the lace curtains they would have had a rather ecclesiastical look. They exuded an air of prudery, of tea and sponge cake, as well as of scholarship. Many of them were inhabited by the intelligentsia of Oxford.

My mother was an imposing women, tall like me, and still good looking at 55 after having brought up five children. We met at the station and I took her to lunch at Elliston's, which was the most popular restaurant in the town. Later I delivered her to Mrs Ruskin in the Banbury Road.

I had not been at all sure how I should entertain my mother but I soon found that this had all been arranged, with dinners and theatre parties with the North

Oxford set. For my own part I decided to ask my mother to tea in my rooms. She climbed the wooden staircase in Meadows 3 and considered that her son had not been given very suitable accommodation but hoped that next year I would have something better. I introduced her to Robert and Philip and took her to the cinema.

At one of the tea parties which I went to with my mother in North Oxford, I met three of the plainest young women I had ever seen. Their names were unusual, Chryseis, Briseis and Antigone, called after three Hellenic women who, I was told, had exceptional wisdom. Their shortened names were Chrys, Brissy and Antig. Their parents must have had great prescience as their daughters were all highly intellectual. The girls were dressed in woollen skirts which came down to their ankles with blouses which buttoned up to their necks, covering what appeared to be remarkably flat chests. They had nondescript jackets, mouse-coloured hair done up in buns at the back and steel spectacles. They were studying at the University as Home Students and were living at home.

Conversation, holding a tea cup in one hand and a piece of cake in the other, was difficult. I started diffidently with Chrys.

"What are you reading?"

"Greek and Ancient History," she replied.

"Do you find that interesting?" I knew no Greek and my history did not extend much further than 1066 and Alfred burning the cakes.

"Extremely."

There the conversation faltered and I offered to get her another cup of tea and decided to try the younger one, Antig, whose blouse appeared to be rather less flat and whose face, more rounded than her sisters, looked as if it could, if pressed, break into a smile.

"What are you reading?" I tried again.

"Music in the Eighteenth Century."

"Well you must be musical. What do you play?"

"Apart from the piano, the harpsichord when I can find one."

Being very unmusical, I was once again getting out of my depth.

"Do you ever go out?" I ventured.

"Oh yes. To concerts."

"Would you like to go on the river?"

"Oh. I don't think I should. Besides I can't swim."

"What about Fullers?" Fullers was the tea shop in Oxford where undergraduates took their girlfriends for tea and cakes.

"No. I don't think I could go without Chrys and Brissi."

"Well perhaps we shall meet again," I concluded weakly.

I decided I had better concentrate on looking after my mother. After tea I took her to the Playhouse in Woodstock Road where we saw *Thark*, a Ben Travers farce with Stanford Holme and Margaret Rutherford. The next day my mother returned home after promising that she would visit me again when I was in my new rooms.

It was during the summer term that *Eights Week* took place. During that week, various colleges competed on the river. If a college *eight* overtook or, as it was called, *bumped* a rival they moved up one place towards the coveted *Head of River*.

On this occasion Christ Church had bumped one of the other colleges, which was a cause for celebration even if you were not a rowing man. There had been a good deal of drinking in the Buttery after Hall and I and some of my friends continued the party in my rooms. Suddenly Robert and Philip burst in.

"We're going to climb out on to the roof and fix something to the chimney," said Robert dramatically.

"Can we use your window?" asked Philip excitedly.

"I don't see why not," I replied.

"It really ought to be a chamber pot," said Robert. " Can we borrow yours?"

"But I might want to use it," I said reasonably. "What about my pyjamas? You can have them."

This seemed to be satisfactory and Robert, who was the mountaineer, opened the window and surveyed the roof.

"That should be easy," he said and he and Philip climbed out and made the precarious ascent to the ridge and chimney.

The next morning my pyjamas could be seen by everyone, fluttering in the breeze as a symbol of the college's success and there they stayed for several days until a firm of steeplejacks was called in to remove them.

Shortly afterwards I received a polite note to call at the Senior Censor's rooms at 10.30a.m. I went with some trepidation.

The Censor was a famous philosopher and an awe-inspiring character. He asked me to sit down and began: "Some garments were found attached to the chimney on top of Meadow Buildings. I think they are yours. Did you put them there?" I replied truthfully that I hadn't and the Censor then said: "I am not going to ask you who did put them there, but you will be fined ten shillings."

Fortunately I had a ten shilling note in my pocket and paid up immediately. On the way to the door I turned and asked: "How did you know they were mine, Sir?"

"Laundry marks are always a good clue," replied the Censor dryly and there the matter ended. I suppose I was lucky not to have received a more severe penalty.

My first outing with Mary had been to Fullers to have coffee and cakes. I had been a bit tongue-tied but it had not been nearly as bad as the tea party at Connie Ruskin's. We talked about books because she was reading English Literature and about the cinema. At least she did because, although I was a keen cinema goer, I didn't seem to know the films she was talking about. However it gave me the idea to invite her out to see a film which she said she wanted to see. It was called the *Blue Angel* and had Marlene Dietrich in it, an actress neither of us had heard of, but was showing at the Ritz. I wanted to see a Hitchcock film that was on at the Electra but Mary didn't like Hitchcock at all.

One of the features of the Super Cinemas of the day was the cinema organ or Mighty Wurlitzer which, in between films, rose from the depths in front of the screen to a background of ever changing coloured lights. Popular tunes were played by the organist who wore evening dress and turned and bowed to the audience at the end of every recital. The Ritz was no exception to this and after we had watched a comedy with Buster Keaton at which I laughed a lot but Mary didn't laugh at all, up came the Wurlitzer and on came the lights. Not that we were doing anything but it made me think of the Capitol at Macclesfield so I turned to her and told her about the jingle: *Banish your cares in Capitol Chairs* and how they had double seats at the back with no armrest in between. Mary looked at me and said: "But Thomas they have them everywhere. They look rather uncomfortable to me," and she gave me an indulgent laugh and looked at me teasingly down her petite nose. I didn't know what to say because I knew that Tony, the one with the caustic wit, had taken her out only the other day to the cinema and said they had sat in double seats. At that point the music came to an end and the organist stood up bowed to the audience and we all clapped. Then the main film started.

It was a sad film. Although Marlene Dietrich looked wonderful, her sultriness was quite unnerving and I felt sorry for the Professor. Mary said it was profound and that it was the Professor's fault in not understanding that his fantasy about the woman would never work. Mary tilted her chin up and gave me that teasing look again which I found so unnerving and yet exciting at the same time.

After the film Mary wanted to dance and I invited her back to my rooms because I had a portable gramophone. I invited Robert and unfortunately Tony also came up.

Although the British Broadcasting Corporation had been formed in 1922, listening to the Wireless did not become popular until later which was partly due to the size and complexity of the early wireless sets. In the 1930s they had become like large pieces of furniture and could incorporate a gramophone with a turntable operated electrically, which meant one didn't have to wind by hand. The B.B.C. advertised that: "You could dance at home to the best bands in London". Dancing was very popular. The dances were mainly the Foxtrot, the Two-Step and the Waltz. The Charleston and the Tango were considered rather showy and in general the dances were sedate, with each couple entwined and solely absorbed in each other. Jitterbugging came much later. Television did not arrive until 1936 when the B.B.C. opened the first television studio at Alexandra Palace.

Despite the fact that I had made wireless sets in my workshop at home, mainly so that my sisters could listen to the dance music, I did not bring one to Oxford but made do with a portable hand-wound gramophone for musical entertainment in my rooms. There wasn't much room for dancing but Mary was determined and Tony jumped up before I had the chance. While they danced Robert and I pushed our chairs back and tried to look interested. Mary also wanted to do the Charleston but it made the floor judder and the record on the turntable jump. I was quite pleased when 10 o'clock arrived and I could escort her back to the *Nippery*.

Since I was already an Officer in the Territorial Army I joined the Oxford Officers Training Corps whose Headquarters were in Manor Road but I could carry out my drills at the Drill Hall in Blue Boar Lane.

I also took up another activity, partly because Mary had mentioned it. It was not connected with the T.A. but it eventually led to my joining the University Air Squadron, something which had a decided effect on my future. As I had acted in some of the plays at school, I joined the Oxford University Dramatic Society (OUDS). This brought me into contact with a different branch of Oxford Society and, although it interfered with my work, I considered the experience to be well worthwhile. In 1932 the OUDS staged a production of *Romeo and Juliet* in which I was given a small part and the job of Property Master. At that time it was the custom for the OUDS to engage professional actresses and producers for their major productions and for this one, Juliet was played by Peggy Ashcroft and the Nurse by Edith Evans. The play was produced by John Gielgud. I, of course, had no idea how famous these actors and actresses were to become in the future. I read later that this production was the turning point in Peggy Ashcroft's career because it brought her into contact with John

Gielgud and the undergraduate actor, George Devine, who were her two closest allies over the following years.

The OUDS had a club in George Street which included a restaurant where I used to go for breakfast and other meals with my friends. Being a member also increased my circle of female acquaintances. In one production of *Much Ado About Nothing* a number of society young ladies were engaged to act as *Attendant Ladies.* They were more of the county and hunting fraternity and somewhat older than the undergraduates but still very good fun.

I was further involved with a dramatic society which was formed at Christ Church whilst I was there and of which I was President. It performed two plays in the Upper library - Kyd's *The Spanish Tragedy* and in the following year Marlow's *Edward II.* The undergraduate producer was a friend of Mary.

I was talking one day to a colleague in the OUDS who I discovered was also a member of the University Air Squadron (OUAS). I was interested as I had always wanted to fly, and discussed it with him. He told me it was difficult to get in but as I was an officer in the T.A. it might help. I decided to apply and see if they would have me.

The first hurdle to be overcome was to obtain *parents' consent.* In those days anything to do with flying was considered highly dangerous and I was doubtful if my father would sign the consent form. However, much to my surprise, he signed it, saying as he usually did: "Mind - Be Careful".

The next hurdle was the medical tests which I had been told were very tough. I duly presented myself before the doctor. The first test was to hold your breath for what seemed an immeasurably long time. I felt I was bursting and would never make it but after something like three minutes I found I had passed. The next test was to blow up a column of mercury and hold it at the set point for a time which also seemed interminable but was not as long as the first. After that standing on one leg and examination *starkers* by the doctor was no problem. The eye test was easy as I knew I had exceptionally good eyesight. However the last test was hearing and it was here that I nearly failed. I was told to stand in the corner of the room. Eventually the doctor arrived behind me and asked if I had heard anything. I replied that I hadn't been listening! So the test was repeated and the doctor who had been saying 'cheese' very softly as he approached his victim was decent enough to make it a little louder. And so I passed the medical.

The final hurdle was the interview with the Chief Flying Instructor, Group Captain Roderick Hill and the Adjutant, Squadron Leader Garrod. The fairly obvious question was "Why do you want to join the Air Squadron?" and the equally expected answer: "Because I want to fly". The next question was whether the candidate was considering a career in the RAF or the Auxiliary Air Force after leaving Oxford. As I was already in the Territorial Army, I replied that I would certainly consider transferring to an Auxiliary Squadron if the opportunity arose, but privately I decided that when the time arose I would keep my options open. This seemed to clinch the matter and I was accepted.

CHAPTER 5

In my second year I had as my mother hoped, been allotted better rooms in Meadows 2. They were much more commodious than my first year attic and were on the second floor of the staircase, looking out over the Meadows.

I had made quite a few friends and social functions proliferated. I was also kept busy with drills, drama, and membership of other societies as well as the OUAS which gave me little time to concentrate on academic work, and not as much time as I would have liked to concentrate on Mary. For all my different activities, my wardrobe had to be extensive. The era of the ubiquitous jeans had not arrived.

At the beginning of the thirties the normal dress for the man who was in work or in business was a suit with a waistcoat and a shirt with collar and tie. The collar would be detachable and therefore washable and if he worked in the City it would probably be a stiff one. On the other hand the manual worker or labourer would have trousers supported by braces or a belt and with a shirt usually collarless and no tie.

For everyday wear, I wore grey flannel trousers which although still rather wide at the ankles, were not as wide as the outlandish *Oxford Bags* of previous years. On top I usually wore a sports jacket or blazer and a shirt with collar and tie. Those who considered themselves *hearties,* such as rowing or rugger blues, could wear plus fours and tweed caps. We seldom wore hats but on trips to London the *trilby* appeared.

For the ladies, the tubular shape, the very short skirt, the Eton crop and the long cigarette holder, which had graced the twenties, had gone out and had been replaced by a much more feminine costume which allowed the curves of the figure once more to be shown. Skirts had lengthened to halfway between the knee and ankle and were worn with either a blouse or a woollen pullover and a jacket. In the summer, frocks of either cotton or the new artificial materials in lovely colours appeared and were worn with wide brimmed floppy hats. Hairstyles were generally cut to just above the shoulder. Mary's hair was cut quite short and curled up at the back of her neck. I was not sure if this was one of the new permanent waves or if it curled like that naturally.

As well as in Hall, we wore gowns to lectures and also in the evening if you were in town. It was an offence not to wear one and if caught by the Proctors in town without a gown you were likely to be fined.

There were special occasions such as taking *schools* (sitting for an examination) when academic dress had to be worn. This required a subfusc suit, which meant a dark coloured one, with a white shirt and a white bow tie, as worn with formal evening dress, and a mortar board, the traditional academic headgear.

Undergraduettes at the four women's colleges and the Home Students followed the fashion for academic dress in which they wore a white shirt and black tie with a dark jacket and skirt and, in place of the mortar board, they had a soft rectangular black hat.

For important dances, such as the Commemoration Balls which occurred during the summer term, full evening dress was obligatory for men with white tie and tails. For less formal occasions a dinner jacket with black bow tie was sufficient. For the ladies evening wear was closely moulded to the body and ball gowns were low cut, frequently backless and with long skirts enhancing the looks of their wearers.

When I went up to Oxford, the rest of the country was suffering from the effects of the Great Depression and the Wall Street Crash which had occurred in October 1929. The General Strike had been in 1926 when I had been so envious of what I considered to be those lucky people who had been allowed to drive railway engines, buses and trams which I was too young to do. In 1932 unemployment rose to nearly 3 million. The basic industries of coal, steel and textiles stagnated as the demand for capital goods diminished. Synthetic fibres were taking over from natural ones. Steam, the normal motive power for factories, ships and railways, was soon to be replaced by the internal combustion engine fuelled by gas or oil.

Meanwhile the living standards of the population, apart from the unemployed, had risen. Prices of goods were falling. Woolworths had arrived: *Nothing over sixpence*, and Montague Burton: *The Fifty Shilling Tailor*. The Lyons Corner House was a popular eating place and the price of food was falling. One could buy a meal of roast beef, Yorkshire pudding and chips for one shilling. Baked beans on toast, known in the North as *Thousand on a Raft*, cost fivepence. One egg on toast, *One on One*, cost sixpence, or if you were feeling affluent, *Two on One* for ninepence.

At Christ Church the cost of food and drink was very reasonable. Sherry could be bought for four shillings and sixpence a bottle and college ale at fourpence a pint. My *battels* which was the name for the bills I received for meals and drinks from the buttery only came to £22 in my first term. The charge for dinner in Hall, which comprised four courses including butter, cheese, bread and a napkin, was two shillings and sixpence. Tuition cost £10 and rent for the room a little over £7. With various other minor items such as electric light and laundry, the total for the term was just over £60. This meant that with the money from my exhibition and other scholarships together with a small parental contribution I was able to live a full social life.

It was unfortunate and reprehensible, that no one in the Government seemed to care about the unemployed who were living in miserable conditions and in appalling houses, with hardly the bare necessities of life. From 1931 a *Means Test* was imposed, ostensibly to target the limited resources to those most in need. Sadly it went hopelessly wrong and in many cases reduced the total income of those who were trying to help themselves. In 1931, during my second year, The National Hunger March took place when 2500 of the unemployed marched on London but achieved nothing. Again in 1936 an event took place known as the Jarrow Marchers when 200 men from the Jarrow shipyard marched 300 miles to the capital but again achieved nothing. Alas there was no easy solution to the unemployment problem until Hitler provided it in 1939.

Various charitable bodies had been set up to try to do what the Government had failed to do. Christ Church was one and had formed the *Christ Church (Oxford) United Clubs* (once called *The Below Bridges Club*) to help unemployed youths from the Brixton and Kennington area in London where poverty, overcrowding and poor housing were endemic. On several occasions I entertained 6 or 8 of the *Bermondsey Boys*, as they were called, to lunch or tea and a tour of the University. I wondered whether, apart from filling their stomachs, they appreciated being shown a window opening on to a life in which they had little hope of participating.

Politically during the whole of the decade the electorate had voted the National Government into power with a succession of Prime Ministers which included Ramsay McDonald, Stanley Baldwin and Neville Chamberlain. The in-fighting within the Government and its attempts to solve the domestic situation, took the attention of the populace away from what was happening elsewhere. Perhaps they did not realise that in Germany Hitler won an alarming number of votes in the 1932 election, and finally came to power in March 1933.

It was in February 1933 that the Oxford Union introduced the infamous motion - "That this House will in no circumstances fight for its King and Country". Although a member of the Union, I did not go as it was the opening night of *Edward II* at Christ Church and I also felt that the debate had been organised mainly for publicity. There was undoubtedly a pacifist element in the country as well as at Oxford amongst those who had read of the flagrant loss of life in the first war and had no wish for it to be repeated. There was also a Labour Club containing a number of communists, mostly intellectuals, who supported the USSR claiming it was the bastion of the *workers* - a class which they themselves had probably never seen and knew little about, as at the time neither did I. However they would have supported the motion knowing that it would cause disruption to the establishment.

The morning after the debate Philip rushed into my rooms with a newspaper in his hands.

"I told you you should go. This is real life Thomas. Now see what they are saying."

There it was. "Dreaming Spires fired by peace debate. Union motion carried." It was headlines across the front page of The Oxford Times and was taken up by the London papers who reported it dramatically so that it would be blazoned across the world.

"But I don't support it," I said.

"Some hope you'll have of proving that now," replied Philip.

After the war some historians have said that the result of this debate influenced Hitler and Mussolini to think that the British lacked the will to fight.

There were also other movements. One evening when I was dining in Hall, one of my friends who was renowned for attending many heavy drinking sessions, suddenly turned to me and said: "I've just joined the Group."

I was thinking about Mary who I felt I was not making enough progress with. I had taken her out to the cinema again and also to the Moorish, a restaurant much frequented by undergraduates but I hadn't seen her for a week or so. I asked rather absently, "What group is that, Harry?"

"Don't you know about the Oxford Group?" he replied. "You have to tell all your friends when you join."

I had heard briefly about the Oxford Group whose beliefs were based on an American Movement called Moral Rearmament. I knew little about it and was not particularly interested but Harry seemed to want to talk, so I asked him: "What is it?"

Harry answered a bit diffidently. "Well I don't really know a lot about it. The chaps seem a pleasant enough crowd and I thought I would join up with them."

"What do they talk about?"

"Oh they talk about absolute moral standards and the guidance of God and they seem to think that these are what the world needs today at this critical time."

"That sounds all very well. But has it done anything for you Harry?"

"Yes," he said, "I've started to clean up my life and to go to church and to work hard."

"I didn't know you needed all that *cleaning up* but if you have started to work - that certainly is a miracle!"

For Harry it provided a turning point in his life and I could not deny the benefit to him. However for me although I hoped I was a Christian, its beliefs were too rigid, its demands too vigorous. Later Harry became a Padre in the Services and we remained good friends.

Since my new rooms were more commodious, they were easier to entertain in. With the arrival of Eights Week, I decided to invite the three Nippies to lunch. It would mean I could see Mary again. I also invited Robert and his friend Derick. The other two Nippies' names were Liz and Audrey. Liz was of medium height with brown eyes, a big sense of humour and was rather a tomboy. Robert, the 'Boy Scout' fell for her in a big way. Audrey was short with dark hair and was already friendly with Derick who was at another college.

The lunch was brought in by Line who was the scout on Meadows 2, and I had provided a supply of four and sixpenny sherry and some wine. The party was going well and most of the sherry and wine had been consumed. The conversation turned to the Summer Vacation.

"What are you doing in the vac?" I asked Robert.

"I'm going climbing and camping in the Cairngorms."

"Can I come with you?" asked Liz boldly. She was very much attracted to Robert.

"Yes I suppose so," said Robert, "that'll mean two tents."

"One would be lighter," said Liz.

"Yes I suppose it would," said Robert slowly, the implication of the reply having only just sunk in.

"What about you?" Mary asked me.

"I shall be going to T.A. Camp in Wales," I replied

"I suppose that'll be all men," remarked Mary with interest, her mind on her favourite subject.

"Oh, I expect there'll be plenty of girls in Rhyl," I said, hoping to make her a little jealous.

Audrey and Derick were talking quietly together on the window seat overlooking the New Walk down which people were strolling in the sunshine.

"Let's go down to the barge and watch some races," said Mary who had drunk rather more sherry than the others and I knew she wanted to show off her new summer dress and floppy hat. She had so many admirers. Had I missed an opportunity, unlike Robert, when she had asked me about the vacation?

We set off, down the Walk, through the Meadows with the tall trees on either side and the cows grazing in the fields. The girls made such a pretty picture with their coloured frocks rustling in the breeze and holding on to their wide brimmed hats, that they caught the eye of a Press Photographer and our pictures appeared on the front page of the Oxford Mail next day.

When we arrived at the College Barge I ordered tea with cream cakes and strawberries and then we watched the races.

I couldn't stop thinking how attractive Mary was. I felt possessive and decided that next time, I must take her out on her own. The prospect was exciting but when this would be was a little problematical because my involvement with flying, although also exciting was going to be very time consuming.

The first part of the training was to attend various lectures on the theory of flight, engines, airmanship and navigation at the Club House. After that the time came for my first flight. I reported to Manor Road and together with other members of the Squadron was driven out to Upper Heyford, an aerodrome not far from Oxford.

The aircraft I was to fly was an Avro 504, a biplane with a rotary Lynx engine similar to the aircraft used in the First World War. In those early machines, the cylinders attached to the propeller rotated whilst the crankshaft was stationary. The 504s we were flying were more conventional as the cylinders, although set radially, were stationary and the crankshaft and the propeller rotated.

I was introduced to my instructor, a young Flying Officer who showed me how to put on my parachute and how to pull the rip cord if the need should arise. I sincerely hoped it wouldn't. Climbing into the rear seat of the aircraft I was shown how to strap myself in, how the controls worked, where the throttle was and what the various instruments were for. The instructor got into the front seat and established communication by speaking through a tube connected to earpieces on the pupil's flying helmet. Easy to hear when the engine was not running but, at times, almost impossible in the air!

Starting the engine was a dangerous occupation for the airman swinging the propeller, and a routine had to be established for his safety. The magneto switches were mounted on the outside of the fuselage where they could be seen both by the pilot and by the man on the propeller. First he had to ensure that the chocks were in place in front of the wheels. Then on the command: "Switches off - Suck in", the pilot made sure the switches were <u>OFF</u> which the man on the *prop* could also see. The airman then rotated the propeller to draw the petrol mixture into the cylinders to facilitate starting. After a couple of revolutions the pilot would call: "Switches On - Contact", and would put both magneto switches <u>ON</u>. The propeller would then be swung in a way so that the man swinging it was well away from it when the engine fired. If all was well the engine burst into life and was allowed to warm up for a few minutes. If not the process was repeated.

The next requirement was to test the engine at full throttle and to ensure that both magnetos were working. Having checked again that chocks were under both wheels to prevent the aircraft going forward, and that an aircraftman was hanging onto the tail to steady it, the pilot advanced the throttle fully and checked the revolutions on the instrument in front of him and tested each magneto in turn to check that the revs didn't drop on either of them. He then throttled back and signalled *Chocks Away* by raising his arm and slowly waving it from side to side. Taxying, my instructor explained to me, must be in a zig-zag direction as in a single-engine machine such as the Avro it was not possible to see directly ahead when on the ground.

So to the downwind end of the aerodrome, a careful look all round for other aircraft, especially from behind, then slowly advance the throttle and we were off.

Although the Avro took off at only about 60 to 70 miles an hour, my first impression was of great speed over the ground and then the exhilaration of leaving the earth and looking down at it from a totally different perspective. The pilot flew steadily at first but then carried out a few turns, increasing the steepness so that I felt the first effects of *G* that force that forces you into your seat as if a giant were holding you down. I was pleased that I did not feel sick. After about 30 minutes the pilot landed and I had had my first flight.

After that there were flights nearly every week so long as the weather was suitable. I learned to take off and land, to do steep turns when the effect of ailerons and rudder were reversed and then spinning.

Spinning was the most unnerving. After reaching a safe height, generally about 2000 feet, the pilot pulled the nose up until the aircraft appeared to be stationary in the air. The nose then fell away and the aircraft having *stalled*, started to spin leaving my stomach where I felt it shouldn't be and the world appeared to be turning rapidly round me. After a few revolutions the pilot applied opposite rudder and stick forward. The spinning stopped and he then pulled the aircraft out of its dive.

Later he demonstrated low flying. I couldn't believe how he could avoid his wing tip striking the ground when he did a steep turn round a windmill and flew at hedge-top height over the ground. It was all very exhilarating.

Now that I was flying in the air, I realised that another social revolution had occurred on land in the preceding decades with the birth of the motorcar. I had been taken to school in the twenties in a Model *T* Ford, a product of Henry Ford's imaginative and innovative methods of mass production. This was now being copied by William Morris (later Lord Nuffield) in producing the Morris cars. These cars were comparatively cheap and could be afforded by many families. As a result the masses were no longer tied to their homes or reliant on public transport, but could go on evening outings and weekend jaunts whenever they wished or on holidays to places they could never have visited before. One result of the staggering increase in the number of motor vehicles was the increase in the number of road accidents. I had already suffered one when driving the family car at home due to the absence of any form of halt sign or traffic signal at a blind road junction.

A second-hand bull-nosed Morris Cowley, 4 seater, open tourer could be had for as little as £25. I, who was the proud possessor of one, was allowed to have it at Oxford during my second year. There were strict University rules as to its use. One was that it must have a small green light fixed to the left hand side of the windscreen so that the Proctors could identify it.

After the lunch party in my rooms during Eights week, I decided that I must make more headway with Mary as I knew that I now had a rival in the Christ Church Dramatic Society. As I had a car I decided to ask her to come out with me the next Sunday.

Sunday came and Mary appeared dressed in suitable attire - a calflength skirt with a blouse, well suited to show off her figure, and a look of anticipation on her face. It was a lovely summer's day - just the day for an outing in the country. My car had bench seats in the front and back. Mary got into the front seat but, instead of keeping to her side of the bench as everyone else I had taken in the car did, she slid over and pressed herself close to me with such intensity that it took me by surprise. No other woman had done this to me before. My sex education was rather limited and I was in some doubt as to how to proceed. Mary was not by any means the only woman I had ever kissed but this sensation was something new. I found it very pleasant and had no wish to ask her to move although it did rather take my mind off my driving.

We drove to some places along the river and as it was hot and we had brought our bathing things, we stopped by a wood and changed demurely into them. After that we swam in the river and spent the afternoon lying on the bank in the sun, close together, with a good deal of cuddling and kissing. I was wondering if I was really in love while Mary, no doubt, was comparing me with her other conquests. When it became dusk I delivered her back to the Nippery and considered what I should do next. Most men would probably have gone on with the eventual hope of seduction but it seemed to me that Mary was unlikely to fall for that. Neither did I want to get too involved so I decided that I would avoid seeing her for a time and perhaps look for someone else to experiment with.

CHAPTER 6

The Air Squadron, like the T.A., held an annual camp which took place in the long vacations at Eastchurch on the Island of Sheppey in Kent.

For the first week I carried out daily flying with my Instructor until he considered me to be competent to go solo. Then the Chief Flying Instructor, Wing Commander Keith Park (later to become A.O.C. in C. Fighter Command in the Battle of Britain) got into the front seat and asked me to take off, do various turns and then to land. He then got out and I was on my own. I suppose that for everyone who flies, the *First Solo* is the thing he or she remembers most, perhaps like the first parachute jump. There is no one in the front seat and, although taking off may be no problem, the realisation sinks in that there is no one else to get you back on the ground in one piece but yourself. However I succeeded and the feeling of achievement was intense. After that I had another flight with my instructor and then two more solos. The greatest danger in flying is over-confidence. The first 50 hours is one danger point and then again at 500 hours so it is important that dual instruction continues as well as solo.

I was now able to do aerobatics. This was great fun. Up to 2000 feet, for safety, and then a loop - dive the aircraft to its maximum speed, pull up the nose and over you go backwards, the horizon which had vanished appearing again as you straighten out. The slow roll was more difficult without letting the nose of the aircraft drop. Then flying inverted with all your weight hanging on the straps. I liked stall turns the best. You dived to get up speed, pulled the nose up until the aircraft was just about to stall, kicked on full rudder and the aircraft did a sort of cartwheel and you pulled out of the dive at 180 degrees to the original direction. I was told it was very useful in dog fights in the first World War.

I was now competent to do a cross country. I flew with my instructor to an airfield near Cambridge and was told to take the aircraft back to Eastchurch. I had very carefully worked out the course, allowing for wind drift, and checking landmarks I would be passing over. So off I set. After a little while, looking at the ground, I did not seem to be passing over the places I had expected. Then

I noticed, from smoke on the ground, that the wind was in the wrong direction. Looking at the compass I saw to my horror that instead of flying due south on 180 degrees I had misread the compass and was travelling due north and might eventually have landed up in Scotland! I quickly did a 180 degree turn and arrived back at Eastchurch rather later than expected, explaining that I had been carrying out some exercises on the way.

In my third year the Squadron moved to Abingdon and was issued with Avro Tutors, a much pleasanter aircraft to fly than the 504 although it had a similar Lynx engine. However all good things come to an end and at the final camp, at the end of my fourth year, I had my last flight with the Air Squadron flying the obsolete 504s back to Abingdon. We were told to keep in some sort of formation but the flight commander must have been in a hurry to get home. We had been told not to exceed certain engine revolutions for long. I found I had to keep the throttle fully forward throughout the flight just to keep the leader in sight. However although the engine was vastly overheated we got there safely and that was the last flying I had until fate decided otherwise.

Not far from the OUAS club house in Manor Road was the river Cherwell with a boat house and landing stage where you could hire a punt. The punt is a long narrow boat of shallow draught propelled by the punter wielding a long but strong pole. It had a small deck at one end rather like the gondolas in Venice and cushions were provided for the passengers to recline on.

It was often assumed that at Cambridge the punter stood on the deck, thinking perhaps that he was a Gondolier, and propelled the punt sedately forward by pushing with the pole. At Oxford, on the other hand, the punter frequently stood on the floor and would propel the punt as he walked along its length, thrusting the pole into the river bed and pushing with all his might. This moved the punt at greater speed but it had its drawbacks. If the pole was too deeply imbedded in the mud when he got to the end of the punt which was only a few inches above the water, and if he couldn't get it out, he had two options - abandon the pole (which he then had to pay for) or hang on to it while the punt disappeared, leaving him clinging like a monkey up a stick as it gently subsided with him into the river. The advantage, if he didn't lose the pole, was that his passenger, usually female, could observe his muscular prowess.

I had decided that in my third year I would not see so much of Mary and would try a little competition. I had already met some of the undergraduettes from the womens' colleges so why not invite one of them to come on a punting expedition?

Josephine from Somerville was a very studious and erudite young woman but, far from being a *blue stocking*, she was stunningly attractive and much sought after by the young men. She was of medium height with hazel eyes, auburn hair and a figure the top half of which I studied with great interest as it was encased in a loose fitting blouse and it was fairly obvious she was not wearing a bra. We set out on our expedition on a summer evening in June. The air was warm. It had been a sunny cloudless day and the river looked idyllic. I had brought a bottle of five-shilling sherry, a couple of glasses and made sure there were plenty of cushions. I was not particularly proficient at punting but having settled Josephine on the cushions and avoided the obstacles round the landing stage, managed to get into midstream. There were other punts on the river, all apparently bent on the same purpose - to find a secluded spot to tie up.

We proceeded up the river, passing *Parsons Pleasure*, a place on the river carefully screened and reserved for men bathing in the nude. Enterprising female punters often had navigational difficulties when passing this spot, their punts drifting accidentally round the screens with apologetic shouts of "Oh Sorry"!

Conversation with Josephine was desultory as I was concentrating on steering the punt, avoiding other craft and not losing my pole. Eventually we came to a part of the river where the trees hung low over the banks and a bed of reeds meant that you could be hidden from both the river and the bank. I tied up and opened the sherry.

Josephine was not averse to a little dalliance and time passed quickly with some kissng and cuddling - a punt being very suitable for that sort of entertainment.

It was getting dark when we both realised Josephine must be in College by midnight whilst I had to be back by twenty past. Untying the punt, I pushed out into midstream and started for home, punting furiously. Sadly as we neared the end of the journey the inevitable happened, the pole stuck in the bottom and refused to budge. I clung to it and walked off the end of the punt and, hearing Josephine's laughter, collapsed into the water. Fortunately for such emergencies the punt was provided with paddles and Josephine, being no slouch and knowing what to do, soon had the punt under control and helped me back into it, sodden and dripping. We tied up at the landing stage and the boatman didn't seem at all surprised. I paid him for the pole even though he could easily retrieve it later. He didn't suggest a refund and I was too cross to care.

I was very wet and drove Josephine back to Somerville where she thanked me for a very interesting evening. She probably thought me an idiot and I was so embarrassed at my ineptitude that I considered myself lucky that I had not taken Mary.

At the end of this my third year, not surprisingly in view of all my other activities, I found that I had done badly in the examinations. I was only able to get a third class honours degree in Physics. It was in a lower class than I had hoped for and meant I would not be able to get an academic post where I could have carried on with research and experimental work which was what I really liked. I knew I would now have to find a job but had not realised that they were not so easy to come by. My tutor suggested that I should stay another year and try to get a degree in Engineering which might make it less difficult to find employment. With what I had already learned on the Physics course, he said it should be possible to obtain an Engineering degree in one year instead of the normal three-year course. In 1933 the School of Engineering at Oxford was very small. If you wanted to get a degree in that subject you would normally have gone to Cambridge or one of the provincial universities.

It was now the end of the summer term in my third year and the OUDS were holding a ball at the Randolph Hotel. As I was the Junior Treasurer of the Society, I was asked to organise it. It was to be a prestigious affair with Henry Hall's dance band from London, a cabaret and unlimited champagne. I and the other men would, of course, have to be in full evening dress with tails, white waistcoat, white shirt, white tie and collar. I always felt like a stuffed turkey when I had to dress up in it.

After the expedition with Mary in my car the previous year, I had not taken her out but had inevitably met her at several parties, generally with other men and frequently escorted by my rival in the Dramatic Society. There was no doubt that I was still very attracted to her so I decided I would try once more and ask her to come to the OUDS ball as my partner. She was pleased to accept my invitation and I looked forward to the evening. She arrived looking entrancing in a long pink ball gown, tight fitting to show off her quite voluptuous figure, backless, the front held up by a halter round her neck and obviously bra-less. The dance started and after I had dealt with the various problems which always arise at such a function, and which the organiser has to sort out, I was able to devote my whole attention to Mary. We danced several dances in which I held her close to me, our bodies fitting perfectly into each other and she not resisting the passionate pressure. After the Cabaret and after some rather more energetic dances and, having consumed a large amount of champagne, Mary whispered to me: "Let's have a rest and sit the next one out."

42

I was not unwilling. She led the way upstairs, by the big staircase in the Randolph, to the billiard room, which was in semi-darkness and appeared to be unoccupied. After a certain amount of amorous exchanges, Mary suddenly unhooked the halter holding up the top half of her dress to let it fall exposing her breasts which she pressed against me whilst kissing me passionately. Unfortunately, as I was wearing a shirt with a very stiff front, along with the white waistcoat and stiff collar, she might as well have been pressing herself against a brick wall. It was all pretty frustrating and I was not prepared to remove my shirt as it was obvious by now that we were not alone, having been joined by another couple with similar ideas. Mary carefully put up her dress and we returned to the dance which went on into the early hours. After it had ended we walked as far as Magdalen Bridge, watching the sun rise and then returned, past the sleeping colleges, to the club in George Street for breakfast. Afterwards we walked back via Carfax and St Aldates to the House. I gave her a last passionate embrace outside the Canon's front door and returned to my rooms.

In spite of all the embraces and the contact with her body, I was not happy. I felt she was just leading me on. Perhaps it was to satisfy her own passion for men. I felt disillusioned. However now that the term had ended it would be the long vacation when I would not be seeing her and with other things to think about, I might perhaps be able to forget her. I knew she would be up for a fourth year doing research on an obscure aspect of Jacobean Theatre, a subject which she had informed me my rival in the OUDS was also interested in. The implication being that I was not.

I also would be up for a fourth year as I was going to take my tutor's advice. One of the qualifications for the Engineering degree was to attend a three-week surveying course which was usually taken in the summer vacation. I decided to do this as soon as the summer vacation started.

The weather that year was fine and warm and the course turned out to be a pleasant occupation in the countryside not far from Oxford. It was run by a retired Army Officer who, I suspected, had practised his surveying in India. The Major certainly kept his pupils hard at work. From 8 a.m. to 5 p.m. we were out with a plane-table, prismatic compass and later a theodolite. In the Drawing Office we prepared beautiful maps which had to be spotlessly clean and accurate. As it needed good light to draw the maps we often had to get up before breakfast and spend time in the Drawing Office in the morning before going out to survey and then again after tea. It left little time for going to the nearest pub and none for girls.

At the end of the vacation, just as the autumn term was about to begin, I contracted appendicitis. In 1933 the normal anaesthetic for such an operation was chloroform dripped on to a mask held over the patient's nose and mouth. I could see it dripping as the lights in the operating theatre slowly disappeared and I felt I was sinking into a bottomless pit with the associated terror. I woke with a terrible headache and nauseating sickness to feel a nurse wiping my sweating brow. I hoped I would never have to go through such an operation again.

By the time my convalescence was over it was half way through the term before I could go back to Oxford where I formally took my degree. At Oxford scientists are awarded a BA rather than a BSc which is the case at other universities. This always caused some confusion when I put BA after my name, although I was a physicist. However, as a graduate I could now live out of college so the first thing to do was to find lodgings.

The best restaurant in Oxford, well patronized by the undergraduates but often visited by the Proctors, was the *George*, situated in George Street and not far from the OUDS club. I had a friend called Malcolm who had obtained a degree in Agriculture the previous year and was now studying Forestry and lived in a flat above the George. Malcolm was a year older than me and more sophisticated. He had dark hair and wore horn rimmed glasses and was quite a bon viveur. As Malcolm had a spare bedroom in his flat, he suggested that he and I should share the flat and split the expense. The flat was very convenient having the restaurant below. On a Saturday there was generally a crowd of people trying to get into the restaurant which was full. I had only to walk up to the door and signal to the doorman to be let in as I was living there, much to the annoyance and angry remonstrances of the crowd.

Another course which the Engineering School provided was to send the students, during one vacation, on a voyage in a transatlantic liner to gain practical experience in the engine room. Accordingly in March 1934, I arrived at Southampton where I met Bill, another student on the course. Bill was younger than me and was still an undergraduate. He was a cheerful character and we got on well together. We learned that we were to sail on the White Star liner *Olympic* to New York and back. First of all we had to obtain white boiler suits as we were to be Probationary Engineers and had to sign on as part of the ship's company for which we were paid a nominal sum of one shilling. Although we were part of the crew we were accommodated in the Tourist Class and when off duty could mix with the passengers. We were not supposed to go into the First Class but, with the excuse of inspecting a winch or some other piece of machinery, I was able to go all over the ship. The Chief Engineer put us on the 8a.m. to 4p.m. watch but our duties were not onerous and I wished we could have been given more to do.

I had always been interested in steam engines and was enthralled with the two mighty quadruple expansion engines with enormous cylinders. The piston rods of gleaming steel moved majestically up and down to rotate the propeller shafts which passed through long tunnels to the stern of the ship, where they went through the hull to drive the screws. I went down these tunnels once, through watertight doors to the stern plates of the ship and listened to the ocean only inches away from my head. I tried not to think what would happen if the lights went out, the watertight doors closed behind me and the sea came in.

The boilers producing the steam to drive the engines were coal fired and the grimy, sweating stokers seemed to be for ever heaving coal into the voracious maws of the furnaces. The heat was terrific and the dust and noise appalling. How much better it was when oil firing came into use.

There was a certain amount of socialising with the passengers in the tourist class but the highlight of the trip for Bill and myself was the arrival at New York, a city which neither of us had been to before. Malcolm had told me that when I got to New York I should contact a friend of his who lived there. As soon as we came ashore, I studied the telephone directory and eventually found her number. I got through, explained who I was, and arranged that we should meet at the Paris Hotel.

Nancy was an attractive young lady and like all Americans most hospitable and keen to show off her city. One problem was language. At first I simply could not understand the different use of words and the American accent but this was soon overcome. We then did a rapid *Cook's Tour*: 5th Avenue, Central Park, Wall Street and so on. With all the excitement, I wanted to pee very badly but could see no signs like in London for such conveniences. I was much too shy to ask Nancy. However the need became so great that eventually I had to ask her and found that the answer was simple. You went into the nearest restaurant or bar and made use of their facilities even if you did not have a meal or buy a drink.

Having had lunch at a little cafe in Wall Street, Bill and I returned to the ship but arranged to meet Nancy at The Empire State Building at 5 p.m.

To go up in the express lift cost $1, the equivalent of five shillings in English money, but when we got to the top it was an experience that was worth every cent and every mile of the 3000 mile voyage it had taken to get there. We stayed at the top of the building until the lights came on across the City. The tops of the high buildings were bathed by the setting sun while the lights of the traffic, snaking in and out of the streets so far below, seemed more fairylike than real. It felt like being in another world looking down on this pulsating city of the New World. Never had two hours appeared to pass so quickly. Afterwards Bill went off on his own and Nancy took me to a little *Actors* restaurant where, with true American hospitality, she stood me the meal. Afterwards we went on to Radio City to see a film. I took her home in a taxi which I was intrigued to see was fitted with radio communication. I thanked her for a most memorable visit to her city and went back to the ship where I sat down and wrote a poem.

New York! That foremost city of the western world.
City of steel and concrete, square and gaunt.
Fashioned by man's most modern ingenuity.
What feelings must it conjure in the expectant traveller's breast?
Three thousand miles from England's shore.
Tossed in a great Atlantic liner by the waves
Which tossed Columbus when he crossed of yore.

That famous skyline! now known to millions by the silver screen
Comes into view, picked out with twinkling lights
Till they come confused with those celestial ones above.
Then - on our left - "Liberty".
Large in herself but dwarfed by the immensity around,
Guardian of this entrance to the modern world.
And so our brave ship docks.
Then after clashes with the port authorities
Comes the moment when we set our feet upon the land,
That land which generations back was source of great conjecture.

We scale the highest building by man's uplifting engines.
Modernity in action, action in modernity,
Then gaze with wonder on what lies below.
Oh city of superlatives - greatest - largest - fastest - highest!
City of a thousand peoples,
All moving - running - hurrying - shouting.
Here time is Money. Speed can save it -
City of speed and money - deified.

I arranged to meet Nancy again at 5 p.m. the next day when we had tea and later cocktails (I don't think I had used the term before), and talked about America and what she thought of England and when she was next going to visit and whether she had a boy friend and was she going to marry? She was so easy to talk to. I thought she was one of the nicest girls I had ever met and promised to give Malcolm her love. Leaving her at 7 p.m., I caught the ship with just 2 minutes to spare!

The ship sailed at 8 p.m. Standing on the deck, I watched the lights of the waterfront and *Downtown* slowly disappear. It was a moonlit night and as I watched the outline of New York fading into the distance I turned and said to Bill:

"You can get a packet full of thrills from this," and Bill agreed.

The return voyage was uneventful apart from a storm which was so severe that it caused another Atlantic liner the *Manhattan*, on a similar course to our own, to heave to. The *Olympic*, however, ploughed on and I, who was on deck duty, experienced for the first time the strength of a gale at sea. To prevent being literally blown off my feet, I had to hold on to any support for dear life. After six days we docked at Southampton. Bill was met by his mother who gave me a lift to the station from where I went home and continued my vacation. I considered how lucky I had been to see New York - at no expense -and to be taken round by such an attractive young lady.

My last two terms at Oxford were the most hectic of my university career. Not only was I trying to put three years' work into two and a half terms but I was also heavily involved with dramatics, first with the Christ Church plays and then with the OUDS of which I was still the Junior Treasurer. I also flew with the Air Squadron and occasionally attended my Territorial drills at Blue Boar Lane. Parties and social functions proliferated and, on top of that, in my last term I was going to interviews with prospective employers put forward by the University Appointments Board.

Peter had ploughed in his examinations and had come up for another year to retake his finals. Philip had got a temporary job teaching at a school in Oxford. Robert was doing an extra years research in chemistry. The medical students, Tony and William were at the Radcliffe Hospital and Bernard was doing research into Arabic at St Johns College.

My romantic life was in a turmoil. I still thought I was in love with Mary but love is a peculiar thing and I wondered if it was just because she was the first girl to give me that sensuous feeling. Although after the OUDS ball she had again been rather aloof, we still had tea and drinks together and met at parties. She was going out with more and more male admirers and I had to admit I was jealous. On the other hand I was able to find solace with other girls myself. The last straw was when I found she was going out with my flatmate, Malcolm. I discussed the situation with Peter. We had dinner together at the George and had a good deal to drink. After dinner, apropos of Mary, Peter said rather ponderously: "There are more fish in the sea, Thomas old boy. You'd better hook another."

"You're dead right," I replied, seeing Peter through a drunken haze. "I'll ditch her and put her out of my life." We then proceeded to have several more drinks.

Next day I had a frightful hangover. Peter called round and asked me if I would give him a hand with a couple of French girls he had promised to look after. I don't know if he intended this to help me to forget Mary but Peter was a good friend and although I felt pretty lousy, I agreed. The girls lived in North Oxford. *Dodi* according to Peter was a Comtesse and *Pip* also a member of the French aristocracy. (Peter always seemed to have exotic friends). He had promised to take them on the river but as he had agreed to play tennis that afternoon with Philip who had some free time from his school, he asked me if I would punt them up to Magdalen where they were to meet a *Prince*. I wondered what I was letting myself in for but as the girls sounded interesting I agreed.

It was a very hot afternoon and having hired a punt at Folly Bridge, the girls, who were young and very French, appeared, got into the punt and we started up the river. By the time we arrived at Magdalen I was sweating profusely, both from the effort of punting and from trying to make conversation at the same time in French (although the girls spoke perfectly good English) as I wanted to impress them. Having arrived at our destination, I disembarked unsteadily and tried to hold the punt still to prevent the girls from falling in the river. Off-loaded safely, we searched for the Prince who the girls knew. Suddenly he emerged from one of the buildings, looking like a very ordinary undergraduate but to my surprise Mary was with him. She laughed at my dishevelled state and said something to the Prince which he seemed to find very funny. They then led us to a party of Indians of both sexes, the ladies dressed in colourful saris, and all chattering animatedly in various languages. I then found to my dismay that I was expected to punt my party up the Cherwell, land by a meadow and have tea with the Indian party who were in another punt and Mary who was in the Prince's punt. As far as I was concerned the whole trip was a disaster. I had a splitting headache and couldn't understand a word of what was being said.

When it was over, still sweating, I returned my charges to Christ Church from where, for some reason, they refused point blank to move. I rang Peter.

"For God's sake come and collect your girls. I've really had enough and they won't move."

"Yes they are a bit wilful," Peter replied. "I'll fetch them and then come and have a drink." I was not sure if I ever wanted to have another drink with Peter again! As for Mary I was not going to let any further thoughts about her trouble me.

I now had interviews for various possible jobs. They were very diverse - from chocolates and sanitary towels to railways and motor cars - but few made me a firm offer of work. Eventually I had an interview with a director of a steel firm in Lancashire. He was a young man who had been at Oxford some years before me and had been in the OUDS. We chatted amicably and he offered me a job as a trainee at a wage of three pounds five shillings a week which was five shillings higher than any of the other offers. I had always been interested in blast furnaces and steel making and so I took it. The works were in Barrow-in-Furness and my future in the Territorial Army was shaped by this decision.

The end of term now approached. I sat for the various examinations and was pleased that I did just pass and obtained the Engineering degree I needed.

Four years at Oxford can make a big change in a man or woman and I at 22 was now very different from the diffident youth who climbed the stairs to his attic in 1930. I had made a wide circle of friends both male and female and felt I was sufficiently mature to hold my own in any social gathering.

The final evening was the *Gaudy* at which Christ Church graduates are invited to dine at a special dinner in Hall. All my friends, including Peter, had now become graduates and were there. I sat between Peter and Philip. Timms, our original scout, waited on us and kept us well supplied with food and drink. It was a great occasion.

Next day I went down for the last time. I wrote in my diary "So Goodbye to Oxford. Four years which no one can say was wasted and which are full of memories - of love and learning - beauty and inspiration - friends and foes - to help me on in life's adventure".

CHAPTER 7

I set out for Barrow in the Morris Cowley, taking the route to Scotland through Wigan, Preston and Lancaster. This was along what is now the M6 motorway but was then a series of roads of indifferent construction which caused the Morris, at times, to leap out of one pothole and plummet into the next. Before starting the climb which would have taken me from Kendal to Penrith and on to the border with Scotland, I turned left at Levens Bridge into a totally new country, the Furness Peninsula.

On my left were the waters of Morecambe Bay and to the right the lakes and mountains of the Lake District. Far to the north was Thirlmere with its dark curtain of pines and fir trees. Then Ullswater, that long and peaceful lake overlooked by towering Helvellyn, but a lake which so quickly can be whipped up into stormy waters. Next Grasmere and Rydal Water, the home of Wordsworth. Then, closer to Barrow is Windermere where Beatrix Potter wrote those books of Peter Rabbit and his friends, that I so well remembered as a child. It is the same lake on which, in 1930, Sir Henry Seagrave came to an untimely end when his boat Miss England II hit a floating object and burst into flames just after he broke the World water-speed record. Close by Windermere are the Hardknott and Wrynose Passes where, as a challenge, I was later to force the Morris over their rocks and boulders to get from Eskdale to Ambleside instead of going by the normal route. After that, the dark waters of Wast Water appear and on to Tarn Howes where, on winter's evenings when the moon was full and frost had turned the trees to sparkling diamonds, young men and women would bring out their skates and cut intricate patterns on its surface, and picnic along its banks. And so to Millom and the coast and back to Barrow.

That was not the route I took that first day. I went by Newby Bridge and Ulverston and entered Barrow by the long straight Abbey Road following the tram lines to Ramsden Square, the centre of the town. Turn left and you are amongst the shops, then turn right past Vickers shipyard and over a bridge and you are on Walney Island, a bird sanctuary. Press on over the sand dunes and you reach the sea-shore looking out over the Irish Sea to the Isle of Man which, on a clear day, you can see from the higher part of the town. Return to Ramsden Square and leaving by the opposite side you pass the gasworks.

One cloudy winter's day I was walking past when I felt some heat on my back which made me think the sun had just come out. Turning, I saw the gas works blazing and a few seconds later heard the explosion. The gasometer was wrecked but fortunately no one was hurt. It made me realise the potential dangers of the industrial life on which I was embarking. Just beyond the gasworks, was the Barrow Haematite Steel and Iron Works and it was here that I was to work for the next three years.

The first thing was to find lodgings, or *digs* as they were called. I had already met Douglas, a commercial trainee at the Steelworks, and Bill who was the Company Secretary and they helped me find accommodation in Abbey Road. Here for two pounds five shillings per week, I was provided with a bedroom and three meals a day, breakfast, lunch and high tea. I met the other two occupants of the digs: Ignatiev, a white Russian who was an engineer working at Vickers, and Allan, a premium apprentice who had just returned from a year's secondment to a firm in Germany. I asked Allan what a premium apprentice was and he explained that, having paid a premium, he was apprenticed to Vickers for five years after which he would become a qualified engineer. In the end Allan decided after he had completed his five years, to turn down the offer of a job in South Africa in order to join a Norwegian expedition to the lonely Island of Tristan da Cunha in the South Atlantic Ocean.

Vickers Armstrong, apart from the Steelworks, was the main employer of labour in Barrow. Many famous warships and submarines had been built in the shipyard but now Vickers was making guns and other armaments as well. The Government was, albeit slowly, realising that war might be looming on the horizon and were ordering arms from their main suppliers. Vickers was one of them. This was good news for their employees who could look forward to continuing paypackets.

The premium apprentices were to some extent similar to the students at a University but obtaining more practical engineering experience. Some were in the local Territorials and I soon made friends and joined in their activities. I had decided that as I was expecting to remain in Barrow I would apply to transfer from the Cheshire Regiment to the local T.A. Unit which was the 4th Battalion The King's Own Royal Regiment (the 4th of Foot). My transfer was accepted and I now found myself to be a Lieutenant in the *King's Own* and wore the Lion in place of the Cheshire acorn. The Headquarters was in Ulverston where there was one rifle company, one at Millom and two at Barrow. I was in one of the Barrow companies and was able to do my drills at the Drill Hall off Abbey Road. The electric trams which ran up and down Abbey Road and into the town were the normal form of public transport and I used them for travelling to and from the Drill Hall and the Works. Their clanking sound as they travelled along the rails and the bell which announced their approach was something I had to get used to as they ran just outside my digs.

The Commanding Officer of the Battalion had served in the last war and had been awarded the Distinguished Service Order. He was an excellent CO, both kind and understanding and respected by all ranks. He lived with his family near Grange-over-Sands overlooking Morecambe Bay.

In the middle of the thirties, although still in the years of the depression, but with thoughts of war beginning to draw ever closer, and perhaps because of it, there seemed to be an endless round of entertainment, cocktail parties, dances, visits to the cinema, games of badminton and squash and I soon became caught up in a whirl of social activities.

It was not long before I found out that the Colonel had an attractive daughter. Sally was tall with short strawberry blonde hair and an athletic figure. She rode to hounds and was very much an outdoor girl. I have to admit I was immediately attracted to her. I soon began to receive invitations to their family parties as well as going to dances and the cinema. Eventually I was asked to stay for the weekend. That Saturday I arrived earlier than expected and, as the family were out hunting, had a luxurious hot bath. However I had a very chilly reception when the hunters returned, I had pinched all the hot water!

The rest of the family came in by degrees, having changed their mud spattered hunting clothes and cleaned their mud speckled faces. The talk gathered momentum on jumps and runs, kills, horses and people, until the day's sport had been minutely dissected. It flowed over me, a disinterested listener, in a somnolent stream. After tea we all went to the cinema. I sat next to Sally and consequently remember little of the film.

The following morning I woke rather late and was called peremptorily by: "Bathrooms finished with now". It rather indicated that if there was any hot water left, I could have it. I breakfasted alone but afterwards we all drove to Church. Although it was raining, Sally and I walked home. Never had an hour's walk in the rain passed so quickly or so pleasantly. Life in Barrow began to look as if it might have possibilities.

When I arrived in Barrow in the autumn of 1934 world events were taking place, and were to happen in the next few years, which would lead up to the war in which I was going to be involved.

In October, King Alexander of Yugoslavia was shot dead in Marseilles by a Croat gunman, causing potential unrest in the Balkans. In 1933 Hitler, who had come to power on the death of President Hindenburg, destroyed the Communists in Germany and secretly planned to destroy the Unions which he succeeded in doing in 1934. In their place he set up an organisation called *Strength through Joy*. This produced incentives for the working classes such as heavily subsidised holidays. For example a ten-day holiday cruise to Madeira cost as little as ten pounds in English money. Not unnaturally this endeared him to the workers whose support he urgently needed to build the armaments that he was soon to require.

Although he was a tyrant, both intolerant and emotionally unstable, Hitler gained the adoration of, not only the workers, but the majority of the German people. They believed he was saving them from the defeat in 1918 which had caused, amongst other things, the collapse of the currency leading to hyperinflation and the ensuing depression. Furthermore he promised to liberate them from the shackles of what he considered to be the shameful Peace imposed on Germany at Versailles, in particular the limitations on the size of the army and navy and the prohibition of rebuilding the airforce.

If anyone had read Hitler's 'bible' - *Mein Kampf* - written in 1923 during a nine month imprisonment for his unsuccessful coup against the Bavarian Government, they would have seen what Hitler intended to do. Sadly those who did read it, dismissed it as a load of Nazi gibberish and could, or would not believe it.

The first shock came in January 1935 when the inhabitants of the Saar, occupied by the French since the end of the War, voted to return to Germany. That a predominantly Catholic country could be so taken in by what was happening in Germany, is an example of how much Hitler had duped the people. The return of the Saar took place peacefully and Hitler then declared he wanted nothing but peace and had no more territorial demands on France. Great Britain and France believed him and declared that if he would renounce any demands on the countries to his east (Poland and Czechoslovakia) they would release him from the terms of the Versailles Treaty. Hitler prevaricated on this as he had every intention of extending his eastern frontiers. In March 1935 he simply repudiated the military clauses of the treaty, instituted military service, started production of tanks and heavy artillery and commenced to build up an Air Force.

This flagrant violation of the treaty which would have fully justified France, who had a massive army, to march into Germany and destroy Hitler once and for all, was simply overlooked and nothing happened. Everyone was fearful of doing anything which might provide a repetition of the 1914-18 conflict but the first opportunity for direct action to avoid the coming war was missed.

All these events in Europe and Germany were forgotten in the rejoicing over the King's Silver Jubilee which took place in May 1935. Then, in January of the following year the King died and was succeeded by the Prince of V ales who was proclaimed King Edward VIII. Teddy, as he was called by the general public, was popular amongst the working classes for whom he had great sympathy and would have liked to help had it not been for the dead hand of bureaucracy. Alas his efforts at conciliation with the German people, to whom our Royal Family are related, and his wish to marry Mrs Simpson, a divorcee, counted against him. The train of events which led to his downfall was triggered by a sermon by one of the bishops and by a complex set of influences. Eventually the Prime Minister, Stanley Baldwin, and the Archbishop of Canterbury, amongst others, caused him to abdicate. It was a sad ending which I saw on the newsreel in the cinema, as he boarded a ship to go into exile. His brother the Duke of York, a quiet and unassuming man who had never wanted to be King, became King George VI and once again the people were in a state of euphoric excitement at his Coronation. I watched this historic event through the first black and white television pictures to be transmitted by the B.B.C. on such an occasion.

It was in 1936 that Hitler hosted the Olympic Games and made it a dazzling propaganda coup for his so-called peace initiative. Nevertheless he refused to shake hands with Jesse Owens, the outstanding black American sprinter who had won four gold medals, because of his skin colour. Hitler was obsessed with the purity of the Germans who were to him the supreme Aryan race. He considered that anyone who was non-white, a gypsy or a homosexual was a threat to the purity of that race. This applied particularly to the Jews who had to be eliminated by torture, degradation and eventually mass murder. The persecution of the Jews, which would culminate with the extermination camps like Auschwitz and Buchenwald, had begun the previous year but none of this was noticed by me nor by Allan who had returned from Germany the previous year nor by the inhabitants of Barrow at the time nor, indeed, by the majority of the British population.

In the Spring, again breaking all treaties, Hitler marched into the demilitarised zone of the Rhineland which had been agreed at the Treaty of Locarno. It was not known at the time that his army had instructions to retreat immediately if attacked by the French army which was still vastly superior in numbers to his. The French did not attack. Instead they appealed to the League of Nations - a useless gesture. Another chance of averting the next World War had gone. I knew little of this at the time which was perhaps just as well considering the unpreparedness of the Territorial Army for a real war.

Trouble also began to erupt in Africa where Mussolini had ordered the invasion of Abyssinia the previous year. Marshal Badoglio entered Addis Ababa in May of 1936 and completed his conquest over the lightly armed and unprotected Abyssinians by the use of high explosives and mustard gas.

In Spain, during the summer of 1936, a right wing revolt started in Melilla, the easternmost city of Spanish Morocco which led to the Spanish Civil War between General Franco's forces and the Spanish Republican Government. Hitler quickly supported Franco hoping for another pro-Fascist state which, together with Italy, would arouse further fears in France whom he hated vehemently for the defeat of Germany in 1918. France with its Left Popular Front Government supported the Spanish Republican party as did communist Russia. In Britain the National government adopted a policy of *non-intervention* which in effect supported Franco.

Meanwhile the Germans were able to test their new guns, tanks and war planes under battle conditions in Spain. The indiscriminate bombing of the open city of Guernica on the 27th of April 1937 which was a forerunner of the bombing of cities and civilians in the war to come, caused shock and horror throughout the world but apart from condemnation nothing was done.

At home there was a General Election in November 1935 and Stanley Baldwin remained as Prime Minister. He presided over a National Government until in 1937 Neville Chamberlain replaced him.

Although it was obvious to some that the slide into war might gather speed at any moment, little effort was being made to re-arm the country. Apart from Vickers and the other armament firms, some Government contracts were being given for more mundane supplies and whilst there was serious unemployment and poverty in many parts of the country, prosperity in Barrow was improving and few were unemployed.

However the Territorial Army was still the *Cinderella* of the forces, and Winston Churchill was, alas, only a *voice crying in the wilderness.*

My first job at the Iron and Steel works was in the Blast Furnace department. Four tall cylindrical columns, taller than the Martello Towers which protected our shores in the early part of the last century, dominated the skyline behind the works. Each had an inclined tracery of steelwork carrying the skips which took the iron ore, coke and limestone, the proportion of these ingredients being known as the *burden*, to the top of the furnaces which devoured their contents continuously.

The working of the furnaces was explained to me by Mr Danks, the Blast Furnace Manager. He told me how the steel shell of the furnace was lined with several layers of firebrick to protect it from the searing heat of the molten iron. In order to reach this temperature, the flammable gas which was produced in the furnace was used to heat the air which was blown into the bottom of the furnace through a series of water cooled nozzles called *Tuyères*.

Once the furnace was lit, and this was done in the same way you would light the kitchen fire by building up a layer of firewood and putting a match to it, it must never be let out during its working life which might be several years. If this should happen, the iron inside the furnace would set to a solid mass and the furnace would have to be dismantled and rebuilt. It was a disaster, Mr Danks emphasised, to be avoided at all costs. When the furnace was running the iron ore, which was called *haematite* (and may have been mined locally at Hodbarrow which was up the coast, or imported from Norway or even from such far away places as Sierra Leone) melted. The iron took up some of the carbon from the coke and with the limestone, formed a slag with the impurities in the ore. Much of this I had learnt from reading about it in the encyclopaedia at home and at school but now it was for real.

Five times every twentyfour hours, seven days a week, every week for the years of its life, the furnace had to be *tapped*. This was done by a man wielding a sledge-hammer who drove an iron bar into the bottom of the furnace. Once he had broken through into what was known as the *hearth*, the white hot glowing slag was the first to appear, rushing out into an iron bogie. The bogie was then pushed by a steam locomotive - the slagging loco - to the top of the slag heap, that unsightly artificial mountain behind the works and typical of iron and steel-making throughout the world. Although the slag as it cooled in the bogie had a solid grey crust on top, it was still molten underneath and, as it was pushed up the mountain, splashes of fiery liquid could be seen spilling over the edge. As soon as it was tipped, a white hot stream, like lava from a volcano, ran down the sides of the mountain and at night illuminated the town and countryside for miles around. I always knew when a furnace was being tapped since I could see the light in the sky from my digs.

After the slag had run out of the furnace, the molten iron appeared, white hot but not as bright as the slag, fizzing and sending out sparks just like a child's sparkler. The fervid stream ran into channels moulded in a bed of sand. From there it ran into subsidiary channels and then into smaller ones to form the blocks known as *Pig Iron*, so called from the analogy with a pig suckling her young.

There were three shifts, each in charge of a foreman, and each furnace had a *keeper*, a *slagger*, and a *cobbler*. I was pleased to meet the furnacemen, some of whom were in the Territorials, and who were a grand lot of Lancashire men. As they saw I was prepared to *muck in* and help with the *pig lifting*, a backbreaking job, and other work, they treated me as one of them, called me Tom and asked me to join in their activities.

I noticed that samples of the iron, before it cooled, were being taken in little cast-iron pots. I asked George, who was the foreman on one of the shifts, how he could tell the quality of the iron from these.

"It's like this Tom," said George. "If it sets like cream it's good but if it whirls round in the pot it's bad. If it's white like a man's bald head it's high in *silli* (silicon) but if the graphite sets out in a ring round the edge of the pot it's low. Then we alter the burden to get it right."

He added. "They check it in the lab but it takes too long and we're generally right."

When sufficient iron had been allowed to run out, the flow had to be stopped. I asked George how this was done?

"Well thou hast to be a strong lad with a good eye. He puts a sweat rag round his throat and picks up that bar." He turned to me and said, "Try its weight." I did but couldn't move it. George laughed. "You'll have to have a mate."

He continued. "He sticks a lump of fireclay on the end and then stuffs it into the hole. It needs a lot of strength and he usually does have a mate."

I have never forgotten my first experience of a *tap* at night. There was the noise of the furnace dropping as the air was turned off, the rush of molten metal flowing down into the sand beds, smoking, hissing, steam rising if the sand was damp, and the furnacemen silhouetted in the darkness by the light from the molten metal, with their iron rods poking the metal if it was not flowing freely. There was also the realisation that here was the method of winning iron from its ores first practised thousands of years ago by our Iron Age ancestors to make their weapons, and now producing the basic material for our modern arms. Without this process our present industrial age would not have developed.

One day George asked me to come and have a drink with him that evening. We went first to the *Travellers*, a public house where, apart from numerous pints of ale, I was invited to eat a quarter of a pound of tripe and a pig's trotter. The thought made me feel sick but I found it not nearly as bad as I had expected. We then went on to George's Club - *The Cemetery* - where we met his brother Jack and consumed several more pints of ale. George was by now very drunk and we went round to Jack's house where Mrs *Jack* and her daughter slated George in good style with much colourful language. However after a cup of strong Lancashire tea we got George home and I felt I had had a very enlightening evening although I suffered for it next morning.

On one of the night shifts when we were having a break the conversation turned, as so often happens when men are together, to more intimate matters. I had to admit that I wore pyjamas in bed.

"Nae lad," George remarked, "thou does'ne want them things. A nightshirt's better when thou'st in bed with missus - ther's not so much messin abart." I felt I was learning more of life than I had at the University.

On another occasion Jack, after much beating about the bush, asked me if I would come to a dance with his daughter and her *young man*. I agreed and in due course arrived at Jack's house. The dance at the Parish Hall was different from any that I had been to before. The girls sat on chairs in a line on one side of the room. When the music started the young Lotharios walked across to pick the girl of their choice. The popular ones were danced off their feet and fights sometimes broke out if they had several admirers. The plainer ones had to wait their turn and if no male escort turned up they had to sit it out or dance together. The dances themselves were rather formal: the Foxtrot, the One-Step, and the Waltz. The man held his partner decorously with one arm round her waist and, with the other stretched out and clasping her hand, he propelled her round the room. One step forward, one to the side, turn, feet together and forward. I never got the hang of it. I was used to holding my partner tightly - depending on who she was - and walking in time to the music whilst making polite conversation o. if more intimate, dancing *cheek to cheek*. I didn't try the Boston Two Step or the Tango but when I started, what I thought to be an old fashioned waltz and twirled my partner round, I found it was a Veleta and had to be danced much more sedately. Supper consisted of fizzy lemonade for the girls and tea and a bun for the men. The total cost for the evening was one shilling. After the dance we returned to Jack's house for more cups of tea and chat. I eventually got back to my digs and wished that some of the other dances I had been to had been as interesting and had only cost as little.

Douglas, the commercial trainee who had helped me to find digs had been in

Barrow for twelve months before I arrived there. He was slightly older than me but seemed a rather lonely type and was not interested in girls. He dressed smartly in a tweed jacket, tweed breeches, stockings with never a crease and brown brogues, which were clean and well polished as opposed to mine which were always pretty rough. He had a dark moustache, somewhat larger than mine, a rather pallid complexion and wore a country-type trilby. He owned two cars, a Morris like mine, and a two-seater Humber tourer, both of which were always immaculately turned out, the paintwork shining and the chrome highly polished.

He was a member of the County Club in Ramsden Square to which he got me elected. We only worked in the mornings on Saturdays and at lunchtime retired to the club where we devoured oysters and Guinness, and met Allan and many of our other friends.

One Saturday Douglas suggested that he and I should have a run in his Humber to the Lakes, ostensibly to climb Helvellyn. We set out but the rain started and before we had got very far we decided it was too wet for our climbing project. The outing then degenerated into a gigantic pub crawl round the hostelries for which the Lakes are famous. After we had exhausted those that we knew, we drove on to Morecambe where we visited the Winter Gardens and spent a hilarious hour on the *dodgems* and other side shows.

By the time we were ready to return both Douglas and I were very drunk. Douglas was driving, and at a speed which would not have been safe had he been sober. We had several narrow shaves and stopping to have a pee on the way back, Douglas fell full length into the ditch at the side of the road, making an awful mess of his smart clothes. I picked him up, put him in the car and drove the rest of the way myself. After an erratic journey we arrived safely at Douglas's digs where I put him to bed and drove his car to my digs and got to my room where I slept soundly. We had been, as might have been expected, well over the limit had there been a breath test. In those days there were very few cars on the road and there was less likelihood of an accident but I think we were still lucky to avoid one and get home unscathed.

After that episode, I decided that the next time I would take an outing by myself and see the *Illuminations* at Blackpool. I could get a railway excursion for two shillings return fare and accordingly, one Sunday afternoon, I set off. There was a cheerful Lancashire party in my compartment consisting of a married couple and three elderly women. The three *E.W.* laughed, swore and chattered continuously but good-humouredly throughout the journey. I had not perfected my Lancashire vocabulary sufficiently to join in the conversation, so confined myself to grinning and uttering a few ayes and grunts which seemed to be acceptable.

Arriving at Blackpool in torrents of rain, I walked up the *Prom*, had a drink at a pub and then walked down again. The Illuminations were magnificent. I saw the Tower but did not go up it. It was still raining and seeing a very modern building by the station which turned out to be an hotel, I approached a door marked *Bar* but, on entering, found that I was at the tradesman's entrance. I retreated and found another door with various modern devices which passed as door handles. Having discovered how they worked I found myself in a Cafe and ordered an omelette. The waitress was affable but definitely *on duty* although she accepted the offer of a drink later but it had to be off the premises. We went to the nearest pub. She ordered a port and lemon and I had another beer. After that she said she had to meet her boyfriend so she left and I went off to the Tower Ballroom. None of the girls were very attractive or forthcoming, so having danced a Paul Jones I retired to the bar until closing time which was at 10.30. The train didn't leave until 11 and I sat in the station feeling depressed. I was surrounded by courting couples all waiting for the last train home. When it arrived I was lucky to find an empty compartment where I slept until arriving at Barrow. It was still raining. There were no taxis and the trams were not running so I walked. I arrived at my digs and was pleased to find Allan still up. He opened a bottle of beer and I recounted the evening's events which I considered a dead loss with no women, getting very wet and costing me nine shillings and fourpence which I thought a considerable waste of money.

"If you will go on these expeditions what can you expect?" said Allan. "Next time you had better take someone with you and you may have better luck."

One night, not long after my expedition to Blackpool, I was awakened by the noise of an explosion shortly followed by another. I looked at my watch. It was 4 a.m. The telephone rang. It was Douglas. "There's been a breakout at No 10," he announced. "You'd better get down to the works at once."

I dressed rapidly and got my car out. As I drove down Abbey Road I saw an ominous red glow in the sky in the direction of the works and when I got to the factory gates there was a frantic crowd, milling round asking if anyone had been hurt. When a blast furnace 'breaks out' it means that it has not been possible to stem the flow of molten metal from the furnace. This could be caused either by a fracture in the hearth or if the tapper had failed to get the plug of fireclay into the hole. In this case there had been a fracture and the molten iron had come in contact with the water cooling the tuyères and this had caused the violent explosions. As a result the metal poured out over the sand beds making it more difficult to get to the furnace to try to stop the flow. Men could be caught in the molten metal and fatally burnt. It was imperative to stop the furnace from emptying itself which would have meant having to rebuild it. The furnacemen, knowing that their livelihood was on the line, would take exceptional risks to seal the furnace up. Fortunately when I arrived, although the iron had spread all over the sand bed and would cause immense problems in moving it when it cooled, the hearth had been sealed, the furnace saved, and no one had been seriously hurt. I went back to bed realising once again the dangers anyone in industry and especially in the manufacture of iron and steel, had to face. I think this realisation remained with me for the rest of my life and made me especially aware of the need for industrial safety.

CHAPTER 8

The Morris Cowley had served me well but when the owner of the garage where I kept it offered to swap it for an unusual car called a Schneider I agreed. The Schneider was an open four-seater tourer very similar to the Morris but rather more sporty and much admired by my friends. It had an unusual addition which I did not appreciate until after I had acquired the car. The back of the front bench seat was held in position by a chain which could be used to adjust its angle. However it could also be released so that the back fell into the gap between the front and rear seats making an upholstered bed the length of the vehicle. This caused much consternation to any female passenger who, when I demonstrated it, on hearing the rattling of chains and feeling the collapse of the back, immediately thought I was going to take advantage of her.

The Schneider was not powerful enough and I hankered after a proper sports car. When a second-hand Wolseley Hornet Sports turned up at the garage, I could not resist it. I borrowed the money from my mother and became the proud owner of a six-cylinder, twin-carburettor, two-seater open sports car with wire wheels. It had a wonderful exhaust note as I drove it down the Abbey Road, showing off to the locals.

Reggie James was another premium apprentice at Vickers and also a Lieutenant in the Territorials. He was short in stature but well-built and played for the Barrow rugby team. He had gingerish hair and a pleasant scattering of freckles and his eyes shone with good humour. He and I were about the same age and we became good friends and spent much of our leisure time together, going to parties, playing badminton and drinking.

One evening when we were at the Saturday night dance at the Victoria Park Hotel, we noticed two nice-looking girls, one blonde and one brunette, who looked as if they might be receptive to an advance. I pointed them out to Reggie.

"I'll go for the tall one and you go for the short," I said.

"That suits me," replied Reg.

We went over and asked them to dance to which they agreed. After several dances and some refreshments, we took them back to my digs which were closer than Reggie's, where we drank cocoa before taking them home. We found out that the girls were sisters and ran a ladies' hairdressing salon in the town. They were Irish. My girl's name was Bridget and Reggie's Sharon.

Next day we asked them to come to the cinema. Reggie and Sharon sat in the row in front of Bridget and myself.

"Do you think Reggie knows what to do?" I said, turning to Bridget with a smile, although I knew very well that Reggie was not inexperienced.

"I think Sharon will show him," she replied, "like this." And she pressed her lips against mine as the lights went out.

I don't remember much of the film only the closeness of Bridget as there was no armrest between us.

After the film we walked the girls back to their home. They lived alone but we didn't go in. Returning to Reggie's digs he produced a bottle of beer and we discussed the evening.

"They're jolly nice girls," said Reg. "I think we're lucky, and we should keep it up." To which sentiments I agreed.

As it was summer we arranged to go for a picnic in the Lakes the following Sunday and it turned out to be one of those lovely hot and sunny days in June, suitable for dalliance in the hills. I borrowed Douglas's Morris as it was a four-seater and the Wolseley could only take two. We set out and eventually reached a pleasant and deserted spot high up on the moors above Coniston Water. It was ideal for a picnic and sun bathing. We decided that the picnic could wait but the sun bathing could not. Reggie and I were already in shorts and the girls changed skilfully into their sunbathing outfits. An hour passed very quickly with a good deal of snogging taking place for which the sunbathing outfits were very helpful. However both girls were prudent and would not go too far which was perhaps just as well. After that we brought out the picnic. The girls had made sandwiches and I had brought a bottle of sherry. The picnic over, we all lay in the sun again until it started to get cooler and then drove home, stopping at one or two pubs on the way. Everyone agreed that it had been a lovely day and we would meet again.

It was not long after that pleasant episode in the hills, that we were due to go to camp. My first camp with the King's Own was on the Isle of Man. Since it involved an embarkation and short sea voyage it could have been considered as training for the landing of an expeditionary force on the continent. The Battalion entrained at Ulverston for the journey to Heysham where we embarked on the ferry to Douglas. It was a rough passage and many of the men were seasick and glad to reach Douglas where camp was set up some little distance from the town.

Although still a Lieutenant, I was senior to most of the other subalterns and therefore felt more confident in the Mess. Training was much the same as at my camps with the Cheshires but seemed now to be more realistic. Perhaps the directing staff thought that it might not be long before we would be doing it for real. The manoeuvres on Snaefell were strenuous but by the time camp came to an end, I felt I had learned more about proper soldiering than on any previous camp.

Shortly after returning I was told I was to move to the steelworks. This was all part of the same factory but its object was to convert the pig iron to steel and to manufacture steel rails for the railways. I was sorry to leave the blast furnaces where I had made good friends with George, Jack and the other furnacemen but, as I was a works trainee, I had to go where I was told.

Steel-making is different from winning the iron from its ore. There are two methods. One, known as the Bessemer process, is to blow air through a molten bath of iron to remove the carbon, which produces a spectacular cloud of sparks, after which the required extra ingredients are added to make the steel. The other method, which uses a proportion of steel scrap together with the iron, is known as the open-hearth process and produces a better quality steel. The steel at Barrow was made by this method.

The Siemens Martin open-hearth furnaces were some 30 feet long and about eight feet high. The outside was constructed of brickwork held together by steel rods and lined, as in the blast furnaces, with firebrick. The hearth was shaped like a shallow pan and access to it was by an opening at the front. This opening was closed by a door, also made of firebrick, which was suspended from a lever with a counterweight. Just below the opening and in front of the furnace was the charging floor made of heavy steel plates. This carried the charging machine, a very rugged and cumbersome piece of machinery with a long arm which picked up the charging boxes from the floor. The boxes, filled with pig-iron or steel scrap, weighed about a ton and the machine pushed them into the furnace and tipped the contents on to the hearth.

To attain the high temperature required to melt the steel a method of regenerative heating was used. The furnaces were fired by the gas which had been produced in the blast furnaces. The gas, mixed with air, ignited and the flame was carried over the hearth heating the steel. The heated gases, having passed through the furnace, were used to preheat the incoming air and gas. By repeating this process of regeneration many times the temperature rose until it reached the required heat to melt the steel. It needed careful control by the furnacemen to prevent the furnace from getting so hot that the brickwork melted, which would be disastrous.

The scene on the charging floor when a furnace was running was, like the tapping of the blast furnace, something that is etched on my memory: the noise from the rush of heated gases and the roar of burning, the clanking of the charging machine, the dust, the heat, the flames escaping round the edges of the door and, again, the outlines of the furnacemen silhouetted by the glow from the furnace.

I was issued with a pair of furnaceman's spectacles, steel-rimmed with lenses about one inch diameter of very dark blue glass. I found it impossible to look into the furnace without them. I was also given a *sweat rag* which, although it was tied by a piece of string round my neck, had to be held in my mouth so that it hung down and protected my throat from the heat. I timidly approached the open door of the furnace. The heat was more than I had ever experienced before. I felt I was about to be consumed. I looked into the furnace through the spectacles quickly before the heat made me draw away, and I saw the molten steel bubbling, as if in a witch's cauldron, throwing up blobs of liquid steel, and with an unearthly vapour swirling above it. Remembering what I had read in the book of Daniel in the Bible, I could well imagine that I was seeing Shadrach, Meshach and Abednego dancing in the fiery furnace heated seven times seven by Nebuchadnezzar, and could well believe that the men who threw them in were consumed by the flames issuing from it.

The furnacemen were dressed in woollen jackets, trousers, and caps, with the blue spectacles and sweat rags. They had to approach the furnace door much closer than I had, as it was necessary for them to poke the surface of the molten metal with iron rods to stir it like soup and to take samples for the laboratory. I couldn't see how they could withstand the heat. They were sweating profusely and had to retire frequently to the back of the floor where they drank copiously of barley water, or sometimes beer, which was brought to them by their families when they also brought their *baggin* - a meal in a bag.

When the charge was ready, the furnace was tapped in much the same way as the blast furnaces. The steel ran down a chute into a series of moulds in the casting pit to form steel ingots weighing several tons.

The next stage of manufacture was the production of the steel rails. The ingots were taken to the rolling mills and were heated in *soaking pits* to a white heat, just below their melting point, and then transferred to the first set of rolls at the *cogging* mill. The rolls were massive cylinders of steel in pairs, like a clothes mangle. They were driven by a steam engine and cooled continuously by sprays of cold water. The ingot was moved up to the rolls which seized it with a mighty crunch, the steam engine roared as if in anger, sparks and steam flew from the steel and the ingot appeared at the far side slightly thinner but longer than when it started. The direction of the rolls was reversed and they were brought closer together as back the ingot came to be squeezed a little thinner. The process was repeated, each time the rolls were brought closer together, until the steel had made its last pass. It was now a *billet.*

In order to produce a rail, a different set of rolls were provided which had a series of profiles of the rails cut into them. The billet was heated and the process of rolling proceeded until the billet had become a long white hot straggling bar which, in spite of the heat, the men had to manipulate with tongs for it to enter the next pass or, in some cases, another set of rolls. If the steel were to become too cold during the rolling process it could break the rolls which would be a disaster. The foreman in charge known as the *Roller* had his own way of checking the temperature. He spat on the steel and from the amount of sizzle knew if it was satisfactory. He had no use for modern pyrometers or measuring instruments and as a result was the highest paid man on the floor.

The final stage was for the rail to be straightened which was done by eye with the help of powerful hydraulic rams. After that it had to be cut to length. This was done by a steel circular saw and the high pitched scream of tortured metal with no ear protection must have left many of the workers suffering from eventual deafness. It certainly gave me a headache.

So the rails were produced and every time I travelled on the railway, I thought of the steel track I was riding on and wondered how many of my friends had helped to produce it.

Summer had turned into autumn, that *season of mists and mellow fruitfulness,* when the Lake District looked most beautiful with the leaves turning colour from yellow through all the tints to deep red with the shiny green of the evergreens in the background. But it was now early December, the leaves had fallen, the sheep were moving to the lower pastures, and one had the feeling that winter was not far away.

I had been at Barrow for over a year and had seen Sally at tennis parties and occasionally taken her to the cinema but she had been away for most of the summer, staying with friends in France. She was now home, so I decided I would ask her to come with me to Cartmel races which were taking place the next Saturday.

Cartmel, not far from Barrow, had a small racecourse which had an oval track a mile and one furlong long with a half-mile run in and sharp left-hand bends. Most races required several circuits. It was the steeplechase season and on this Saturday there was, in addition to the other races, one Hunter Chase in which amateur jockeys took part.

I asked Douglas and Reggie to come along with me but, as I was picking up Sally, they went separately in Douglas's car. I duly collected Sally who was looking very attractive in a full-length fawn coat with cap to match. We arrived at the racecourse in time for the first race and mingled with the crowds. It was fine but cold with a touch of snow in the air. The scene was like all racecourses, a milling crowd round the bookies' stands with their colourful umbrellas and their boards quoting the odds which they were shouting and making signs in a language that only the knowledgable racing professionals could understand. The Tote was for those who preferred a sedate and probably more modest gamble. The grandstand was filling up but the more enthusiastic racegoers were by the saddling enclosure where the horses were walking round led by their grooms with numbers displayed on their arms. The rugs which had been protecting the horses from the cold were removed and the jockeys with their bright racing colours mounted and, after parading in front of the stands, cantered down to the start.

Sally was more interested in the third race, the Hunter Chase, as one of her friends was riding No.3 which happened to be my lucky number, and was a horse she knew well. We all went down to the saddling enclosure and Teddy who was riding No.3 winked at Sally as he went past.

I had already seen several of the men from the works as it was a popular outing for them and, when I saw Jack and his daughter and her *young man*, I brought Sally over and introduced her. They chattered for a moment about the prospects for the race and then Sally and Douglas went off to the Tote. While they were away Jack turned to me and said:

"Tha's got a gradely lass tha Tom." To which I heartily agreed.

We went down to watch the race from the rails where we could see the last two fences. As the horses came round on the first circuit, No.3 was lying third which Sally said was a good position for that stage of the race. On the last circuit No.3 was neck and neck with No.6 at the fence before the last. The crowd was cheering, the noise rising to a crescendo and, as they came to the last fence, No.6 misjudged his take off which cost him the race. Sally flung her arms round me in her excitement and kissed me effusively. She then rushed off to the unsaddling enclosure to congratulate Teddy.

After that the rest of the afternoon was rather an anti-climax. When the races were over we went back to Sally's house where she introduced Douglas and Reggie to her father and mother and we all had tea. One of Sally's friends whom I had met before at one of the parties turned up, as well as Sally's younger sister. We decided we would all go to the cinema. I sat next to Sally, and as it was one of those cinemas with double seats, was able to put my arm round her. After the film we had drinks at a pub which, in those days, meant you had to buy a sandwich if you wanted to have a drink after 10 p.m. After dropping Sally at her home where she gave me a lingering kiss, I returned to my digs with romantic thoughts filling my head. Feeling restless I decided to go and call on Reggie who was just about to go to bed, but seeing me he got out two bottles of beer and glasses.

I lit a cigarette. "Well, what do you think of Sally?" I asked.

"She's a cracking nice girl," he replied.

"Yes she is. I've rather fallen for her."

"That's pretty obvious, but don't go and get yourself tied up too soon or you'll miss out on the others."

Reggie's philosophy was to meet as many girls as possible before he considered settling down with one of them and he still had a long way to go.

"That's all very well but you're not in love."

"You'll get over it. Take Bridget out," was Reggie's final reply.

I finished the beer, thanked Reg for his advice which I had no intention of taking and went back to my digs.

Sleep took some time to come, but when it did I dreamt of Sally.

I had still kept contact with some of my Oxford friends. One weekend I went over to Sedbergh school where Philip was now a master and together we climbed Winder, the hill behind the school. Shortly afterwards Peter came over to Barrow and brought his girl friend Polly and stayed, rather grandly, at the Furness Abbey Hotel. Sadly he was to be killed a few years later in a farming accident in Australia. Robert had already married Liz and joined the Navy where he lost his life in the first year of the war. Audrey was to be married to Derick, and Philip, Robert and Liz, Peter and I all went to the wedding. I no longer had any contact with Mary who, I had heard, was engaged to my rival in the Dramatic Society and was living somewhere on the East coast.

It was not long after the Cartmel races that a letter arrived from Sally's family inviting me to go with them to the Westmorland County Ball. This was a prestigious affair, akin to the Oxford *Commems*, with lashings of drink and a host of attractive females. There was one who had green fingernails and another who thought she should be a film star and modelled herself on Katherine Hepburn, and one in what I can only describe as a tantalising dress. The dinner party at Sally's house went on for rather a long time and as a result we arrived at the dance very late. The dances were arranged by programmes and most of the girls had already made their engagements. I was content to dance with Sally when she was not taken up by other admirers. The dance went on until the early hours and breakfast of bacon and eggs was served at 5 a.m. Sally's father, the Colonel, had arranged for some taxis to take his party home and I was able to sit in the back of one and hold hands with Sally.

The next day we were to follow the local Harriers. The Harriers hunt the hare and the field can either be mounted or on foot. The latter have to be pretty fit to keep up with the hounds which although faster than Beagles were not as fast as Foxhounds. Sally was to be mounted and her horse box was driven to the meet. I decided I would run as I had hunted with the beagles when at Oxford, and was pleasantly surprised to find that I kept up with hounds until they were called off at the end of the day. I found Sally who was looking for her horse box and I walked beside her until we found it. Sally's father then kindly agreed to drive it back while I took Sally home in my car.

When we were nearly home I turned the car into a side road and, pulling Sally towards me, kissed her passionately. I felt myself being carried away with thoughts of the times we had had together and then the dance the night before and now with Sally in my arms.

"Will you marry me?" I suddenly said.

Although Sally was undoubtedly fond of me, she was taken aback. "I'll have to think about it," she said with surprise. "It's rather sudden."

"I know," I replied. "But that's how I feel," and with that I started the car and drove back to the house.

The next morning I felt rather embarrassed by my impulsiveness but did not mention the matter. After saying goodbye, I drove back to Barrow.

As I thought about it I realised I had got myself into an awkward position. I hadn't taken Reggie's advice and didn't really want to get myself tied up so soon, much as I thought I loved Sally. The solution came rather unexpectedly. Her family heard of my liaisons with the hairdressers in Barrow and decided that if I wanted to run with the hare and hunt with the hounds I would be better doing it somewhere else. Sally, I heard, was not too unhappy with this solution. So perhaps it was all for the best. Reggie certainly considered that I had had a lucky escape.

CHAPTER 9

I had not been at the steel-making plant for very long when the Chairman, Sir Robert Riscombe sent for me. He explained that they had a problem due to the shortage of supplies of good quality steel scrap. Scrap varied from old iron bedsteads and pots and pans to heavy steel ships' plates from the breakers' yards. It was supplied by Scrap Merchants from all over the country and varied very much in quality and therefore in price. The Chairman wanted me to inspect the scrap coming into the works and assess its quality. He explained that one type of scrap which we used was the turnings from the machining operations in engineering factories such as Vickers. These turnings could either be long spring-like lengths of steel known as curly turnings or heavier pieces known as heavy turnings which fetched a higher price. The unscrupulous merchants would fill a wagon with curly turnings and cover them with a layer of heavy turnings and pass the wagon off as the more expensive material. He went on to tell me that to check it I would have to climb into every wagon and jump up and down. I would soon find the feel of the curly turnings if they were underneath. I couldn't believe that Sir Robert had ever climbed into a wagon and jumped up and down to see if there were any curly turnings underneath but no doubt the Works Manager had told him about it.

He warned me that I would be up against an unscrupulous crowd who would try anything, including bribery or worse, if they found I was impeding their profitable business. This seemed an interesting and perhaps exciting opportunity to learn another aspect of the industrial world and I said I would certainly do my best at it.

In order to learn more about the Scrap business before I started work as a Scrap Inspector, it was arranged for me to spend some time at a reliable firm of Scrap Merchants in Sheffield. I went by train with the Chairman and the Hon.Gerald Coleshaw who was the director who had interviewed me at Oxford. We travelled First Class, something I had never done before although I knew that T.A. officers, if in uniform and on duty, were entitled to first class travel. Arriving at Sheffield, I was booked into a hotel near the Scrap Yard whilst the directors went to the Grosvenor House Hotel in the centre of the town. They invited me to dinner and I had a pleasant evening discussing life at Oxford and some of the aspects of running a Steelworks.

Next morning I presented myself at the scrap yard. Cookson and Dankson was the firm where I was to learn the business. Mr Cookson the Managing Director had been responsible for the raising of the German Fleet, scuppered at Scapa Flow after the First World War. He was a very alert and forceful character but his health had been undermined by working at Scapa, probably in diving equipment. Nevertheless he was uncompromising in his views and it was obvious that he was a man who would get things done. I next met Mr Jackson, the Manager of the yard. He was a well built, medium sized man with spectacles and growing bald. He had a volatile and excitable temperament which seldom ran to real anger. I discovered that this was due to his upbringing in Andalusia about which he gave a most romantic description, and explained how different was the outlook on life of the Andalusians, how prosperous they were, living on the best of the land with no care for the morrow. He was married with one son and was, of course, an expert bargainer when it came to scrap.

There were other characters. Mr Wordsworth, the chemist, was tall, dark and stooping, troubled with sciatica but quite loquacious on his two subjects: *foundry practice* and *himself.*

"Of course this is only a stop-gap until I go back to foundry work when my back improves," he said loudly and continued. "There are three branches of the family - one in the Lakes - the Poet you know, and ------- ." It went on and on but he was not a bad sort.

Just after I arrived the jib of the big crane in the yard had broken loose in a gale and there were great lamentations and many suggestions as to how it could be fixed. I was lucky enough to hit on a solution which was adopted and enabled the jib to be replaced. This increased my reputation in the yard. During my stay I learned how to differentiate between the various types of scrap: heavy steel, light cast-iron, pressings, motorcar scrap and many others. I also made friends with Joe, the chief burner. He taught me how to use an oxy-acetylene torch for cutting up scrap. It was a wonderful tool and cut through heavy girders like a knife through butter. He warned me of the danger of a heavy girder falling on you if you didn't watch what you were doing and kept clear when you were nearly through a cut.

After I had been there for two or three weeks, I returned to Barrow and commenced work as a scrap inspector. It was quite an athletic job, climbing into fifty or more wagons and jumping up and down to see if there were any curly turnings underneath. It certainly kept me fit. I then met several of the scrap merchants who tried to persuade me to accept their inferior material but I refused all bribes and soon the quality of the scrap began to improve.

The shortage of good quality steel scrap was by now so acute that the Chairman sent for me again. He said he understood that there were supplies to be had in Ireland and asked me to go there and see if I could buy any. I had never been to Ireland so I was pleased to have this opportunity. It was also a chance to learn something of the commercial side of the business.

I travelled first to Belfast where I visited the shipyards which should have been a good source of supply but found the scrap merchants had been there before me and I was only able to buy a few small parcels. I then went on to Dublin where I had no success with the scrap but stayed with the family of a girl I had met in Oxford. I had heard that I might be more successful in the south so I went on to Cork. I found a quantity of old railway lines which, when cut up to fit the charging boxes, were suitable, so I bought them. I returned to Barrow. The Irish trip had not been very productive and we had to continue to rely on the scrap merchants.

Towards the end of 1937 the country and the Government were at last waking up to the fact that a war with Germany might be inevitable. Most of the armament factories, including Vickers, were already working on the manufacture of weapons, ships and aircraft but now attention was being turned to the Armed Services. The Territorial Army was to be doubled and reorganised. One result was that the King's Own, an infantry battalion, were to become Gunners. This was a drastic change for those who held the traditions of the Regiment at heart. Overnight they became the 56th Anti-Tank Regiment of the Royal Artillery and now had to wear the Gunners' badge, depicting a grenade, on their headdress, instead of the lion although the officers were allowed to retain the Kings Own Lion insignia on their Service dress.

It was annoying for me and some of the other officers who had recently purchased full mess kit which included a scarlet jacket with buff facings and a buff coloured waistcoat. The Gunners' mess jacket required dark blue facings and waistcoat. I don't suppose this was going to be of much importance if we were going to war! Anyway the facings could be changed by a competent tailor.

The Battalion became a Regiment and Companies became Batteries. The Non-Commissioned Officers became sergeants and bombardiers and the other ranks, Gunners. The Regiment was to be armed with the 2-pounder anti-tank gun, which was a new weapon about which we knew little. However when we eventually saw one, it turned out to be a beautiful little gun carried on a chassis with two wheels, and towed behind a 15 cwt truck. It fired a 2 lb solid steel armour-piercing projectile which, with a muzzle velocity of 2600 feet per second, was reputed to be able to penetrate 2 inches of armour-plate as well as effective against reinforced concrete and could therefore be of considerable use against pill boxes. It was a semi-automatic weapon capable of firing 12 to 30 rounds a minute providing the loader could keep up the supply of ammunition. However, when we were converted in 1937, no one in the Regiment had even seen one and it was several months before a single 2-pounder was issued so that training in gun drill could be commenced.

To bring the gun into action it was detached from the towing vehicle, manhandled into position, the wheels removed, and the legs unfolded. The layer sprang into his seat, looked through the telescopic sight and brought the gun to bear on the target and then fired. In the Drill Hall this was supposed to take 40 seconds. On manoeuvres in the country it often took considerably longer!

When the gun arrived, gun drill took place in the drill halls. I was rather surprised that at first the officers took no part in the gun drill and stood around watching the gunners doing it. I suppose that as we had only the one gun it was more important for the gunners to become proficient although I would rather have done the gun drill first myself. There was no ammunition and none was available until 1938, which was the first time anyone had a chance to fire the gun. We were able to get some practice on the miniature range by means of a .22 rifle attached to the barrel of the gun.

After the reorganisation I found myself in 221 Battery along with Reggie. Our Battery Commander was a Captain, a pleasant enough chap, rather older than us and married. 222 and 223 were commanded by Majors and 224 by a Captain. The Adjutant with the rank of Captain was a Regular Officer which was the normal establishment for a Territorial unit in peacetime. Our CO was now Lieutenant-Colonel Baslow. He was a gunner Officer who had served in India. He was thin and athletic and had an inexhaustible supply of swear words, mostly connected with a monkey's anatomy which he used in a very quiet and precise way which made them even more effective.

Around the same time as the change to anti-tank artillery, I became friendly with a family who lived in Barrow who invited me to cocktail parties or to join them for badminton or the cinema. One evening when I arrived at their house I was met by the *au pair* who was looking after their two young boys.

Mr and Mrs Slowcombe had gone out so I found myself alone with the girl. Her name was Helga and, although German, spoke English fluently but with a seductive intonation. She was a tall girl with blonde hair, voluptuous bosoms, inviting lips and alluring eyes. The children had gone to bed and we had not had much conversation before she drew me to the sofa and indicated that she was not averse to some pretty heavy petting. Before I knew it, I found myself rolling on the floor with her in a series of sizzling embraces. We disengaged ourselves just in time before the Slowcombes returned who may have wondered why we both looked a little dishevelled. As I left, Helga came up to me and, when the Slowcombes were out of earshot, whispered: "We must meet again on our own." This seemed to me to be a pretty good invitation and one to which I was prepared to agree.

The last occasion on which the local T.A. Unit was able to wear its old uniform was at the King's Own Regimental Ball at the Victoria Park Hotel. I decided that I would invite Helga. The Slowcombes arranged dinner before the dance and asked some of the other Officers including Reggie, who decided he'd better not bring Sharon, and Allan, who also had a girlfriend, and several others. The dance was a colourful affair with the Officers in their mess kit but it was also a sad occasion as it was the last time we should be the *King's Own.*

Although Helga had been dancing with me she had not had much opportunity to get me alone. When the dance ended, the Slowcombes went to get the car. I was giving Helga a goodnight kiss when I heard her whisper to me again: "Next time, will you take me out somewhere where we can be by ourselves?"

The plot seemed to be thickening and later I told Reggie about it. He remarked that I seemed to be on to a *hot cookie* and as usual, advised me to be careful of getting too involved.

Next Saturday Helga told the Slowcombes that, as it was her day off, she was going out to do some shopping. She took a tram and got off opposite my digs. I already had my car out. She got in and pressing herself close to me said: "Let's go somewhere quiet."

We drove to a pub in the country, which I knew was not frequented by my friends, and had lunch together with a bottle of sparkling wine. Helga told me something about herself and how she had had several boyfriends, but they had dropped her and she had come over to England to forget them.

After lunch we got into the car and I drove to a secluded spot. The hood of the car was up as it had been raining, and somehow we both got into the back seat of the Wolseley. It was not really a seat but intended for the luggage and was extremely cramped.

Helga proceeded to remove her knickers and handed me a contraceptive. I don't understand how I managed it in that confined space but somehow I was successful.

Helga didn't consider this arrangement to be very satisfactory and said that next time we must go to an hotel. I had never done this before but as I had, so to speak *broken the ice*, I thought I might as well try it.

A few weekends later, Helga made another excuse to the Slowcombes. This time she said she wanted to see some more of the country and took the tram to the station. I met her there and booked tickets to Blackpool. On arrival we hired a taxi which took us to a large hotel which looked like a castle and which, I had been told, did not ask too many questions. I booked in at the reception desk as the ubiquitous Mr and Mrs Smith and the receptionist made no comment. There was no lift and, although large, the hotel looked as if it could do with some renovation. The porter carried our bags up to our room but on opening the door Helga was disappointed to see two single beds! I in my confusion, had omitted to specify a double bed. I told Helga we would have to make do with the singles. I was far too embarrassed to ask for a change of room. The weekend was not a success and I decided that Helga would have to be dropped and after that I avoided seeing her.

I often wondered later if she was really a beautiful spy getting information from me about the new Anti-Tank gun and the Regiment. I think that was highly unlikely as the change to anti-tank was common knowledge although perhaps the performance of the gun might have been secret. Still it was true that after the War when some of my men, who had been taken prisoner, were repatriated, they told me how much the German interrogators knew of my personal background in their efforts to gain the confidence of their prisoners. There was probably no connection but I still wonder how the enemy knew so much about me.

At the beginning of 1937 the Steel Works was doing badly. Its equipment, which at the beginning of the century had been the most modern in the Industry, was now out of date. It required large amounts of capital to bring in the improvements necessary.

The need for armaments was increasing but the Barrow works were not able to produce the type and quality of steel required. Their main production had been rails for the railways and their speciality was the conductor rails for electrification, which were only needed for the London Underground and suburban services. They did not have the equipment required for making heavy plates for shipbuilding, nor for alloy steels for guns and shells.

The directors, charming aristocratic gentlemen, had little real knowledge of the technology of iron and steel making. They were concerned with finance, the profit and loss account, and how to raise the capital they required to modernise the plant. Having heard of a firm of American efficiency experts, the Bedaux Company, who were reputed to have improved substantially the profitability of companies who employed them, the directors agreed to engage them in the hopes that they would do the same for the Steel Works.

Sadly *Time and Motion*, as it was then called, was not readily adaptable to iron and steel making. After all, how do you measure the time taken by a Roller to spit on a rail in order to check its temperature? When the Bedaux engineer arrived I was appointed as his assistant and did most of the timing work for him. However it was not long before the directors found that the Bedaux Company's fees, which were very substantial, were too high for what they were achieving, so they dispensed with their services. They then decided that I, who was much cheaper, should do the work that the Bedaux engineer had been doing. As a result I found my job changed from Scrap Inspector to what would now be called a Work Study Engineer.

The work involved timing the men on their various duties by means of a stop-watch and clipboard, two items which came to be synonymous with the job. Timing their work was something quite alien to the British Working Man and anathema to the Unions. Shortly after I started work on the timing, large headlines appeared in the newspapers - "Worker says the timing made him go Wibberley Wobberly" - and - "Made him ill". I stuck at it for some months but it was obvious that timing was not the answer for a workman who carried out his work in a non-repetitive manner.

I thought about it carefully for some time but I was not happy with this sort of work. Reluctantly, I decided that I should have to leave.

My father had always wanted me to go into one of the large chemical works in Cheshire as he knew some of their directors. I travelled home and an interview was arranged with the Managing Director of the General Chemicals Division of I.C.I.. The result was that I was offered a job as an engineer in their chemical works at Runcorn.

I was sorry to leave Barrow. I would miss Reggie, Allan and my other friends, but Reggie was still in the T.A. and I would see him at camp as well as the other officers. I would keep in touch. Leaving at that time was probably a good thing from the point of view of my private life as I had become rather too heavily involved with some of the girls of the district. I thought that perhaps *pastures new* would be a good thing to try, and might get me out of some of the scrapes I had got myself into.

CHAPTER 10

I arrived in Runcorn in the summer of 1937. The first thing was, as always, to find suitable accommodation. I had been fortunate in Barrow so I was prepared to spend some time looking for the right digs. I eventually found just what I wanted in Greenway Road near the War Memorial and only a fifteen-minute walk from the works. There were three other lodgers in the house: a young man older than myself who worked in a tannery of which there were several in the town; a Scotsman who was a trainee in the chemical works where I was to be, and whose brother would be killed in the battle of Arnhem in 1944; and a woman of about thirty who worked in a bank. I had some qualms about sharing lodgings with a female but felt I was now sufficiently mature not to get involved!

I was also able to find a garage for the Wolseley. It was not usual to leave your car on the road as it was in later years, not so much from the fear of theft or vandalism - a word which had barely entered the vocabulary - but on account of the lack of street lighting. A car parked on the side of the road would have been a hazard to other users of the road, and pedestrians might walk into it at night unless the side lights were left on which would have had disastrous results for one's battery.

I set out for my first day at the chemical works walking past the War Memorial, passing a sandstone cliff on my left which hid the common and the disused sandstone quarries, and looked out on my right, towards the Manchester Ship Canal and the Runcorn Docks, and across the Mersey estuary to the Lighthouse at Hale. In the distance was Liverpool where, on a clear day, the Anglican Cathedral stood out starkly on the skyline. The road sloped sharply down to Sandy Lane where as I neared the bottom, the unmistakable smell of the works assailed me - I recognised the sharp smell of chlorine, but this was mixed with the sweetish smell of solvents and tar to which I was soon to become accustomed. I approached a long brick edifice which must surely be the Office Building and at the door was confronted by a smartly uniformed commissionaire who took me to the Works Manager's office.

The Works Manager was a bluff Cheshire man with greying hair and spectacles who had been in the chemical industry throughout his working life. He welcomed me and took me across the corridor to meet the Works Engineer who, although younger than the Works Manager, had hair which was silvery white and spoke so fast that it was like the staccato bursts of a machine gun. From what I can remember from the rapid interview, it was emphasised that I was an engineer and, according to the Works Engineer, engineers ran the factory and chemists just got in the way! It was a somewhat surprising suggestion for a chemical works but one which I took with a pinch of salt and later found out was certainly not true. Finally I was taken to the Section in which I was to work.

The Section Manager, Don, was a pleasant, middle-aged university graduate with a brilliant brain who chatted to me and explained how the Section worked. I could not avoid looking at the deep scar on Don's cheek which, I learned later, had been caused by an experiment in a laboratory when a flask of chemicals blew up in his face. The Section Engineer, whose name was Fred, was to be my immediate boss, and was a rather quiet character who tended not to interfere and let us all get on with our jobs.

The other occupants of the Section office were the Plant Managers, both chemists and as different as chalk from cheese. Patrick was an Irishman, brilliant at solving mathematical problems which he could do almost as fast as a modern calculator, but living in a world of his own. You could see him walking through the works oblivious to everything that was going on around him, his mind far away amongst the bogs and hobgoblins of his native land, or perhaps involved in some obscure mathematical calculation. His brown laboratory coat was always filthy, generally from food which had spilled out of his mouth or from cigarette ash. He frequently reduced the middle-aged typist in the Section Manager's office to tears with his outlandish and frequently bawdy remarks. The men under him treated him as a joke and pulled his leg unmercifully. At the time there was no formal training in man-management and it did not seem to be taken into account when appointing technical staff - a university degree in chemistry was sufficient. The other chemist, Jonathan, was a smart and dapper young man with a military moustache who ran the solvent stills and was looked up to by the men under him. He had been in the Oxford University Air Squadron but was two years senior to me so I had not met him. He later joined the Auxiliary Air Force and was killed while flying a Fairy Battle bomber powered by the famous Merlin engine, in the Battle of France, protecting the evacuation of the British Expeditionary Force. As for Patrick, being in a reserved occupation, he remained at the factory throughout the war.

I next met the engineering Foreman for whom I was going to be responsible. A foreman in the works acts rather like a Sergeant-Major in the army, controlling the men under him but taking orders from his manager. Alf was a character. He had a slight impediment in his speech but every sentence included at least one f... and generally several. He was one of those individuals who are unable to express themselves verbally without swearing and he also put in a few extra f...s to impress me as the young engineer from the university. I, having had three years in the steel industry, was well able to out f... Alf, which impressed him not a little and we became good friends.

I was the maintenance engineer on our Section which contained the solvents plant and I had also been appointed its Safety Officer. This meant I had to ensure that all the machinery was correctly guarded so that no moving parts could be touched by the operatives. This was not very popular with the production staff when I had to have machinery shut down in order to fit the guards. The idea of industrial safety was only just beginning to be accepted as essential by law and by the management.

One of the products made on the Section was a dry-cleaning fluid. Alf scrounged an old washing machine and, tipping several gallons of *Tri* into it, offered to clean anyone's clothes. One day, seeing my extremely dirty trilby lying on the bench, he put it, without asking me, into his washing machine. The hat came out a shapeless mess. I discovered it and accosted Alf. "What have you done to my f...ing hat? I can't wear that."

"Well at least it's clean," replied Alf, for once forgetting to swear.

Talking of dry-cleaning, it produced another colourful character. The sales representative for the dry-cleaning fluid was Joshua Culbertson-Smith. He was known as Jos and with his large handlebar moustache, bushy eyebrows, ruddy complexion, and wearing a deerstalker cap, he was certainly colourful. He drove a Vauxhall open tourer which had a body shaped like a boat and an exhaust which could be heard by everyone in the Office building as he drove past. He appeared to work what would now be called flexible hours. In his case they were pretty *inflexible* as regards the opening hours of the Fiddlers Arms to which he repaired during his lunch hour and was seldom back before 3 p.m. As a result he was always in a 'jolly' mood and, being a salesman, considered it his duty to keep his customers happy which he managed to do, so long as they were not teetotallers. He was so successful in this that in spite of his rather flamboyant life style, he never got the sack.

The lunch hour was from 12 until 1 and the works provided a canteen for both the manual workers and the staff, although they were separated. I went to the staff canteen which was near the Office building. It produced an acceptable meal of two courses at a reasonable cost. I was interested in the arrangements for carving the meat: roast beef, mutton or sometimes pork. One of the office staff volunteered for this job. He was given an extra ten minutes before the start of the break and a free meal. We lined up, collected our vegetables, and passed in front of him as he slapped a piece of meat on each of our plates. If you were friendly with him, he might put in an extra piece, hidden below the potatoes. It was not long before I made friends with him but was always embarrassed by this special treatment.

It was the custom in most canteens that you picked a table and sat with your friends. As I was a new boy I had to be invited to a table and it turned out to be with what were some very interesting and differing characters. Dr Harding was an erudite and distinguished chemist in the Research Laboratories. Mr Todhunter was an engineer in a department which he said was so secret that he could not talk about it, although he frequently did. Mr Bunbury, much older than most of us and in charge of the Factory Services and Estate Management, was a great help to me in finding my feet in a new environment. These with the *carver* were my new friends.

The women, typists, secretaries and laboratory assistants, sat at separate tables. There was no mingling of the sexes.

So the first weeks in my new job were very pleasant and I looked forward to the future and what it would hold.

I soon found that, as in Barrow, there was a round of social engagements to which I was invited and not long after I arrived there was a Regimental Ball in Warrington organised by the local Infantry Territorial Battalion. The manager of the bleach Section at the works was one of the old fashioned managers of which I had seen pictures taken in the early part of the century. At the works he always wore a dark suit and waistcoat, with an upright starched collar and a bowler hat. He lived up Sandy Lane and had a daughter who was tall and dark but very quiet. He asked me if I would partner her at the ball to which I agreed.

At the dance during the evening I was introduced to several parties in one of which there was a Mr and Mrs Pickup. They were not that much older than me, but right from the start Mr Pickup addressed me as *my dear boy*. I'm not sure why but it seemed to go with his slightly old gentlemanly manner. Mr Pickup was manager and owner of one of the tanneries in the town, his father, who had died, having run the business before him. The Pickups were very hospitable and they asked me to come to dinner one evening. Mr Pickup was short in stature with a twinkle in his eye. He had a sense of humour which often ran to practical jokes. He rode to hounds and was a prominent member of the local Council. He knew a lot about Runcorn which Don, my section manager who had been invited to dinner with his wife Margaret, and I soon discovered.

When we had finished eating, the ladies, Margaret and Mrs Pickup whose name was Cecily, retired and the men were left to drink port. Mr Pickup passed a box of cigars round and I accepted one but Don preferred his pipe which he proceeded to pack and light.

"Mr Pickup," I began but Mr Pickup who was already beginning to be enveloped in a cloud of smoke as he started his cigar, waved his hand at me: "Geoffrey," he said, "call me Geoffrey my dear boy."

"Geoffrey," I began again, "can you tell me a little about Runcorn's history which I am sure you must know?"

"Well," Mr Pickup settled himself in his chair and passed the port to Don. "Yes I do know a bit about it. Did you know that in 916, the Countess of Mercia, that magnanimous virago known as Elflede, built a fort in the village of Runcorn?"

"No," I replied, "I wasn't all that good at history at school. I could never remember the dates."

"I've always been good at dates," said Mr Pickup rather smugly.

"What did they need a fort for?" asked Don.

"To guard the approaches of the river and to repel the marauding hordes of Danes who were invading the province of Mercia. Runcorn was strategically important, much more than Liverpool which hardly existed at the time, because the river's narrower here, easier to defend. After that the village must have fallen into decay because there's no mention of it in the Domesday Book. 1086, you know," his eyes twinkled mischievously and he took another puff on his cigar. "You'll have seen the remains of the castle overlooking the town. That's Halton castle, part of the Barony of Halton which included the villages of Over and Nether Runcorn. Along with the castle, a parish church existed before the Conquest and also a Priory at Norton, next door to Runcorn. Sadly, the priory, well it became a mansion really, built by Sir Richard Brooke on top of the old priory, was pulled down about ten years ago."

"I've seen the entrance to it, quite impressive," said Don.

"That's the old priory entrance and it is impressive but not nearly as magnificent as the whole estate used to be. Thomas you should visit the church.

It has a connection with your old college. After the Dissolution of the Monasteries, Henry VIII gave it to the Dean and Chapter of Christ Church. I wonder if they still collect dues?" I said how I expected they did in the way that old traditions linger on.

"Some traditions," said Mr Pickup cheerfully, "though I think I will enquire about that. Some traditions are better not left lingering on. Now bringing things a little more up to date, I bet you didn't know that at the start of the last century, Runcorn was known for its sea bathing and salubrious air. In fact it was a health spa and people were sent from Liverpool and Manchester to get well here. The Mersey was a pleasant uncontaminated river abounding in fish, and also an important seaport importing china clay from Cornwall for the Potteries, and exporting sandstone from the local quarries."

"Well it isn't uncontaminated now," said Don bluntly, for with all the industry that had sprung up along its banks it could hardly be called salubrious.

"No," Mr Pickup sighed, because it was a problem that his own tanneries with their effluent was also responsible for. "Transport," he stressed the word like the opening of a speech at a council meeting. "Up to the middle of the eighteenth century everything was dependent on what could be drawn by a horse along a road. Then the canals appeared and one of the first ones was built by James Brindley from Worsley to Fiddlers Ferry on the Mersey. He then advised the Duke of Bridgewater on building a canal from the Runcorn Docks to bring materials further into Cheshire. Have you seen the locks? You can see them from Waterloo Bridge, a tremendous feat of engineering. I expect you know all about it, being engineers."

"Chemical engineers," said Don, "not civil. But the Manchester Ship Canal was built first wasn't it?"

"No it was built much later. 1884 in fact, but it caused another tremendous feat because the Bridgewater Canal had to cross it. Up at Barton they built a swinging lock. Have you not seen it?" Even Don shook his head at this one. "It's fascinating. You see a barge, apparently floating in mid-air in what looks like a steel box which is swung to allow the ships with their tall masts to pass along the Ship Canal."

"Geoffrey?" said Cecily putting her head round the door and raising her eyebrows towards her husband. "Are you coming to join us?"

"Oh yes, dear, won't be long, just finishing a story," said Mr Pickup but when Cecily closed the door, he passed the port again and continued: "Transport," he repeated, "that was the thing. George Stephenson built his steam locomotive, the Rocket, for the Manchester-Liverpool railway line in 1829. Quite early on and as a result the importance of Runcorn increased. Industries began to be established. They including a soapery, precursor to your chemical industry, Don. Then there's the Evans and Webb Biological Institute, started about 1911. It produces anti-toxins and vaccines against diptheria, tetanus and cholera. Near your lodgings, Thomas, you will have seen a number of horses grazing. Not for hunting, those ones, but they're kept well and not killed but are used to produce some of the anti-toxins. Of course the main industry has always been tanning."

"Better join the ladies," said Don knowing that this was the precursor to what Mr Pickup really wanted to talk about, but I was interested and wanted to hear about tanning. As we got up I said: "I know nothing about tanning and would be interested to hear about it from the horse's hide's mouth, so to speak."

Mr Pickup smiled. "I do know a bit about it. I've been in the business all my life." As we went through to the drawing room, he began: "Leather can be made from the skin of any animal, even horses but it's mainly cattle that we use. It's been used for clothing ever since our cavemen ancestors were clad in it."

"Coffee?" asked Cicely.

"The skins would of course go rotten until it was found that certain trees produced a substance which, if the skins were immersed in it for a long time, preserved them. That substance was called tannin and of course the process became tanning. In England the bark of the oak tree was used but other countries had there own recipes. So in France they used the Spanish Chestnut. Originally the farmers who produced the animals did their own tanning but as demand for leather increased, the process was centralised in the towns."

"Geoffrey, must you talk about business? Thomas, do you take sugar?" asked Cicely,

"But why Runcorn?" asked Margaret.

"Because Cheshire is a dairying county with plenty of cattle for the supply of hides and also abundant oak trees to supply the tannin. And Runcorn has a good supply of water as well as a river to take the effluent away." At this point Cicely glared at her husband so that he turned quite pink and became silent whilst the conversation turned to other things. Don and Margaret talked of golf as Margaret was captain of the local club. I did not play golf so could not join in.

Shortly before the party broke up, Geoffrey Pickup said rather gloomily,

"What do you think are the chances of this war starting? The Government all seem to be for appeasement. That is except for that old warhorse Churchill."

"If you want to know what I think," said Don, "I think it's pretty close. All that secret work going on in the drawing office, and the hush hush factory that's being built at Astmoor must mean that the powers that be are thinking of chemical weapons. And it's being pushed on with all speed. I expect you and I, Geoffrey, will have to run the factories at home."

"Yes you're probably right," said Geoffrey and the two women looked at their husbands as much as to say they were relieved.

Turning to me Don said, "I suppose you will be in at the beginning and I shall lose you and Jonathan from the section.

"Yes I expect you will," I replied, "My father suggested I should join the Territorials way back in 1930 so that I should be ready for it."

After thanking Geoffrey and Cicely for a very interesting evening and saying good night, Don and Margaret gave me a lift to my digs, and then went home.

Not long afterwards Mr Pickup phoned me at work to ask me if I'd like to see round his tannery. I accepted and a few days later arrived at the works where the hides were being immersed in a mixture of lime and water for several hours to soften them. The smell of the hides waiting for treatment was like putrefying flesh and nearly made me vomit. How the operators who worked in it all day could put up with it was extraordinary.

As we were going round, Mr Pickup suddenly asked, "Do you know why the sixpenny piece is called a tanner?"

"No," I replied.

"Ah," he nodded happily and began. "The story is this. Tanners and dealers in hides would meet in Leadenhall market in London and after business spent the rest of the day at the local inn. There were no cabs in those days so the dealers, who lived in Bermondsey, would hire a hackney coach to take them home, for which the charge was sixpence. The locals called this coin a tanner and that's how the sixpence got its name."

Going back to the process, Mr Pickup explained that after the hides were taken out of the lime, the hairs were removed and used for making felt. The surplus fat and flesh from the other side was used for making gelatine and glue. Nothing was wasted. He went on to show me the next stage of the treatment. Here the hides were immersed in the tannin liquid which had been made from the oak bark, and allowed to remain there for several months. They were then dried, passed through rollers under considerable pressure, inspected, and sent to the warehouse.

After we had completed our tour of the tanning factory Mr Pickup took me to lunch and started to tell me the history of the tanning industry.

"You must remember that up to the beginning of the twentieth century, the horse was still extremely important, not only for riding but on the farm, drawing wagons and carriages and for pulling barges on the canals. It meant that leather was required for all forms of saddlery and harness."

I remarked that the First World War must have seen an enormous increase in the demand for leather.

"Yes," he replied. "Guns were pulled by mules or horses requiring leather harness, rifles had leather slings and Officers had leather belts. It was required everywhere. Then there was the expansion of Industry. Before electric power was available in the factories and cotton mills, they were run by huge gas engines which required hundreds of leather belts which passed from shaft to shaft up through the floors and down to the looms. After the war, although leather was still required for boots and shoes, the arrival of synthetic materials and the rubber Wellington boot has reduced the need. Now we're working on short time and tanneries not only in Runcorn but everywhere are contracting."

Not surprisingly, Mr Pickup was rather disconsolate when describing this, but he hoped that the shoe trade, at least, would keep his factory going for the time being. If there was to be another war the demand for leather would increase.

I thanked Mr Pickup for the lunch and a most interesting conversation and returned to my digs.

On the other side of the River Mersey from Runcorn is the town of Widnes. I thought I would have a look at it and when I arrived went to the Town Hall where I met the Archivist. He, like Mr Pickup was a mine of information.

He pointed out that at one time the river Mersey was fordable at low tide, at the site of Elflede's fortress, which was the real reason for its military significance. In 1190 a ferry, called the *Navis de Widness*, was established at this point. In more recent times there was a ferry, made famous by the comedian Stanley Holloway as costing "Tuppence per Person per Trip", which landed its passengers on the Widnes side at Snig Point from where they had to scramble over slippery rocks to the local hostelry, known as Snig Pie House. There they, no doubt, partook of *snig pie* after having been fortified by several shots of brandy to compensate them for their rocky crossing.

"A *snig*, by the way," said the Archivist, "is the name for an eel which was considered a great delicacy."

With the arrival of the railways, an Act of Parliament was obtained to construct a railway bridge to cross the river at this point. This was started in 1864 and, when completed, put Runcorn on the direct line between Liverpool and London. The bridge, which was high enough to allow ocean-going ships to pass to the Port of Manchester, included a walkway by which foot passengers could cross to Widnes. The Manchester Ship Canal was contiguous with the river at this point but separated from it by a wall which meant crossing by ferry was no longer possible. It was therefore proposed that a road bridge should be erected. He told me how several schemes were considered by Thomas Telford, who was the engineer who constructed the suspension bridges at Conway and across the Menai Straits. When these schemes were looked into it was found that the cost of the approach roads in Runcorn and Widnes would be prohibitive. As a result a transporter-type of bridge was designed, erected and opened in 1905. 1000 feet long, it was the largest span of any bridge in the United Kingdom for carrying road traffic at that time.

From towers at either end a gantry was suspended again high enough for ships to pass underneath. Along it ran a trolley and suspended from the trolley was a platform called the transporter car. It was originally intended to hold 'four two-horse loaded wagons and 300 passengers'. When I was at Runcorn the load was 12 cars, or the equivalent in lorries, and as many pedestrians as could be squeezed in.

Motorcars and lorries were driven on to the platform and pedestrians followed. A gate came up to stop anyone falling off. The driver, who considered himself part-seaman and part-landsman and had red and green navigation lights on top of his cab, sounded a hooter and the contraption commenced to rattle its way to the other side where the process was reversed. It took about 3 minutes for the crossing as long as there was nothing passing on the Ship Canal. If there was, the car had to stop. With loading and unloading it could take at least twenty minutes for the car to return to its starting point. This was acceptable when the Transporter was built as the amount of traffic was not great. When I came to Runcorn the delay at peak periods could run into hours and the frustration of drivers arriving at the bridge just as the car was departing, can be imagined.

The Transporter became a way of life for the Runcornians and Widnesians.

At the works during the first Christmas week after I had arrived, I was told there would be an Office Party. We had not had one in Barrow as the number of staff at the Steelworks was much smaller and also these office parties were a new idea.

Bottles of sherry were issued to each department and managers and office workers were expected to let their hair down and have a good time. This generally meant that any inhibitions between the men and the female staff which during the year had been suppressed, rapidly evaporated. The party was held in the staff canteen. During the afternoon everyone was getting very merry and I noticed that one of the typists who I knew slightly, was giving me what I had come to interpret as the *come hither look*. Shortly afterwards she came towards me, staggering slightly, after which she collapsed into my lap. I took advantage of the situation by giving her a lingering kiss on the lips which I found was returned with considerable enthusiasm. The afternoon progressed and everyone was looking rather the worse for wear, clothing and hair becoming disarranged and couples locked in embraces they had looked forward to for many months. As it was getting dark I suggested I should take Josie home. I found that she lived in Widnes so we got into my car and drove down to the Transporter. There was quite a queue and a long wait before the transporter car was able to take us. Whilst we were waiting, Josie pressed herself against me and, after a few more kisses, it was obvious that the evening was going to continue in an amatory fashion. We eventually got on to the car which, once it had left the landing, was in darkness and made our situation even more alluring. When we got to the other side Josie said she knew of a secluded spot we could drive to. Now I didn't want to get too involved. I had had enough of *girls* when I was in Barrow and I was trying to remember Reggie's advice not to get too caught up. However the effect of the sherry and the proximity of Josie was too much to resist so we spent a pleasant and amorous half-hour before I returned her to her home and drove myself back to my digs. The Transporter was not really a very romantic venue, but it did seem rather empty on the return journey.

Although when I was in Barrow I had transferred my allegiance from the Cheshire Regiment to the King's Own which had subsequently become the 56th Anti-Tank, I decided not to make another change. The RAF were trying to persuade me to join the Auxiliary Air Force and with this in view I was given a flight in a Hawker Hart at the nearby Cheshire Auxiliary Air Squadron's base at Hooton. I found the experience of being in an aeroplane diving at over 200 miles per hour, faster than I had ever flown before, both exhilarating and attractive, but to join the squadron would have entailed more time for training at the weekend and in the evenings than I was prepared to give. The Territorial Army was less demanding.

I found another Anti-Tank T.A. unit not far from Runcorn where I could do my drills and where the training was more practical and interesting than at Barrow. Officers got down to doing gun drill themselves instead of watching the gunners do it. This was good fun and I enjoyed taking part as a member of a team to get the gun into action in the shortest possible time.

Meanwhile world events were taking place which were to have shattering results in the coming months and years. In the very first paragraph of *Mein Kampf* Hitler had stated that 'The reunion of Austria and Germany *(the Anschluss)* was a task to be furthered by every means our lives long.' It was not surprising therefore, that in the spring of 1938 he marched into Austria on the flimsy pretext that it was the wishes of the Austrian people. Chancellor Schuschnigg, who tried to save his people from subjugation, was imprisoned and spent seven years in various concentration camps. Meanwhile I read in the papers that Neville Chamberlain, the British Prime Minister, in what was considered to be one of his first misleading statements to the House of Commons, had said that Hitler and Schuschnigg had agreed to incorporate Austria into the Reich. It may be that Schuschnigg did agree but only under severe duress and to avoid the bloodshed of his people. Later, as the paper reported, the Prime Minister had to admit: "Nothing could have arrested what was happening unless this country and other countries were prepared to go to war." The implication was that Britain was not so prepared.

Although I was doing my drills in Cheshire I continued to go to camp with the 56th. In 1938 the camp was held at Trawsfynydd in Wales amongst the barren moorland and hills of the Cambrian mountains, southwest of Snowdon and overlooking Trawsfynydd lake. Here for the first time we were able to fire the 2-pounder on the ranges with the limited amount of live ammunition available. Now that we had done this, I felt a lot more confident about the Territorial Army than I had before.

I had not seen Reggie since I left Barrow but had kept in touch with him and was very pleased to see him at camp.

"What's the news of our friends in Barrow both male and female?" I asked.

"Allan's left to go to a job in South Africa, but got sidetracked on the way to go to some godforsaken Island in the South Atlantic. Douglas has joined the Navy, and the hairdressers have gone back to Ireland, so I'm without a girlfriend at the moment. Oh! Helga has been going the rounds as far as I can gather. Quite a lot of red faces when she's mentioned. I think she's about to go back to Germany. I hope she's not a spy."

"If she is, it looks as if we shall be together again sooner than we expect if this war catches up with us."

"You're always so optimistic," Reggie said sarcastically. "Anyhow as there doesn't seem to be any girls around here we might as well go to the Mess and drown our sorrows."

CHAPTER 11

When I got back from camp, I found I was being moved to the Cell Room. There were many products made at the Castner Kellner chemical works but the most important was chlorine and caustic soda. These were made in the cell rooms.

Caustic soda is used in making soap which is why Mr Pickup had pointed out that the soaperies were the precursors of the chemical industry. I remembered when I was at school being taken on a trip to visit a soap works in Warrington. The soap was being made in vats containing mutton fat which must have gone putrid as the smell was as bad as the smell of the hides at the tannery. Chlorine, on the other hand, is an acrid smelling greenish-yellow coloured gas. It was made at Castners and was used in the First World War as a chemical weapon, for which purpose it had been compressed into heavy steel bottles which were then transported to the trenches. When the wind was blowing towards the enemy the gas was released and was carried over the enemy positions where it caused choking, damage to the eyes and lungs, and eventual death. The disadvantage was that the direction of the wind could change carrying the gas over our own troops who, even though they were protected with rather inefficient gas masks, suffered. I had read that the chlorine used at that time had been made in the cell rooms in which I was about to work. Apart from this unpleasant use, chlorine is an essential constituent of many useful industrial and household products.

Chlorine and caustic soda are made from common salt. Near Northwich, not far from Runcorn, there are large underground deposits of salt which were laid down millions of years ago when the sea covered this part of Cheshire. The towns of Nantwich, Northwich and Middlewich are salt towns, the name *wich* being an old English word for *salt spring*. At Winsford there is a salt mine where rock salt is cut out underground and used for salting the roads in the event of snow or frost.

The salt used in industry is obtained from brine. Water is pumped down to the salt-bearing strata under the ground where, when it has dissolved sufficient of the mineral, it is brought to the surface and pumped to the factories.

The method of separating the products in the brine is to pass an electric current through it. Although I had learned the principle at school, I was intrigued to find out how this would be done industrially. It involved the use of mercury (sometimes called quicksilver) which I remembered as the little silver globules which appeared if you happened to break a glass thermometer.

The cell rooms were housed in single story flat-roofed buildings the size of a tennis court with a series of trenches which ran the length of each building and allowed the workmen access to the underside of the cells. The cells themselves were flat concrete troughs about two feet wide and twenty long, slightly inclined so that the mercury when introduced at the top end flowed in a silver stream to the lower end. The troughs were covered by pieces of slate to which were fixed blocks of graphite. To make the cells reasonably gastight they were sealed with a mixture of china clay and tar, known as *luting* - a filthy, smelly mixture which seemed to cover everything including the workmen and my lab coat.

The cells were fed with brine and an electric current passed between the graphite blocks and the mercury. Chlorine was released and collected and the other component, which was the sodium, dissolved in the mercury forming an amalgam. Here it ran into a steel trough sloped in the opposite direction so that it arrived at the beginning of the concrete trough where it had started but eighteen inches lower, The steel trough was filled with water which removed the sodium to make the caustic soda solution and left the mercury as it had been before.

Now the question was how to lift the mercury those eighteen inches so that it can re-circulate round the system? This was solved by an ingenious method originally devised by the ancient Greeks when Archimedes found a way of raising water from a river so that it could irrigate the land. It is a method still used today in Bangladesh. The principle is simple. A piece of steel is bent into a corkscrew shape and inserted in a tube. When rotated the water is pushed up the corkscrew and is discharged at the top.

Mercury gives off a vapour which is poisonous. So long as it is always covered with brine or water this does not cause a problem. A more serious hazard occurs if the power supply should suddenly fail, the pumps sucking the chlorine away would also fail and the chlorine remaining in the cells would then escape through the luting to the atmosphere.

One day I was caught under these conditions. I had occasion to go to the machine shop which was on the other side of the factory and as it was raining, decided to walk through one of the trenches in the cell room. I was about half way through when the lights failed and everything went very quiet. It was an eerie feeling as there is always noise in a factory. I suddenly realised what had happened. The power had failed. Immediately I felt a choking sensation in my chest, my eyes started watering and I could not see. Panic struck me. I had no gas mask and the end of the trench was a long way off. I remembered reading somewhere that the soldiers in the trenches had soaked rags in urine and stuffed them in their mouths. That was a hopeless idea at the present juncture. I couldn't have peed if I had wanted to and there wasn't time. I tried holding my breath and staggered forward in the darkness, feeling my way along. Eventually I couldn't hold my breath any longer and took a gulp of chlorine-laden air which made me want to vomit. A sort of paralysis set in. My legs no longer seemed to do what my brain was telling them. I thought, what a silly way to die when I was training as a soldier and more likely to die in a battle which would be more glamorous than being gassed in a factory. I pulled myself along holding on to the cells. My chest was burning and I was gasping for air. At last I saw, dimly, a light which must be the daylight at the end of the trench. I made a superhuman effort to drag myself the last few yards and emerged into the open air where Fred found me, my face as green as the gas itself. They took me to the ambulance station where I was treated with large doses of oxygen, sweet tea and enforced rest which soon put me right. I vowed I would never go round the works again without my gas mask.

Since mercury is an expensive commodity, there were always some individuals who would try to steal it. They would then sell it to unscrupulous merchants who, no doubt, then sold the mercury back to the company. One enterprising individual filled a hot water bottle with mercury and, concealing it under his coat, walked out of the factory. Unfortunately for him, the weight of the mercury soon burst the hot water bottle and a silver stream of globules followed him down the street much to the amusement of the Security Man who apprehended him.

Shortly after the unpleasant incident in the cell room, I decided to change my digs. The present ones in Greenway Road were too noisy with the three other lodgers. I moved to a house in Maryhill Road on the outskirts of Runcorn which was quieter and from which I could still walk to the works through the Common and down Sandy Lane. I shared these digs with a man of my own age who was a chemist in the company's research laboratories. Jim was tall with dark hair and a very pale complexion which gave him an air of fragility. He had graduated well in chemistry from Manchester University and was set for a successful career in the industry in which he eventually became a director.

The company for which we both worked was in the forefront of those enlightened firms who were beginning to realise that their workers were their most important asset. They looked after them carefully, in contrast to many businesses in the last century who considered the worker as expendable - to be hired and fired at will. As part of this policy the firm provided facilities for recreation and relaxation.

Not far from the works was the Recreation Club - *The Rec* as it was called - with playing fields for cricket, hockey and football. There were some excellent tennis courts, both hard and grass, bowling greens and a miniature rifle range which I made use of. There was also a large club house with billiard rooms, a dance floor, a stage and, of course, a bar.

Jim and I were having a drink at the bar one evening when we noticed a man standing a little away from us who was about to order a drink. He was rather short but what struck me about him was that he had an unusually large head and face, out of proportion to the size of his body. He came over to us, introduced himself as Bertie, and asked us to have a drink. It transpired that he ran the club's Amateur Dramatic Society and had heard on the grapevine that I had been involved with acting at the University.

"Would you be interested in joining our society?" he asked after the second drink. I explained that I had not been an actor but was more concerned with stage management.

"That's just what we need," said Bertie. "We're putting on a play called *Death takes a Holiday* and we want someone to design the set."

Jim had been listening and interjected: "Are there any acting parts going? I'm quite interested in acting."

"As a matter of fact we do need someone to take the part of Death," said Bertie, looking with interest at Jim's pale face.

And so it was fixed up. I designed the set which included a cyclorama illuminated with an ethereal blue light, and had it built with the assistance of the joiners' shop in the works. The script called for a white grand piano so the joiners constructed a very good imitation from timber and plywood.

Jim acted the part of *Death*, his pallid complexion and dark hair suiting the role admirably and not requiring a great deal of make-up. We rehearsed his part several times in the digs, preparing Jim for Bertie who produced and directed the production.

The show took place in the Rec and was a great success. I asked Don and Margaret and the Pickups to come to one of the performances. Cecily was very interested in the plot in which *Death* takes a three day holiday and takes on the form of a Ruritanian-type Prince. During the three days, of course, nothing dies and people survive the most appalling accidents. At the end Death falls in love. The girl wants to go with him and we are left with the unanswered question of which is stronger - death or love. I think Cecily thought that love should triumph. Even if it meant the girl would die.

Don was interested in the white piano.

"Did you have to hire that?" he remarked.

I took him round behind the scenes and showed him how it was made.

"That must have been a bit of a *foreigner* in the joiners shop," he smiled.

Jim and I were talking in the digs one evening. I admitted that I had no regular girlfriend but had taken Josie out on several occasions. Jim knew about Josie as we all worked in the same building. His advice was much the same as Reggie's - don't get too taken up with her. She's probably out to get you. Something which I think might well have been true.

Whilst we had been involved in our playacting, giving *Death* a holiday, the tension in Europe was mounting. In September 1938 Hitler demanded that the Sudetenland, a part of Czechoslovakia with a German-speaking population, must be returned to Germany. The Sudetenland was vital to the Czechs. It contained its mining and industrial base as well as being an important part of its road and rail transportation system. Not only this, it also contained the formidable fortress line without which the Czechs could not defend themselves against the Germans. Dr Benes, the President, stood firm. The Czech army was strong and well trained and, with the backing of the French, who by treaty were to have come to their assistance, could easily have repelled the Germans, but this would mean war. A war of which everyone was terrified. Chamberlain continued in his efforts to prevent war. It was reported in the papers that he had agreed to meet Hitler at the latter's mountain retreat at Berchtesgaden. Here he was deceived by the Fuhrer into thinking that peace was possible and as a result he had a further meeting with Hitler in Munich. He returned from Munich with what became known as the *piece of paper.*

At the cinema in Runcorn I saw pictures of the Prime Minister emerging from his aircraft at Croydon and then standing on the steps of Downing Street holding the piece of paper and announcing: "My friends! This is the second time there has come back from Germany to Downing Street peace with honour. I believe it is peace in our time." How wrong he was! I wondered, if this was the second time, what was the first? I asked Geoffrey Pickup who I felt sure would know. He told me that it must have referred to when Disraeli in 1878 returned from the

Congress of Berlin with an agreement between England and Turkey which successfully avoided war with Russia.

Although I had seen signs of it when I was at Barrow, I had forgotten that there were a number of people in this country, led by Sir Oswald Mosley, who approved of Hitler and were impressed by the way he appeared to have unified his country. They also supported the Italian Dictator saying that at least *he made the trains run on time!* They were not by any means pacifists - they wanted Hitler to triumph. There were however people who from religious or ideological grounds refused to consider fighting. However the majority of the population were relieved that war had been put off, even at the sacrifice of the free people of the Sudetenland. It remained for Mr Churchill to rise in the Commons to brand Munich "...as a total unmitigated defeat." - a statement which aroused a storm of hostile shouting.

Now that I had moved to the cell room I was promoted to Section Engineer, but still had Alf as my foreman and the same maintenance gang. I shared an office with Alec, my new Section Manager. Alec was of medium height, slightly rotund and balding. He was an expert with anything to do with mercury cells and his hobby was fishing. We sat on opposite sides of a large desk.

One morning I was trying to design a modification to a piece of plant but at the same time my mind kept being sidetracked by thoughts as to whether I should invite Josie out again, in spite of having decided I was not going to get further involved. Alec had got an old fashioned calculating machine which required a handle to be turned several times to get the answer. He was working at this and it made an awful clatter. I couldn't concentrate. Everytime I tried to work out the size of the motor required to drive the piece of plant, Alec wound the handle and the noise nearly drove me mad.

Suddenly the telephone rang. It was Alf.

"The f...ing flap on the salt hopper has jammed and we can't get any of the f...ing salt out," he said. "Better come up and have a look," he added.

The salt hoppers held 50 tons of common salt. They were cylindrical steel containers, 8 feet in diameter, 16 feet high and tapering at the bottom to a 12 inch opening with a flap which controlled the flow of salt into the process below. It was essential to keep the flow of salt going as otherwise the plant below would stop and freeze solid with untold trouble to get it going again. It was a similar problem to the one with the blast furnaces at Barrow.

I put on my brown lab coat and safety helmet, slung my gas mask over my shoulder, and hurried up the yard to the plant which was at the other end of the works.

I found Alf and his gang cursing at the flap valve which was obviously jammed on some solid object which must have got into the hopper. They started to dismantle the valve and found the blockage was caused by a rubber boot as worn by the processmen.

"Some f...ing fool must have f...ing well thrown it into the f...ing hopper," said Alf. "Lets get the f...ing thing out," he shouted to his men.

But the boot refused to budge. It was held by something else higher up in the hopper. The only thing to do was to cut some of the steel away with an oxyacetylene cutter which was sent for.

As the steel came away and tons of salt started to spew out on to the floor they saw, to their horror, that the boot was connected to a human leg and there were two of them.

It was obvious that someone must have been in the hopper but whether he was still alive was very doubtful.

By now there was general panic. Alec had arrived together with the Works Manager and his deputy along with the Works Engineer, the Safety Officer and the Works Doctor.

Looking into the top of the hopper there was no sign of a body but if there had been the salt would have covered it. It was agreed that more steel must be cut away rapidly to get the salt out of the hopper to release the body. By now the Police and the Ambulance had arrived. The question was: who could the victim be? A quick roll call showed that one of the process trainees had not been seen for an hour.

Eventually they got him out but there was no sign of life. He was identified as the missing trainee. Everyone was told to keep away as the body was laid on the floor. It was the first time that I had seen a corpse, but I noticed that the legs were tied together loosely with a piece of cloth.

The questions mounted up. How had he got into the hopper? Was it accidental? Or suicide? Or foulplay?

There was a manhole at the top of the hopper which was closed by a loose iron plate. It was necessary for a processman to enter the hopper occasionally through it, to check if the salt had *voided*. This was when the salt, on being withdrawn from below, had left a void with a crust on top which had to be broken up with a bar.

It was a mystery which was never cleared up. A verdict of misadventure was reached at the inquest. But why did he go into the hopper? Was it just *skiving* for an hour in a nice warm atmosphere, or was he pushed by one of his mates as a prank? If so, and there was a void, he would have gone through the crust the moment he stepped on it and been engulfed and suffocated by the salt.

But why were his legs tied together? Several people disputed this although it was mentioned at the inquest. But I had seen it and couldn't get it out of my mind.

The tragedy of the salt hopper was still worrying me after the inquest but the tragedy of what was happening in Europe disturbed me as well.

In the spring of 1939, not satisfied with the annexation of the Sudetenland, Hitler struck again, breaking all his promises, and occupied the remainder of Czechoslovakia. The mood in Britain changed. Mosley and his followers ceased to have influence. Eventually they would be interned. Those who were against war whatever the cost became silent. Genuine pacifists would become conscientious objectors and although some were imprisoned, the disapprobation of the First World war was not delivered in the form of white feathers. Disapproval there was, but many worked in ways that helped the war effort without compromising their ideals. However more importantly it was Chamberlain who at last woke up to the fact that Hitler had cheated him and was not to be trusted.

This was a fateful turning point in history and two weeks later the Prime Minister rose in the House of Commons and announced: "In the event of any action which would clearly threaten Polish independence H.M.Government would feel themselves bound, at once, to lend the Polish Government all the support in their power". Chamberlain knew Poland was next on Hitler's list and he knew that if she was invaded, this would mean war.

By the Treaty of Versailles, Danzig (Gdansk) had been detached from Germany and made a free city, under the protection of the League of Nations, in order to give the Poles access to the sea - The Polish Corridor. Hitler now intended to take it back. And so, once again, and for the last time, the authority of the League of Nations was to be flouted. It was an organisation with such high hopes of maintaining a lasting peace after the horrors of the First World War but which failed dismally. Danzig was an excuse. Hitler wanted the whole of Poland.

Meanwhile Mussolini, the Italian Fascist dictator who had aligned himself with Hitler, not to be outdone by his friend, invaded Albania. He then informed Britain and France that in the event of an invasion of Poland his country would remain neutral. How could anyone believe him?

In March the papers were full of the surrender of Madrid to Franco and what was left of Republican Spain capitulated. France was now surrounded by pro-Fascist adversaries on three sides - Germany, Italy and Spain.

Throughout the summer rumours were spreading as to the position of Russia. If there was to be a war with Germany we needed Russia to be on our side to attack from the East. Sadly the British Government was suspicious of the Bolsheviks as were the Poles who hated them. Negotiations dragged on until August 23 when a great shock rocked the nation - Russia signed a pact with Germany. It had never been thought that two countries with such opposing ideologies could ever agree to support each other. But they did.

On the 27th of April 1939, conscription for military service had been announced in Britain but as I was in the Territorial Army I knew it would not affect me. I was glad my father had made me a volunteer as I had had more training and more choice of where I would serve. I realised that I might have claimed to be in a reserved occupation but I was in the Territorial Army and had no wish to leave it.

CHAPTER 12

Reg came down to spend a weekend at my home. We swam in the river and lay in the sun discussing the possibility of a summer holiday. Reg wanted to go abroad as he had never been before, but I had been twice to Switzerland on walking and cycling holidays with my school.

The deteriorating international situation might well mean that this would be our last chance of seeing Europe before war engulfed the world. We decided to take my car. This was not so simple as it is today. A *carnet* had to be obtained which was a document to be stamped by customs on leaving or entering each country with the car. A *green card* was also required to cover insurance abroad. In addition, for some countries it was prudent to purchase petrol coupons in advance. Also a spare parts kit for the car was essential as it was unlikely that spares would be available for one's make of car if one had the misfortune to break down.

After we had attended camp where we had more practice at firing our anti-tank guns, we set out at the beginning of August, driving the Wolseley down to Dover. There were no drive-on ferries as we have today. The car was driven on to the quay and each wheel was encased in a kind of rope basket suspended from a frame attached to a crane. On a signal from the stevedore the crane lifted the car up and dumped it on to the deck of the ship. Seeing it swinging about like a stack of cotton bales, I imagined the rope breaking and the holiday disappearing into the dock. However all was well and after a rough crossing, we arrived at Ostend with the Wolseley still in one piece.

As we were driving through Belgium there was suddenly a loud bang. A tyre had burst on the rough *pavé*. Most of the roads in this part of the Continent were paved with small square blocks of stone which, although no doubt very durable and suitable for horse-drawn transport, were very hard on motorcar tyres and the suspension. The tyre had to be mended. We found a *depannagé* or repairer not too far away but as a result we had to stay the first night at a little village in Flanders.

Before leaving England we had decided that the first stop should be Paris, where neither of us had been before. Reg had always wanted to drive in Paris, something I had no great wish to do. On the second day we finally entered the city from the North, drove to the Place de la Concorde, up the Champs-Élysées, round the Arc de Triomphe, crossed the Seine to see the Eiffel Tower, then along the Left Bank by Notre Dame. The number of cars was nothing like what it was years later but, with Reg driving, I gripped my seat anxiously as angry Parisians shouted and gesticulated at the little *GB* darting in and out of the traffic. Having seen enough of Paris by day, we put up at a pension in Montmartre where we hoped to experience the night life of the city. We were able to get some tickets for the Folies Bergère where we saw the famous cancan danced by the girls in black stockings, suspenders and voluminous petticoats. We also hoped to see some nudes.

Most young men are interested in the feminine form of the opposite sex. In 1939 there were no *girlie* magazines such as proliferate on the bookstalls today. The nearest approach was 'Health and Efficiency' - the naturist journal - but pictures of the nature clubs showed only back views generally taken from some distance away. The Scandinavian and German magazines were more explicit but more difficult to obtain. Theatres and films were subject to strict censorship. In London the Windmill Theatre in St Martin's Lane did display nudes on the stage but only if they did not move. I had been twice, entering rather furtively to purchase my ticket in case I was seen by anyone who knew me. I had then passed down a darkened passage to be accosted by a young lady, in very limited attire, who persuaded me to buy an expensive illustrated programme. The theatre was small and the performance continuous. The nudes who were draped across the stage, were statuesque and woe betide any of them who so much as twitched. The dancers were scantily clad but occasionally a bosom and a nipple might slip out, in which case the girl quickly disappeared into the wings. The programme stated categorically that *no additional artificial aid to vision is permitted,* so opera glasses were out. The audience was predominately male and whenever the curtain fell, there was an unseemly rush from those behind, climbing over the backs of the seats, to seize the seats in the front row. The dances and tableaux were interspersed with comic turns and many comedians made their names at the Windmill. One of them, who became a celebrated character, was Jimmy Edwards later to join the RAF and win a Distinguished Flying Cross when he was flying troops to the battle of Arnhem.

At the Folies Bergère, after the cancan, the next scene was of a buxom lady taking a bath. There was a good deal of build-up in French which neither of us understood, but at the end she leapt out of the bath, naked, and rushed into the wings, concealing the more intimate parts of her anatomy with a large sponge.

When we were planning the holiday Reg and I had agreed that in Paris we should find a couple of French prostitutes. We had been told that the French 'pros' were medically inspected and therefore safe from venereal disease, something that was probably more wishful thinking than fact. Finding them was not difficult because as soon as we came out of the theatre we were accosted by two women who indicated in elementary English what they were. We walked the short distance to the women's lodging which consisted of a small room up some stairs which they shared. The room contained two couches and a wash basin. All I can remember of the evening was the two women laughing and screaming to each other in French as to the comparative performance of their clients, one of whom they claimed was *comme un français*. Which of us that was I don't know but for me it was not a very satisfying experience.

The next day we set off for Luxembourg where we stayed the night. Visiting a night club where the girls were dancing semi-nude, we invited two of them to come over to our table where we were drinking some rather rough red wine which we shared with them. Reg, who was slightly drunk, tried to persuade one of them to come to bed with him but his German, consisting of *kommen* and *bett*, didn't seem to go down very well and Reg had no luck.

We arranged to enter Germany by way of Strasbourg and we wondered, after crossing the Rhine, what our reception in that country was going to be. Presenting ourselves at the French frontier we were let through, the officials muttering - "Ils sont fou les Anglais". Crossing the bridge to the German side which appeared to be well-fortified, there was some amusement at our car with the GB on it. A number of brown shirted 'Hitler Youths' then appeared and shouted "Englanders" in derogatory and hostile tones. The customs official was about to stamp our carnet when he noticed some Belgian newspapers in the back of the car which I had used to pack the luggage to stop it moving. The police then approached and said it was *verboten* to bring such propaganda into the country. I did wonder what the propaganda was but they took the newspapers and, after some more argument, let us through. I drove away as fast as I could.

We had not gone very far when rounding a bend we came on the scene of an accident. A car had run off the road and overturned. It was an open-tourer and the German occupants appeared not to be hurt apart from a girl with blonde hair who was lying in the ditch with her legs in the air. She was not unattractive and Reg ran to her. Forgetting all the rules of first aid he put his arms round her and, with me hanging on to her legs, we hauled her out of the ditch. She seemed to recover and was obviously keen to show her appreciation. I, seeing complications if the police were to arrive, told Reg to forget the girl and get into the Wolseley which he reluctantly did. I drove off rapidly putting as much distance between ourselves and the accident as we could.

We stayed that night in the Black Forest where the inhabitants showed us no animosity and then drove on to Lindau on Lake Constance where we crossed into Austria, the scene of the recent *Anschluss.* After that to Innsbruck and via the Wipp valley to the Brenner Pass - that great trade route into Italy since the 14th century and where, during the coming war, Hitler was to meet his friend Mussolini on several occasions. Descending by the Adige valley we skirted Lake Garda, the largest of the Italian lakes, and then to Verona, the setting for Shakespeare's *Romeo and Juliet.* Finally we arrived at Venice where we stayed for a couple of nights. We watched the gondoliers and travelled by *vaporetti* and took pictures of the Bridge of Sighs. Drinking coffee in St Mark's Square we saw the pigeons, and walking by the Rialto Bridge I remembered that here it was that Antonio heard his ships were lost and his bond with Shylock of a pound of flesh, had to be paid. We bathed in the warm waters of the Adriatic from the Lido and then it was time to return.

We drove back across the scorching plain of Lombardy to Milan. Then Aosta and on to France across the Grand St. Bernard pass. I had previously pushed a bicycle up its slopes and remembered the excitement of the descent - never touching the pedals for thirty miles and rounding the hairpin bends at breathtaking speeds. We stayed a night in Geneva. Crossing France, we reached the coast. The boat was full but the crossing was without incident.

When we arrived in London, even in the two weeks we had been away, it had changed. Air-raid shelters were being prepared, barrage balloons were rising in the sky, people were carrying gas masks and there was an air of preparation for what now seemed to be inevitable. We managed one night at our respective homes and then Reg returned to Barrow and I to Runcorn.

I had not been back at Runcorn for more than a day when I received a message from Colonel Baslow asking me if I would go to South Wales to take charge of all the Regiment's guns which were on the artillery ranges on the Gower Peninsula carrying out intensive target practice with live ammunition. I had to obtain special leave from the company for this purpose and, although I did not know it at the time, this was the last time I would see the works for six years.

I drove in the Wolseley to the ranges which were on the bleak western edge of the peninsula, looking out over Rhossili Bay towards the Bristol Channel. Apart from firing the guns, there was little other amusement and nothing to do apart from visiting the local pub.

It was the first of September when Hitler started his invasion of Poland and general mobilization in Britain was declared. I received orders that day to bring all the guns back to the Headquarters at Ulverston with the greatest urgency. I calculated it was about 270 miles, much of it through central Wales. Towing a gun, the speed of the 15 cwt trucks would be restricted and, taking into account that we would be travelling in convoy, something with which we had not yet had much practice, I estimated it would take two days. We drew rations for the journey, and blankets, and arranged to set off at once.

In Britain it had been a wonderful summer, one of the best for years and similar to that glorious hot summer of August 1914 which was the start of the First World War. That war had sent seven hundred thousand British and Colonial youths to their deaths, as well as two million Frenchmen, a million Italians, and untold millions of Russians, Turks and members of the Austro-Hungarian Empire. The Germans lost two million. Amongst the Germans, Hitler, thrice wounded, survived.

Throughout the country the air of complacency had gone and was replaced by apprehension. The barrage balloons, now being put in place, were to defeat the bombers which it was thought would attack London as soon as war was declared. Arrangements for blacking out all lights at night were being made and signposts on roads were being removed to confuse the enemy parachutists who were expected to arrive prior to an invasion.

On Friday morning, 1st September, thousands of children left home for school only to be told to return home, pack a bag, carry their gas mask, and be ready for evacuation out of the capital. Many went to the country, a new world for them to explore and a new home to live in.

The first part of our route that Friday was to Llandilo and then skirting the Black Mountains to Llandovery. I led the way in the Wolseley. I had two motorcycle despatch riders, known as *Don Rs*. At each road junction, one Don R would stop to direct the convoy and when the last vehicle had passed, would roar up to the front to take over from the other one. We drove on from Llandovery and then to Builth Wells. The roads through Wales were narrow and twisting. The road signs were sparse, some had already been removed, so that in spite of the Don Rs' efforts, vehicles still took a wrong turning and, with the occasional breakdown and stops for a *brew up*, the speed was desperately slow. From

Llandrindod Wells we followed the valley of the river Ithon between the mountains of Central Wales to Newtown. It was a lovely sunny autumn day, the sunshine reflected off the leaves just turning to colours on the trees and forests through which we were passing. The river sparkled in the valley and the dark pines covering the surrounding heights hummed with a deeper green. The thought of war and the rape of Poland seemed far away.

From Newtown we followed the Severn to Oswestry and then struck across to Whitchurch, going north, aiming to cross the Mersey at Warrington. We had been going for nearly ten hours and I decided that we should spend the night in Cheshire. I knew that the little village of Frodsham had a wide main street where for 300 years a weekly market had been held and in which the convoy could be parked. The men bedded down in their vehicles although some found friendly billets in the village. I, not surprisingly, spent the night at home where I appeared in uniform, something I would remain in, except for occasional leaves, for the duration of the war.

The following morning we started rather late as I considered we would make better time than the day before on the roads through Lancashire. Setting off just before 11 a.m., as the convoy was going up the hill out of the village, I stopped the Wolseley for a moment to go over to the house where I knew my friend Jim's parents lived. The door was open and the wireless turned on. It was 11.15 and I heard the fateful announcement by Mr Chamberlain "....a state of war now exists between this country and Germany".

We pressed on, with a brief halt on the straight road approaching Warrington before entering the town with its complicated streets. Opposite the spot where we had halted was the house of another of my friends from the works. He was at home and, seeing me for the first time in uniform, rushed out to offer me a tot of whisky which I gratefully accepted.

As we moved North we noticed sandbags, in front of Police Stations and other important buildings, being filled and rising higher and higher as the afternoon wore on and we got further north. Just before we reached Lancaster, one of the Don Rs rode up to me to say that a wheel on one of the guns had come off. We would have to stop to repair it. We were still some distance from Ulverston and it was then that I realised that I was in charge of the whole armament of the Regiment and moreover we were now at war - no longer on training. I drove to the rear of the convoy and urged the men to get the damaged gun into the truck instead of towing it, so that we could proceed. After some delay we got going again and without further mishap arrived at the Drill Hall at Ulverston just as it was getting dark. I thankfully handed the guns over to Colonel Baslow and went to the local hotel for the night while the men, being mainly local, went to their homes.

The next morning Colonel Baslow sent for me and told me that I was to be promoted to Captain and appointed as Adjutant to the Regiment. In peace time the Adjutant of a T.A. unit was a regular officer, but as soon as War was declared and the T.A. *embodied* he returned to his regular unit and the T.A. had to appoint an Adjutant from its own officers. It was some time later that I received my embodiment papers which had been sent to the digs in Runcorn. These indicated that if I did not report to the Drill Hall at Ulverston immediately, I would be prosecuted and also that I should bring my unemployment book with me. As I was already at the Drill Hall I took no notice of it and never found the unemployment book which seemed a little superfluous anyhow. Although on the day that war was declared there had been an air raid warning in London which turned out to be a false alarm, there had been no other incidents. However the war at sea had started in earnest as was apparent on Monday morning when news of the sinking, by a German submarine, of the *Athenia*, with the loss of 112 lives, was reported in the newspapers. I learned later that my younger brother, David, now aged 18, who was returning from Canada in the *Aquitania*, was half-way across the Atlantic when the news of the sinking was received. This resulted in my brother and some of the other passengers being recruited as extra lookouts for the rest of the voyage, which was completed with apprehension, but with no further incidents.

CHAPTER 13

And so at last war had come. The war which my father had forecast and for which he hoped his son was now prepared. Sadly the army was not as prepared as it might have been. In the South African War we had become cavalry-minded, but in the 1914-18 war cavalry was seldom used and although the horse was essential for transport and for moving the artillery we became bogged down for four long years in trench warfare. In 1939 the Allies, with memories of trench warfare in their mind, relied on defensive positions such as the Maginot Line, built at great cost, only to find that the Germans, in a war of movement, outflanked the defences with their tanks. The tank was a weapon which had been invented and used by the British but improved and put to deadly use by the enemy. Poison gas, although outlawed, had been used in the last war and it was thought that it would be used in this one as well.

For me the outbreak of war was a peculiar feeling. For the past few years I, and many others like me, had thought that war would come and being in the forces we would be intimately involved. Now that it was real I felt a confused mixture of apprehension, excitement and, at the same time, the dreadful inevitability of it all.

As Adjutant I was responsible for the administration of the Regiment, disseminating my Commanding Officer's orders to the Battery Commanders and in turn keeping him informed of orders from the higher command. I was in charge of Regimental Headquarters which consisted of an Intelligence Officer who also acted as my deputy, and a Warrant Officer who, with a clerk, looked after the office. The Regimental Sergeant-Major (RSM) was responsible for maintaining the discipline of the troops, whilst the Quartermaster was in charge of the stores. There was also a Medical Officer (Doc) and an Ordnance Officer (Spanners). Spanners had a Light Aid Detachment (LAD) manned by artificers who were responsible for the repair and maintenance of guns and vehicles.

My first task, in order to get the Regiment ready for war, was to weed out the men who were medically unfit, under age, or in reserved occupations.

In January 1939, after the Prime Minister returned from Munich with the *peace in our time* message, the Government had made two important decisions - they created a Directorship of Mobilization and issued a Schedule of Reserved Occupations. The latter was to avoid the haphazard enlistment which happened in 1914 when some industries, vital to the war effort, were crippled by the loss of their most essential workers. The Military Training Act, passed at the end of April, was simply conscription by another name but was something unique for Britain in time of peace. This act was superceded at the outbreak of war by the National Service Act and only a small number of Militiamen had been enlisted into the Regular Army before the National Service men arrived.

At this point there were more men in the Territorial Army than the Regular Army because, at the beginning of the year Mr Hore Belisha, the War Minister, had opened a campaign to double the strength of the T.A. However, in order not to inhibit recruiting, the Reserved Occupation Schedule did not apply. As a result, I found that I had a large number of men from Vickers Shipyard, the Steel Works and the mines who had to be returned to industry and replaced by men who were not reserved. This was not an easy task as the new men from different units had to be assimilated into the Regiment. At the same time the Territorial Army was officially merged with the Regular Army.

Equipment and clothing had also to be issued. The Regiment already had some guns and towing vehicles but many of the administration vehicles had to be impressed from civilian sources. The Mobile Regimental Office, for example, was for a long time housed in a van belonging to one of the local grocers.

The Commanding Officer, Lieutenant-Colonel Baslow, who had taken over when the King's Own had been changed to Anti-tank, was still in command. His second-in-command, Major Stanley, a rather portly but very cheerful officer, was also in charge of the Officers' Mess. 221 Battery was now commanded by Major Shannon, who had been in the last war where he had won a Military Cross. Reggie was a troop commander in his Battery.

The other Battery commanders had not changed since I left Barrow. Major George Wilcox was still with 222 and Major Ike Proudlove, with 223. 224 was now commanded by a Captain, Noel Nickson. The Quartermaster, Captain Kershaw, was known as Uncle as he had been in the last war and at 45 was the oldest officer in the Regiment. He, like Major Shannon, wore the medal ribbons of the '14-'18 war. Lieutenant Peter Williams, my Intelligence Officer, was a young man of medium height and ruddy complexion who wore glasses and had a great sense of humour. He had been studying to be a solicitor and was very bright and energetic and a great help to me.

The last time I had been at home before war broke out, I tried to explain to my sister Janet how the army was organised.

"What are these Battalions and Regiments you keep talking about?" she'd asked.

"A Battalion is an infantry unit consisting of four or five companies, each of which is then split into platoons and sections," I'd replied.

"How many men are there in a Battalion?" Janet liked accuracy.

"It varies but you could say about eight hundred to a thousand. The lowest rank is a private, then lance-corporal, corporal, sergeant, sergeant-major and then the officers. It's commanded by a Lieutenant-Colonel like Baslow my CO who wears a crown and one star on the shoulder."

"Is that what's called a pip?" she asked and I nodded.

"So what's a Regiment?"

"A Regiment generally covers all the infantry units in an area such as a county, like the Cheshire Regiment. But then you also have gunners like me who are part of the Royal Regiment of Artillery - RA for short."

"So that's the Regiment but what about Batteries, you keep mentioning them."

"In an infantry battalion you have companies. The equivalent in an artillery unit is a battery and in a cavalry unit or tank unit it's a squadron like in the Air Force. Don't ask me about the Navy or I shall probably get it wrong."

Janet smiled. "Alright I won't, but going back to the Regiment. In a Regiment you have Brigades and Divisions?"

"No! In a Division there are generally three Brigades and within the Brigades there are perhaps four Battalions which can be from different Regiments. Then there are Divisional troops which consist of the gunners, sappers and other specialist troops. Two or three Divisions may make a Corps and one or more Corps becomes an Army. If you command a Brigade you will probably be a brigadier. A Division would be commanded by a major-general, a Corps by a lieutenant-general and an Army by a general or a field marshal."

Janet laughed. "You seem to have mugged it up very well. It'll help when you're a general," she replied with good humour.

After war broke out, Janet joined the Field Ambulance Nursing Yeomany (FANY) and served throughout he war. Both Nancy and Sybil had married and had families to look after. Nancy's husband was an officer in the Navy and Sybil's a major in the Black Watch. Eventually my brother David would join the Coldstream Guards.

The 56th Anti-tank Regiment of which I was now the Adjutant, were Divisional troops and as such their Batteries could be dispersed within the Brigades. 42nd Division was part of Northern Command which covered the north of England up to the Scottish border. It had six Divisions, each having three infantry Brigades. As a result orders and instructions emanated from both the Division and the Brigades and all filtered down to me. I soon found the amount of paperwork escalating. It seemed as if we were trying to win the war by paper.

One of the most nonsensical things to land on my desk was a request which read as follows: "Subject - trouser buttons - it has been brought to notice that trouser buttons are pulled off within a few days of issue. Please report to this HQ whether this failure has been found to be general in your respective Divisions."

This was signed by a Major-General at Northern Command, passed on by the Divisions to the Brigades and from them to the Battalions and Artillery Regiments. It eventually arrived on my desk having involved at least a hundred separate letters. I showed it to Peter and asked him what he thought of this particular piece of administrative nonsense.

Peter read it slowly and, applying his legal mind, replied: "Yes they may have a point. It might be awkward if the buttons happened to fail during a bayonet charge. Of course the Scottish Regiments wouldn't have that problem."

"Well that might make them laugh and I could also say that soldiers caught with their trousers down during a bayonet charge might be more vulnerable, but I don't think I can reply on those lines. I shall just say that metal buttons do tend to cut the thread and have been known to come off at awkward moments."

"I think that would be a very diplomatic reply, Sir," said Peter and I told him to get a letter out.

After three weeks the 42nd Division moved nearer to the East Coast and the 56th were ordered to move to Hexham in Northumberland. Arrangements had to be made to transport the whole Regiment by rail as petrol was rationed and even the services had to husband it as much as possible. I appointed Peter as Railway Transport Officer. His job was to liaise with the London and North Western Railway Company and arrange for the guns and vehicles to be loaded on to the railway wagons. He also had to ensure that the troops were ready to entrain at Ulverston station.

I had already said goodbye to my friends in Barrow and no one was at the station to bid me adieu, but a large crowd came to see the troops off. Many of the lads were locals and some heartbreaking farewells took place on the platform. Eventually the train slowly pulled out of the station and it seemed now that for us the the first phase of the war had begun.

The Quartermaster, Peter and I shared a first class compartment. The train gathered speed and Uncle started to regale us with a lot of lavatory humour after which he suddenly said rather gravely: "This reminds me of 1914 - I wonder how many of us will come back?" It was certainly not the most cheerful thing to say at that juncture.

When we arrived at Hexham the first thing to be done was to set up Regimental and Battery HQs and to arrange for the billeting of the troops. In each town there was a Billeting Officer who was responsible for allocating households who had one or more spare rooms to take in soldiers. Battery commanders then liaised with him to accommodate their men. Officers were generally put in hotels or guest houses. Regimental HQ would be in the Town or Drill Hall. Communications had to be set up between Headquarters and the Batteries. Wireless communication was not very reliable and could be compromised if the enemy were listening-in so field telephone cable had to be run out to the Batteries by the signallers.

The first excitement, shortly after arrival, was the eerie sound of an air raid siren. A lone aircraft appeared very high up over the town. The anti-aircraft platoon, who were armed with an ancient Lewis gun, collected their gun and set it up in the Town Square. It then transpired that they had not been issued with live ammunition which was kept securely locked in the Quartermaster's stores. An urgent request for the ammunition was made to Uncle who refused point blank to issue any without a signed requisition from the C.O. By then of course the aircraft had long since departed. Perhaps it was just as well as it was too far away to identify it either as hostile or friendly.

Almost immediately after the outbreak of war, whilst we were moving to Hexham, the British Expeditionary Force, known as the BEF, began to move to France.

On the 27th of October the 7th Cheshires, which was the unit I had joined in 1930, was the first Territorial Battalion to arrive in France as part of the four British Divisions who took up positions on the Franco-Belgian border. Belgium had insisted on retaining her neutrality with the catastrophic result that the Allies were not allowed to cross her frontier nor even make reconnaissances until the Germans had actually invaded. It was then of course too late.

From the news coming from France the war was at a standstill with the belligerents glaring at each other across no-man's-land, between the Maginot and Siegfried lines. Apart from occasional patrols to probe each other's defences there was no action for the troops.

Christmas came and with it little change. Most of our troops were able to go on Christmas leave. As the expected bombing of London and other cities had not materialised many of the children evacuated in September began to return home, only to be re-evacuated later when the bombing began in earnest.

The war at sea was a different matter with U-boats a continuing menace. There was also a new weapon, the magnetic mine, which was detonated by the proximity of a ship's steel hull. Early in the war, one of these mines was washed up on a sand-bank without exploding. A bomb-disposal officer, risking his life, was able to defuse it and, as a result, countermeasures were developed which saved thousands of lives and allowed the vital supplies we required to reach this country.

In October, the news of the sinking of our battleship, *Royal Oak*, shook the nation. A German submarine had penetrated what had been considered the impregnable anchorage at Scapa Flow, fired a torpedo and escaped. In December came better news. The German battleship, *Admiral Graf Spee*, had been scuttled outside Montevideo harbour after a running battle with the Royal Navy. Her auxiliary vessel, the *Altmark*, was still at large and was known to be holding as prisoners the merchant seamen from the vessels *Graf Spee* had sunk. Two months later the *Altmark* was cornered in Norwegian waters by *HMS Cossack* who boarded her and, to the cries of "the Navy's here", released 299 prisoners.

By November the Russians, who were at this time allied to the Germans, violated Finnish neutrality and invaded along her one thousand-mile frontier. The indignation of the Allies at this unprovoked attack was followed by astonishment and relief at the lack of success by the Russians. Plans were now made to come to the relief of the gallant Finns via Norway although that peaceful country was also neutral. To do this it was planned, if the agreement of the Norwegians could be obtained, to occupy Narvik, a port on the coast of northern Norway. This would allow access for our troops to the Finns and, as a bonus, would also cut off the iron ore supply from Sweden which was vital to the German war effort. The Narvik expedition was fraught with indecision until it was too late. The port was taken by the valient efforts of the Royal Navy, and contingents of French, Polish and Norwegian troops, but was almost immediately given up when the Germans invaded central Norway. They captured Oslo but the Norwegian King escaped to Britain where he remained in exile for five years.

Although it had been agreed that the 42nd Division would be going to France in February, it was kept back in case it was required for the Norway expedition and the relief of Finland. As a result the Division was rapidly brought up to war establishment with issue of weapons, ammunition and vehicles, and was moved to the South of England, where it underwent intensive training. The 56th were moved to Wantage where I set up our Headquarters in the Town Hall with the guns and vehicles parked in the Town Square. It was one of the coldest winters on record which might have been a help for our arctic training but was not pleasant as we had not yet been issued with the appropriate clothing. The cold was so intense that, in spite of anti-freeze, the vehicles had to be started up and run for a short time several times during the night to stop them freezing.

However our training had hardly got under way when I heard, in the middle of March, that the Finnish expedition was cancelled. As a result we would shortly be going to France and we now made ready for this move.

Colonel Baslow was a keen racing man. It was the Cheltenham Festival, and the Gold Cup which the Colonel had been looking forward to had had to be postponed because of the weather. Now it was on again and the Colonel was in a rush to get there. He invited me to go with him.

The Colonel was a friend of Freddy Foxton the well-known jockey who had now retired. Freddy was a friend of Liam Harvey, the trainer. Liam Harvey was running two of Grimey Wishbone's horses at Cheltenham. Grimey Wishbone, the glass manufacturer, son of Lord Wishbone and owner of a string of racehorses, had a box on the racecourse. Grimey invited Liam who invited Freddy who invited Colonel Baslow who had invited me, to join him in his box for the day.

Although it was wartime, entertainments such as racing continued as the Government felt it was necessary to keep up the morale of the population and not curtail what sport there was. The Colonel borrowed a 15 cwt truck, I drove and we arrived just after the first race had been run. Despite the postponement there were crowds of people and we made our way to the box where the Colonel introduced me to Freddy and Liam Harvey. Liam had a patch over one eye.

I was not all that interested in horse racing or betting but if I did bet, it was generally on No.3 which was my lucky number. It had stood me in good stead at Cartmel races. As this was a prestigious race meeting, I thought I'd better have a bet and went down to the bookies and put five shillings on No.3 which I found was at 6 to 1. Going back to the box, as I was going up the stairs, I passed a tall young woman with long blonde hair, who was going down. The race was run in a flurry of snow flakes and I was very pleased to see that No.3 was the winner. I went down to collect my winnings and noticed that the young woman with the blonde hair was collecting hers from the next bookie.

"No.3 must be your lucky number as well," I said to her.

"Not really," she replied, "I know the horse's trainer," and she smiled.

I went back to the box to celebrate with a glass of champagne and, to my surprise, found the girl standing next to me. She was a friend of Liam Harvey's. No.3, unbeknown to me, was one of Grimey's horses so the whole box was celebrating. I started a conversation with the girl.

"Do you come racing often?" I asked.

"Only in the mating season," which seemed to be the normal reply to that sort of question. She laughed. "You see I live rather a long way away."

"Where is that?" I continued with interest.

"Just now I'm working at Wantage"

"What a coincidence! I'm stationed at Wantage myself."

The conversation continued and I asked her about Liam Harvey's eye patch.

"He lost it in the last war in no-man's-land," she said. "He was with my father in the Gordon Highlanders, in Italy. They were transport officers who supplied the horses, and Liam when he got back set up a racing stable." Her own father was a farmer in Oxfordshire and did some dealing in horses as well. As to why an Irishman and an Englishman were in a Scottish Regiment she only smiled and said: "They called my father Jock and Liam they called Scottie, that seemed to sort it out."

The girl was very attractive and must have been about 25 with blue eyes and a fresh open-air complexion. She was dressed in a warm woollen jersey with a tweed jacket and skirt and wore a hat under which her long blonde hair fell to her shoulders. Her name was Julia and she was a mathematics teacher at a convent in Wantage and was living in lodgings. I had forgotten all about the racing but when the next race was announced, it was the Gold Cup itself. Everyone in the box became quiet and tense, eyes glanced down at racecards and several of them left the box in a surrepticious but purposeful way. I asked Julia if she would like to go down and put on a bet. We went together and bet again on Grimey Wishbone's horse, which Julia said Liam had assured her had a good chance. We watched the race from the rails and it won. This gave us an excuse to return to the box for another celebration.

I introduced her to the Colonel who gave me a wink indicating that he approved before he was swept back amongst the important people surrounding

Grimey Wishbone. Julia and I continued chatting and when the racing was nearly over I suggested that we should meet again, telling her that I was staying at the Bear in Wantage and she gave me her address

The racing over, I drove back to Wantage. The Colonel, who was not a great drinker fell asleep almost immediately, his body relaxed but his face a little red from having drunk rather too much of the generous supply of Grimey's champagne. I drove automatically, my head in a dream about Julia and what a lovely girl she was. I had to see her again.

The next day the Regiment received orders that in three days time it was to be ready to move for embarkation for France. I went round to Julia's lodging and, as it was the weekend, asked her if she would like to come out with me, to which she agreed. One of the officers still had his own car with him. It was an open Alvis and he very generously offered to lend it to me for the day including some much prized petrol coupons. I collected Julia and we set out and drove to the Downs where Julia said she had a horse which she kept in some riding stables. She said we could both have a ride together if she borrowed another horse. I was already dressed in breeches and field boots which I had bought when I was appointed Adjutant. Julia changed into jodhpurs, and mounting our horses we cantered over the Downs. It was still cold and the wind was blowing Julia's hair. I kept thinking how attractive she was and how lucky I was to have met her. For once I did not have too much difficulty with my horse in spite of two low-flying Spitfires which caused both our horses to *kettle*. Mine was a very much better animal than those provided by the army at that T.A. camp when I had first sat on a horse.

It was a wonderful ride and afterwards we returned to Wantage and had supper together and talked. Almost like myself, she had two elder sisters and a younger brother, still at school. When war broke out she had wanted to join the Services but she still had this teaching job at the convent.

"You ought to join the WAAF," I said. "The uniform would suit you."

"Well I might," she replied laughing, "but not for that reason."

I told her how I had come to join the T.A. and about my home in Cheshire. We got on so well together that I felt I might have known her all my life instead of a brief two days. I told her I would shortly be going to France - it didn't seem to be careless talk as everyone now knew we were off. I took her back to her lodgings. As I said good night and kissed her, I put my arms round her and held her close to me. She was nearly as tall as me and every part of her body moulded into mine. The effect on me was electric.

The next day was Sunday and as I had left Peter to do most of the work in the office, Julia and I were able to spend that day together as well. As it was my last night I asked her to have dinner with me at the Bear.

Julia arrived at the hotel dressed in a long coat and underneath she wore a light blue frock with a single string of pearls round her neck. I had already noticed that she wore no rings. We went into the restaurant and sat at a table in the corner. I ordered a bottle of champagne. Peter and Doc were sitting at another table in the restaurant and were watching us with some interest as they had heard of some of my escapades in Barrow. I felt this was much more serious. Julia was a lovely girl and, although we had only known each other such a short time, we seemed to be in tune with each other. I ordered another bottle of champagne and suggested we might take it up to my room. Julia agreed and we sat on chairs in the bedroom and talked. I was not sure how to proceed. I need not have worried. Julia came over to me and kissed me.

"I'm not a virgin," she said, "and I don't do this sort of thing usually, but this is your last night and tomorrow you are going to France and maybe you may not come back." So saying she undressed and got into bed where I followed.

Next morning I took her back to her lodgings and kissing her a lingering farewell, promised to write and to tell her where I was and hoped she wouldn't forget me.

That morning the Regiment started to move but I still couldn't stop thinking of Julia and swore that come what may I would come back to her. The Regiment eventually arrived at Southampton where we embarked on a ship which was to take us to Cherbourg, France, and the War.

It was a night crossing and there was no moon. The Channel was comparatively calm. For most of the crossing I stayed on deck watching the dark shapes of the destroyers, on the look out for U-boats, on either side shadowing the convoy. An occasional aircraft passed overhead, flashing the recognition signal to prevent the trigger-happy sailors from shooting at it. My thoughts were far away, in Wantage, thinking of Julia and our last embrace.

We came into Cherbourg just as dawn was breaking, and disembarked. There were a few stevedores in blue overalls standing about on the dockside and an occasional French Gendarme with a *gauloise* drooping from his mouth.

The first move was to Le Mans which was the HQ of the BEF. It was a hive of activity and having, with difficulty, found the billeting officer, the men were dispersed and guards mounted on the guns and vehicles. I was able to see Reggie who was with 221 Battery. He was his usual cheerful self and pleased to hear I had found a nice girl at last.

The next day we started the long trek towards the Belgian frontier where we were to take up our positions.

We stopped for the night at a village in the Mayenne. Although part of Normandy, the Mayennois were proud of their independence which they had held for many generations. The Batteries and their troops were billeted in the village while the Headquarter officers were accommodated in Fontaine Daniel, an ancient Abbey owned by the Comte de Brabazon, an aristocrat who still had a pack of boarhounds and had no intention of changing his way of life because of a war with *les boches*.

The Abbey was a long and narrow edifice which had been built in the sixteenth century. It housed a large family who were ruled with a rod of iron by Tante Anna, a French grande dame of the old school. Peter, Doc, Uncle and Spanners were placed in various parts of the Abbey but the Colonel, Major Stanley and I were given the guest wing which reminded me of some of the shooting lodges in Scotland to which I had been invited occasionally. My bed was in an alcove hidden behind curtains. A washbasin and ewer stood on a side table and a chamber pot was provided as no lavatory was in evidence. What took my attention as soon as I entered the room, was an unopened bottle of Scotch Whisky and one of French Cognac on a table by the bed, together with a glass. I felt I really couldn't impose on my host's hospitality and decided not to open either of the bottles.

The officers were asked to dine with the family. The dining room was large, with a long oak table illuminated by candles in silver candelabra. The Comte sat at one end with Colonel Baslow on his right and Major Stanley on his left whilst I was at the other end with Tante Anna. The rest of the family and the officers were spread out along either side. The meal was simple and served by an elderly retainer. After the meal was over and the family and the other officers had retired, the Comte, the Colonel, Major Stanley and I continued to sit at the table drinking Calvados, that powerful liqueur made from apples and for which Normandy is so famous. The Comte started to recount how he had lost so many of his kinsmen in the last war and how difficult it was to keep up the old style of living. Nevertheless, he had decided that he would build a church by the Abbey which was now complete. It was dedicated to St Thomas, a name of which I heartily approved.

The next morning after a breakfast of fresh bread and strong black coffee, the Comte and Tante Anna said goodbye to us, wishing us well and good courage.

The Comte swore again that *les boches* were not worth considering. They'd soon be defeated and the war over, but behind his long aquiline nose his grey eyes looked worried. When I looked back I could see that Tante Anna was angry with him about something, and then he turned on his heel and walked off towards the kennels and his adored boarhounds.

Having rounded up the troops from their billets, we started the trucks, and the Regiment set out on the last stage of its journey, which finished on the outskirts of Lille. Leaving 223 in reserve close to our Headquarters, the other Batteries were dispersed to the three Brigades which had been deployed to positions from which they could cross over the Franco-Belgian frontier as soon as, but not before, the Germans started their invasion.

RHQ was at Lambersart, a suburb on the west side of Lille. Peter, Doc and I were billeted in a house close to the Police Station. Spanners was in one down the road by a garage which he said might be useful. Doc set up his Regimental Aid Post in one of the rooms in our house and liaised with the local doctor. Major Stanley fixed up the Officer's Mess in the local estaminet where he and the Colonel were billeted.

And so we settled down to a routine and to await events.

CHAPTER 14

It must have been about the tenth of May when the first bombs fell in Lambersart. It was at four a.m. that I woke. I lay in bed listening to the sound of the guns and the shrapnel pattering on the roof, the bombs whistling as they fell. I noticed how the German bombs made a high pitched scream as they came down which, no doubt, was intended to make them more terrifying.

Doc came in - he was next door - and we both went into the bathroom to watch what was happening. Opening the window, fortunately as it turned out, we saw streams of Anti-Aircraft fire, known colloquially as 'flaming onions', going up and heard the noise of aircraft overhead. As nothing much else seemed to be happening, we turned to go. Doc had just reached his bedroom when there was a sickening crash and I was propelled forcibly through the bathroom door into the corridor. Having picked myself up and grabbed my steel helmet and respirator from my bedroom I ran downstairs to see if Peter was alright. Peter's room, which he was sharing with Spanners, was on the ground floor and Peter was sleeping by the window. There was a scene of considerable confusion. Peter was picking himself up, having been suddenly ejected from his bed, and was covered by glass and the window frame which had been blown in, but he was not hurt. Spanners who was on the other side of the room had also been tipped out of his bed by the blast. Dust and fumes were everywhere. Immediately our thoughts turned to gas but we had still to become accustomed to the fumes of cordite. Going outside, the day had dawned and it was a beautiful May morning, and except for a certain amount of smoke and broken glass, all seemed peaceful. There was a nice-looking new crater in the field on the other side of the road but that was all. Going into the office I was met by more broken glass, and the RSM cursing roundly.

Peter soon joined me and, having found the Passive Air Defence scheme, came to the conclusion it was a little late in the day to make any use of it!

However the quietness of the morning was soon broken when we found that the bombs had hit a row of poor people's houses opposite the Regimental Headquarters, injuring and killing some civilians. Spanners and his men from

117

the Light Aid Detachment formed a rescue squad and started to extricate those who were trapped. The Doc quickly organised a First Aid post and did his best for the injured.

Meanwhile our own casualties were reported. There were only two. The Quartermaster Sgt. and the clerk from Ike Proudlove's Battery, which was stationed in a farm just down the road, had been slightly injured. The rest of the Battery had been remarkably lucky as one bomb had landed in the centre of the courtyard of their billet. Beyond wrecking the cookhouse and the water truck it had done no other damage.

When things had settled down a little, Peter and I set out to make a survey of the damage caused by the bombs. We had not had time to change and were dressed in pyjamas, gum-boots, raincoats and wearing steel helmets. There must have been at least fifty bombs of various sizes, some of which were unexploded. We made an incongruous procession, walking from house to house, entering the back gardens to see what was reputed to be unexploded bombs but which were, more likely, pieces of bomb casing which had buried themselves in the earth. We tried to assess the damage to property. In one house the big French bed with its thick feather mattress was soaked in blood where the occupant, an old woman, had been hit by a bomb splinter. It was our first taste of war, but as such it seemed strangely impersonal.

We soon got tired of the bomb hunt and went back to breakfast where we learnedthat the Germans had marched into Belgium.

"So much for their guarantee of neutrality," remarked Peter.

"Well it's started and we seem to have been one of their first targets," I said proudly.

Orders to march were expected at any moment. But when the Divisional Commander visited us during the morning he seemed in no hurry for us to move.

"Everything is going according to plan," he told us. We were in reserve and might not be required for days.

And so it was. Day after day we sat at Lambersart listening to the news of our army advancing into Belgium. There were no great excitements apart from one or two incidents.

One morning a Frenchman came into my office and from amongst his voluble French, I could only make out the word *cadavre*. Apparently he had lost a corpse and was accusing me of having stolen it. It transpired that on the morning of the raid Doc, who had his hands full coping with the living, had told his orderly to take away an old man who was very dead and for whom he could do no more.

The orderly had put the corpse in a cellar at our Headquarters and, in the stress of the moment, it had been forgotten. Investigation showed, only too well, that after the lapse of several days it was still there. The RSM was detailed for the unpleasant job of removal.

Spy hunts also started about this time. The first one was a Gendarme who came to my office to tell me about a suspicious soldier speaking in French to the proprietor of the café up the road. The soldier turned out to be a member of the British Field Security Police who would not have been much use to us had he not been able to speak and understand French.

Then there was the probably quite inoffensive gentleman who boarded a tram in the Rue de l'Hippodrome and who, for no apparent reason, was asked for his papers by a suspicious sergeant. When produced they were quite unintelligible to the sergeant who reported the matter to Headquarters where on investigation we found the papers quite genuine and instructed the sergeant to let the gentleman go.

And then, of course, there were the lights in the café across the way. This no doubt had a perfectly rational explanation. However it was reported that lights had been seen flashing from the windows. This was enough! The café, which was reputed, amongst other things, to be the local brothel, was surrounded, albeit a little slowly. In fact it would have allowed time for any self-respecting fifth columnist or spy to escape at leisure. The RSM, Louis (our French Liaison Officer) and I, brandishing our revolvers, went in and demanded to be allowed to search the place. The proprietress who, no doubt, thought we were quite mad was only too pleased. We combed the place from attic to cellar in true melodramatic style - kicking open doors, revolvers at the ready, hoping to find a beautiful spy in the process of seducing a member of Divisional H.Q. with a copy of Routine Orders in his pocket! We did find one room occupied by two of the ladies of the establishment, obviously unemployed and drowning their sorrows in a bottle of cognac. Alas our efforts were abortive, even the cellar producing nothing more than empty bottles and a lot of water. We decided that spy hunting was not very productive.

Life again proceeded uneventfully for the next few days. We provided guards for vulnerable points (known as VPs) such as bridges, railway stations or electricity substations. Men were sent out to climb to the top of the church in Lambersart to watch for parachutists. There were occasional air raids and rumours of parachutists, none authenticated but always growing in intensity, and the nightly vigil by the telephone, testing the wire every hour. Peter and I slept with our revolvers handy - just in case - not that there seemed much likelihood of our using them.

The Sunday following the first raid was a gala day for the inhabitants. The crowds were almost like those at Blackpool on a Bank Holiday. Mothers, fathers, uncles, aunts, boys and girls, soldiers, shopkeepers, prostitutes and nuns - all were dressed in their best and all filled with a morbid desire to see the damage caused, and where their fellows had met their deaths.

It was one of those wonderful spring days when the air was warm and balmy. The trees had begun to put out their leaves, flowers were blooming, the birds were singing and summer seemed just round the corner. That morning, amongst all the crowd moving about in a mass of colour, the women in their frocks and the men in their Sunday best, the thought of war seemed to have dissolved. How different was the setting I was to see at this same place barely a fortnight later.

The first indication that all was not as well as had been hoped was a message received one night, and long delayed in transmission. "A body of enemy mobile troops has broken through in the vicinity of Sedan and are moving West". Sedan was a town far to the south east and it was not until later that I found out that this was where the Twelfth German Army with five Panzer Divisions had broken through and outflanked the impenetrable Maginot Line.

We were told: "The situation is well in hand and the enemy are being mopped up."

It was only during the following days that we found out how wrong that information was. At the time scant attention was paid to it. It was just another message and paper had started to roll into my office at almost peacetime rate.

Shortly after this I had occasion to send a despatch rider with a message to the outlying Batteries. Gunner Townley was a reliable man whom I had trained to ride a motorcycle when we were at Hexham. Unfortunately Townley lost his way and arrived at Tournai, a town fourteen miles to the east and inside the Belgian frontier, at the same time as the German dive-bombers arrived. His motorcycle was damaged but he was not hurt. As a result he had to leave the motorcycle there and return by alternative means. He reported to me and I had the feeling that things were not going as well as we had been led to believe.

For the moment the only worry was - one motorcycle out of action at Tournai. However the indefatigable Spanners set out and soon had it put right and brought the motorcycle back. On returning, his report on the state of Tournai did nothing to allay our growing sense of apprehension.

The next day we had definite orders to move. The move, in a southerly direction, should have been a simple one. Ike Proudlove's Battery had already gone off to join one of several separate forces which were being formed during this part of the campaign. The remainder of the Regiment was to act in an anti-aircraft role along the route that the rest of the Division was using. I wondered if someone at HQ had thought that our 2-pdr anti-tank guns could be used as an anti-aircraft weapon. It would be totally useless unless an aeroplane happened to be taxying on the ground when it would be like shooting at a running pheasant with a rifle. Nevertheless the Regiment was ordered to mount their Lewis Guns and deploy troops with rifles along the route. The object being to take on low-flying aircraft. It occurred to me that it would be a brave man who would wait until a dive-bomber was low enough to present a reasonable target to a Lewis Gun before it released its bombs, but those were the orders. RHQ was to follow up in the rear of the column until we reached the town of Seclin.

The date was the 24th of May. Again it was a lovely day. Everything looked green and tranquil. The move was just a routine convoy along roads which luckily the enemy did not attack. We arrived at Seclin, a town about 6 miles south of Lille, about midday and proceeded to look for billets. The office was set up in a house. We were still worrying about such details as separate rooms for Adjutant and C.O., the Second-in-Command, the IO and the QM. The war was still a long way off - or so it seemed. The Officers' Mess was organised in the estaminet across the road and was a great success. It appeared to have all that we required including an excellent cellar.

After lunch Colonel Baslow decided that he and I should pay a visit to Divisionel HQ to see if we could get any information from the Royal Artillery. It was still fine and there was a warm breeze, the sun was shining and spring was in the air. Possibly because of this, Colonel Baslow put on his red forage hat. The Royal Artillary red forage hat is a very distinctive headdress. It is long and narrow, rather like a paper boat, the centre portion being a very bright red surrounded on the edges by a dark blue band. It had produced some rival factions in the Mess at first. Some thought it was rather too showy. When we were in England, Major Shannon had arrived in one but this was not looked upon with approbation by the Colonel. Shortly afterwards the Royal Artillery HQ blossomed out with them and one of the Battery commanders surreptitiously bought one. After arriving in France we had found a shop which sold these hats at a very reasonable price. I had purchased one but found it was the wrong size. I brought it back to the mess and suggested to Colonel Baslow that he might like it. After a little discussion the Colonel, who had sworn never to buy one or wear one, agreed with some reluctance to take it off me as a favour. As a result we were committed to the *red hat*.

However, that afternoon I felt the red hats were not a success, for they seemed to mark the beginning of the end, and certainly RHQ never settled down again after that.

The Colonel and I set out. We did not find the Royal Artillery HQ where it was supposed to be but, as we were returning the way we had come, we suddenly came on the Commander Royal Artillery (CRA) driving at high speed in his car.

"Follow me!" he shouted to us after jamming on his brakes and skidding to a halt.

Accordingly we turned round and followed him down a very narrow road. Not far along it we had to slow down as the road was blocked by two lumbering French army wagons pulled by horses and driven by two French soldiers. The CRA stopped his car, leaped out, brandished his revolver, uttered curses in French and English, and bore down on the unfortunate soldiers.

"Get to hell out of the way," he roared, and continued in a somewhat picturesque mixture of French and English, ending with: "And all the guns and cannons in the British Army are following behind me."

He was certainly a terrifying figure with his red staff cap and choleric countenance. I had seldom seen anyone as astonished as the French drivers, which was not surprising as, apart from our two cars, the countryside was as devoid of artillery and vehicles and as peaceful as any English countryside in summer.

However thinking, perhaps with some wisdom, that the English were completely crazy the Frenchmen pulled their wagons to one side and our little party continued up the road.

As there appeared to be no artillery or vehicles following us, the CRA went off to try to find them. Before leaving he told Colonel Baslow where he wanted his anti-tank batteries to be located. As Seclin was an obvious target to be bombed by the enemy he suggested the Colonel had better make his Headquarters outside the town. A suggestion which I felt eminently sensible.

We set out again and stopped at the little village of Camphin en Pevèle, about three miles from Seclin, which we decided would be our Headquarters and which became our home for the next few days.

It was a pleasant country village with one street, the village green, an estaminet, a church and the village shop. Typical of many French villages, the locals were sitting in the sun smoking and drinking their glass of wine. The blossom was on the fruit trees and all was quiet.

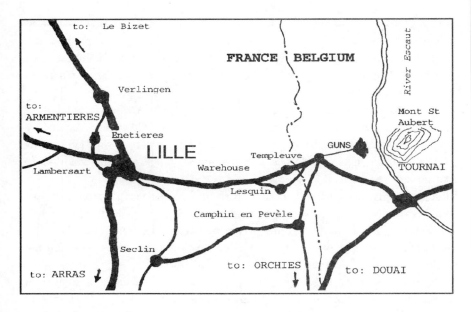

But not for long.

I went back to Seclin and gave orders for the Batteries to move to their new positions. I then shook up RHQ, just as they had completed making themselves comfortable, and gave them the order to follow me and move at once to the new location. Unfortunately, through a misunderstanding, some of the trucks went the wrong way and, as I did not find this out until we had reached Camphin en Pevèle, I had to go back to Seclin once again. This time I collected everyone, but it was dark when I returned and after a welcome meal at the estaminet, found my billet and went to bed.

This was the last billet which still housed its owners, an elderly couple who were very kind, but who were obviously on the point of departure. During the next day, for no obvious reason, the whole village departed in cars and carts, on bicycles or on foot, their belongings packed and strapped on to themselves or their vehicles.

The office had been set up on the village green under a chestnut tree whose branches gave welcome shade. We used, for the first and only time, the *Office Truck*, a modern army vehicle fitted with desks and filing cabinets. Later we decided to leave the truck and move the office into a derelict cottage about half a mile outside the village which seemed to be less of a target. From there, for two days, we watched the dive-bombing of convoys and the shooting up of refugee traffic on the road which passed below the village. We realised later that this shooting up of the refugees was being done intentionally by the enemy to block the roads and hinder military movements. Although we were not near a target, the bombing seemed unpleasantly close but our battle inoculation was only just begining. Peter and I slept in a dug-out which we made from bales of straw in a hayrick opposite the office. Desultory shelling started but it was going over our heads and we could never tell whether it was ours or theirs.

Our Batteries meanwhile, except for Ike's with which we had lost all touch, were digging in their guns at positions on the east of the river Escaut. The Colonel had already reconnoitred the high ground on the east side, and had left only a short time before the Germans arrived. Division now ordered our defences to be on the west of the Escaut, so at least we would have the river in front instead of behind us. Guns were moved and dug in once again. Unfortunately the high ground - Mont St Aubert - north of Tournai and now occupied by the Germans overlooked all the ground on the side of the river containing the new gun positions. The enemy's occupation of the high ground was a considerable embarrassment. Their observation was excellent and any movement, in the dry weather, raised a cloud of dust. As a result a visit to a gun position was not welcomed by its occupants since it generally brought down a salvo of shells on them.

All the villages, including Camphin en Pevèle, had now been evacuated and the farms around RHQ were deserted. The civilians had gone in a tremendous hurry, leaving their livestock just as they were to fend for themselves. The chickens and pigs were shut up. The cows were unmilked and were a piteous sight. Large numbers of dogs appeared.

An old woman from one of the farms arrived in the afternoon and begged us to buy her butter. She seemed terribly upset so I bought some - it was very cheap and wonderful farm butter. I hoped that those few francs would help her when her present stock of food ran out. In the cellars of one of the farms there were four enormous stone jars, two feet in diameter and four feet high, containing the thickest and most delicious cream that I had ever seen. It was intended to be made into butter but what a shocking waste that it all must be left to go rancid.

A Staff Officer arrived from Division. "All dogs must be shot," he said and added, "you'll have to live off the land for the present. We can't get any rations to you."

I sent for Peter. "Have we any farmers in Headquarters?" I asked.

"Gunner Townley was a farmer's son and Reagan was a butcher," he replied, "and I think Spanners had a dairy farm."

"Well get one of them to milk the cows and Reagan can kill a sheep and a pig and we should be able to have some mutton and bacon. I expect someone can find the poultry house and we can have bacon and eggs."

"I don't think you will have any bacon unless we are here for a long time," said Peter, smiling.

Regimental HQ had been in the derelict cottage for about two days when we received news of Ike's Battery which was reported to be at Orchies, southeast of Lille. Peter was sent out on a motorcycle by the Colonel to contact them. Somehow he got on the wrong road and arrived at Douai just as it was being bombed. He escaped unscathed and managed to get to Orchies. He returned with the rumour that the Germans were in Boulogne. This news was met with incredulity by all of us as we could not believe that the Germans had actually been able to get as far as the coast.

Things were certainly looking worse and everyone was getting nervous. Every time there had been any bombing someone noticed that an old windmill started to turn its sails. Perhaps it was an enemy agent signalling to someone?

Patrols were sent out to investigate but found nothing.

Then there was the rumour that was brought by one of our gunners, and which may have had some foundation. At dusk, an alleged British officer drew up in a truck beside him, got out and pointing to two French peasants walking along the road, said to the gunner: "Shoot those people. Don't you know that all civilians have to be got off the road. If they won't move you must shoot them."

The gunner was a little taken aback by such an order, but before he could question the 'officer' further he had gone and fortunately the gunner took no action beyond reporting the matter. It was becoming apparent that the Germans were using fifth columnists dressed as Allied officers both as spies and to spread alarm and despondency amongst the civilian population.

I went down to Divisional Headquarters to find out if this was true. A Staff Captain to whom I spoke said it most certainly was and told me the following story:

"We ordered the Royal Engineers to blow the bridges over the Escaut. Whilst one of their engineers was preparing one of the bridges for demolition, he reported that a German Staff car with a white flag drew up and the occupants started conversing with a *French Officer*."

"That sounds a bit suspicious," I remarked. "What happened next?"

"The Germans having seen what was happening on the Allied side, returned. Our engineer was about to blow the bridge when one of the *French Officers* appeared and asked him to desist as there was a body of French troops just about to cross from the other side. When asked where they were he said they were just round the corner but when our man went to investigate there were no troops and the *Officer* had disappeared. He then pressed the plunger to detonate the charge but nothing happened. The charges had been sabotaged. However he managed to repair them and blew the bridge. He then waited and, as he now expected, some German motorcyclists arrived followed by lorried infantry. Their surprise at finding the bridge blown was complete but did not last long as the engineers had the bridge well and truly covered by fire, and few of the Germans survived."

"Well it certainly looks as if we'll have to watch out," I said and returned to my Headquarters.

There was another incident which occured shortly after the gunner had been ordered to shoot the civilians. As usual Peter and I were taking it in turns to sleep by the telephone, testing it every quarter of an hour in view of a warning about fifth columnists cutting the wires. All was well until about midnight when, on makimg the routine call, there was no response. Peter went out to investigate and found a break in the wire just outside HQ. It was no sooner reconnected when Noel, commanding 224 Battery, rang up: "A party of people are approaching my headquarters from the direction of Tournai," he said. "What do you want me to do?"

I reported this to the Royal Artillery Headquarters where the Staff Captain took the message and seemed very perturbed and called for further investigation. Noel, on being questioned, said they were rapidly approaching his HQ but that they seemed perfectly peaceable and were led by a priest.

Having heard rumours of enemy dressed as nuns this was viewed with grave suspicion and, as the Staff Captain seemed to be even more worried, he instructed me to order Noel to send an armed party to bring them in to my HQ.

It was nearly daylight when the suspicious party arrived. It turned out that they were lunatics who had been evacuated from the asylum in Tournai, and were indeed in charge of a priest. A more pathetic crowd of miserable, dirty and helpless people lying on the grass on the side of the road outside our Headquarters I have seldom seen. However everyone was still very suspicious and Louis our Liaison Officer interrogated them. The priest admitted that they had some field glasses and a map of Tournai. Ah! Our suspicions were confirmed. The RSM pounced and confiscated those nefarious objects. Alas, when brought to me, the field glasses were an extremely ancient type of opera glass which had long since ceased to function - in fact no matter how you used it, the object you were looking at appeared smaller than with the naked eye. The map was a gaudy coloured piece of paper with a rough sketch of the town, such as might be exhibited on a poster showing points of interest to a tourist. Truly the lunatics were confirmed, but I wondered afterwards who of us were the madder?

The tempo of events was hotting up. The shelling was increasing and there was considerably more air activity. Major Shannon of 221 Battery came in with the story that Phil East, one of his troop commanders, had been caught literally *with his trousers down* by a shell whilst attending to a call of nature. Although blown off the latrine he was not hurt. A story also came in that Dicky Noden, a Troop Commander from 223, had taken on a sniper in a house in Tournai with his 2-pdr anti-tank gun and silenced him effectively. We, at RHQ however, had so far not seen any sign of the enemy.

The Colonel brought the news that we were to move that night. I didn't think at the time that it was a withdrawal, merely a tactical move in conjunction with the plans of higher command. The move from Camphin en Pevèle was to commence at 2300 hours but no positions were to be evacuated before 2230 hours. We had a good dinner that night of mutton stew, boiled pork and scrambled eggs.

A little before the time of move, I set out on a motorcycle taking a despatch rider on another motorcycle with me to reconnoitre the route. We had difficulty in finding the way to begin with but I picked up my bearings in time to meet the convoy at the first crossroads. We proceeded through a village after which the convoy became split and I found myself with one half of it whilst the rest, I assumed, was with Majc Stanley. It was now quite dark.

I knew the rendezvous where we were to meet and had a map to find it so there should have been no difficulty. Unfortunately where the map showed a serviceable road, there was only a road in the very primitive stages of construction and which eventually disappeared and degenerated into virgin countryside. As there was no alternative I struck out in the direction shown on the map using a compass bearing. Necessity is a wonderful thing. The convoy covered ground which, unknown, trackless, and on a dark night without lights, they would normally have considered impossible.

When the road had finally petered out I had to admit that I was very worried. Still sticking to the map and the compass bearing, I pushed on, still on the motorcycle, in the direction the road should have been. Riding a motorcycle across country in the dark was something I had not done before but I was learning fast. At last when I was about to give up hope I saw some trucks and figures moving in the semi-darkness. It was Major Stanley with the rest of the convoy who had just arrived at the rendezvous by another route. I was certainly relieved and glad I had stuck to the map and used the compass bearing which had brought us out at the correct place.

When it became light we found we were on an aerodrome - Templeuve - which the enemy had recently bombed. We decided to move our Headquarters to an adjoining village where we found some billets, and parked and camouflaged the vehicles. I then located the Royal Artillery Headquarters and obtained from the Staff Captain the administrative arrangements. After that I went soundly to sleep - so soundly indeed, that when the Colonel came to wake me, it took all the effort of will I could muster to overcome my bodily craving for sleep and become conscious.

It was just as well. The Doc came in with the news that Gordon, a Troop Commander from 224, had been hit, wounded in the legs, and he wanted the location of the Regimental Aid Post. I was glad I had been to the HQ before turning in as I now had that information for him.

In the morning we set about fixing up an office in the cellars of a house on the edge of the airfield. The move had apparently been successful as far as we were concerned. Gordon was the only casualty, but we had lost a 2-pounder owing to the gun-towing vehicle breaking down.

The new positions the guns had to occupy were in concrete pillboxes which had been designed by the French to face to the east, from which direction the Germans had been expected to attack. Sadly they now pointed the wrong way. Due to the Germans having outflanked our Armies, the attack was expected to come from the west. Furthermore the pillboxes had been designed for French guns and our 2-pounder anti-tank gun simply could not be got in. They had to be dug in as usual.

The next morning we moved our Headquarters to a village about two miles up the road. Here we took over the cellars of a house which was occupied by some of the Cheshire Regiment. I was pleased to meet some of the men who had been in the T.A. when I joined them in 1930.

Our Mess was just across the road. Peter and I slept in a cellar by the telephone. The Colonel slept in a room upstairs. The HQ of the Divisional artillery was about 500 yds down the road and I went down there several times to see the Staff Officer in order to pick up any information of which there appeared to be very little.

Shortly after we arrived, we found a large warehouse in the village which was still full of goods of every description and which in later years might have supplied a supermarket. Its owners had left and Division asked me to detail a guard which I did but no one seemed to take any notice of him. Everyone from the Divisional Staff downwards was helping themselves to whatever they liked. I went down there myself and had half a dozen new towels thrust into my hand. I really didn't want them. However when I was offered a large box of Cerise en Kirsch, I didn't refuse.

There was a good deal of bombing going on, fortunately not very close. I watched a German bomber flying over the adjoining village - Lesquin - in which 222 Battery were billeted. I could see the bomb doors open and the bombs fall, rather like spawn coming out of a fish. They took quite a long time to fall. Then there was a terrific explosion, clouds of black smoke and I wondered what had happened to the poor devils below. I went over to the village shortly afterwards and found, to my surprise, very little damage, although some civilians had been killed. The Battery itself had not been hit and had paid little attention to the bombs.

There was a number of Anti-Aircraft guns round our position and not long after we had been there, two planes flew over very low and almost immediately were shot down. Everyone cheered but, alas, we heard later that they were French machines. It was a sad fact that the shooting down of our own aircraft by Allied gunners was not by any means uncommon.

CHAPTER 15

The following day Peter went back to Seclin to contact one of the Batteries which was stationed near the town. Peter seemed to be unlucky as he always arrived at the same moment as the German dive-bombers and Seclin was soon in flames. Once again he escaped without being hit, contacted the Battery and returned safely. Rumours now began to come in that a move would have to be made soon, but where to was not known.

That afternoon the Colonel came back from Division HQ looking, if possible, more worried than usual. He called for a conference as soon as the Battery Commanders could be contacted and brought in. This took a little time as they were not all connected by field telephones and despatch riders had to be sent out. Eventually everyone was there - Battery Commanders, myself, and the rest of the officers from RHQ. We waited for the orders.

The Colonel came in and speaking very gravely, said:

"The British Expeditionary Force is withdrawing to the coast and it is hoped to embark some of it in the Dunkirk area."

This was a metaphorical bombshell. I certainly did not expect a total withdrawal and neither did the others. Nor did we fully understand what it would mean.

That night we were woken by the noise of a terrific battle going on in the distance. Getting up, we saw brilliant flashes, flares and smoke, and heard heavy gunfire and explosions from the west. The enemy must now have encircled us as we had been led to expect when we were siting our guns at Templeuve. No longer was the threat only from the east.

The orders were to move that day. At midday the Colonel went off on a reconaissance with the CRA leaving instructions for myself and RHQ to meet him at a rendezvous (RV) at Verlingen, where we would get further orders. The Batteries with their guns would make their own way to the RV.

I set off on a motorcycle to visit the Batteries in order to give them the route and the RV. I went first to 126 Brigade in the hopes of finding George Wilcox. This was difficult as Brigade had no idea where George was. However I found him eventually, gave him the information and then went on to the other Batteries. Finally I arrived at the farm where 224 Battery were billetted and had just put the motorcycle up on its stand when an enemy plane flew over and dowsed the farmyard with bullets.

I took cover in no small haste and watched the tracer flying past me. When the plane had departed I picked myself up and went into the farm house. Noel was cooking breakfast.

"Like to join me?" he said cheerfully.

"Yes I certainly would," I replied, smelling the aroma of bacon and eggs sizzling in the pan.

"We've managed to find some bacon and there are plenty of eggs. We're not doing too badly really and the chaps have had plenty to eat."

While we ate I explained to Noel the location of the RV to which he was to bring his guns.

"The Germans seem to have got round us and we're in a narrow corridor. It's not going to be easy getting up it to the coast, it looks pretty grim," I said.

Noel looked at the map. "Never mind, we'll make it, and perhaps knock out a few Jerry tanks on the way," he replied optimistically.

I got back on the motorcycle and returned to RHQ where I found Major Stanley who was about to move off with an advance party to the RV where he would set up Headquarters.

As the RV at Verlingen was to the north-west of Lille and we were to the south-east, our route would be through the city and Major Stanley had made arrangements to leave a guide at our old headquarters in Lambersart who would lead us to the RV. I was to follow up with the remainder of Headquarters, which consisted of the office, medical section, signallers, LAD and the RSM. We were to start at 2330 hrs at the same time when everyone else was pulling out.

It was a lovely evening. I had a cup of tea with Doc in his Medical Inspection room and then went down to the warehouse to see if anyone was still there. Going in, I saw Dicky Noden who was making sure his troop wasn't going to be short of grub. His truck was full of tinned food of every sort which he had purloined from the warehouse.

"Excellent idea," I told him as I saw no reason why anything in the warehouse should not be made use of.

Having checked that Dicky knew where to go after he had collected his guns, I went to Division HQ to see if I could get any further information. Everyone there was utterly frustrated. The situation was chaotic. There was no information on which to base an operation order. No one knew what my Batteries were to do, apart from heading for the coast.

As 2330 hrs approached, I had the feeling that we were starting the long trek home. At least there was an objective - to move the Regiment intact to the coast. Could a bridgehead be established there from which we could start again?

Just before leaving, I went down to Division HQ again and found it completely deserted. Everything was strangely quiet and I felt that a German tank might come trundling down the road at any moment.

Outside the village the roads were choked with a never-ending stream of refugees on carts and bicycles but mostly on foot, and there were also masses of French soldiers looking tired and forlorn. The Regiment was not without its own stragglers. I had had a ceasless influx of odd soldiers who had lost their unit and just tagged on to us. The RSM was detailed to put them into some sort of order.

We left on time and very shortly ran into an almighty jam of French trucks and infantry. It would have been a wonderful target but fortunately the enemy planes did not attack us. Several times later we presented an equally attractive target and yet were not attacked. Was there a reason? It was a mystery.

After some time we got under way again and reached the place where I intended to meet Dicky and also Reggie with his guns from 221 Battery, who were the last two troops to pull out. I wanted to make sure they were on their way. I waited for what seemed hours. More and more troops came through and then gradually thinned out. The road was deserted. Any moment I expected the enemy to arrive. At last Reg appeared but there was no sign of Dicky. I asked Reg if he had seen him.

"Oh he'll turn up," said Reg. "He's probably gossiping with some girls!"

I went down the road but there was still no sign of Dicky. More troops went past and then thinned out again. Would the enemy be next? I hoped not. At last a truck appeared with a nonchalent figure smoking a cigar. It was Dicky followed by his troop of guns. As usual pulling guns out had taken longer than estimated. Alas, that was the last time I saw him, as after fighting a gallant battle later on, he was taken prisoner and spent the rest of the war in Colditz Castle where, like many others, he made attempts to escape but without success.

The Headquarter's convoy now proceeded along the road to Lille. It was a slow process as the road was jammed with vehicles. A large oil tank was blazing in the distance, lighting up the sky. When we reached the centre of Lille we had taken so long that I decided to get on the motorcycle and go on ahead. The Adjutant normally travelled in a *pick up* (PU) - a small snub-nosed two-seater

Morris truck with a canvas roof over the back, and in which his kit was carried. The despatch rider who travelled beside him was available to exchange his motorcycle when required. It was pitch dark under the trees, and was a pretty hectic ride up the Rue de l'Hippodrome. However I reached our old HQ at Lambersart and, somewhat to my surprise, as things never seemed to be going according to plan, found the guide waiting there. George Wilcox of 221 Battery with his guns had also arrived and said he was making it his headquarters for the night which turned out to be rather wishful thinking.

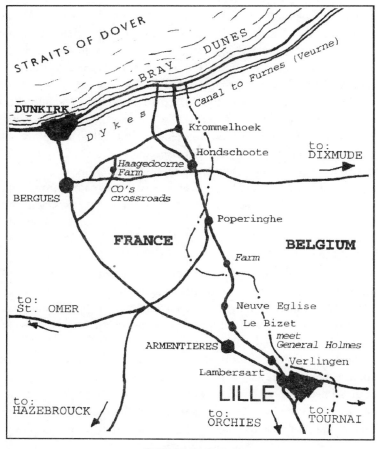

"THE WAY BACK"

We had some time to wait until the rest of the Headquarter's convoy turned up. One or two shells whistled past overhead. Then taking the guide and Doc with me, I set off in my PU in the direction of Verlingen, about three miles to the north, which, according to the guide, was where Major Stanley's party was supposed to be. We arrived at the house which the guide swore was the one he had just come from, but it was empty! Doc and I went through it carefully but it was completely deserted. It was in a frightful mess and had had either a bomb or a shell in it. We found a glove which might have belonged to someone in the Regiment but no indication of where they had gone. This was a bit of a poser! Our only link with the Regiment had gone. We had no idea where the British infantry was and there were ominous noises going on around which might mean we were to be involved in a battle any moment. I told Doc to settle down in the house for the time being while I went out to see what information I could find. I went on foot down the road to the crossroads and, as luck would have it, ran into one of the Divisional Staff Officers. Unfortunately he was as lost as I was but was able to give me the location of the Divisional Commander who he said was in a house further up the road. I decided to go there. En route, I was stopped several times by French soldiers who appeared to be very frightened and kept asking: "Où sont les Boches?" I told them, as best I could in my bad French, that they better try finding them and start fighting. They didn't seem very enthusiastic. It was so frustrating. So many soldiers were lost without leaders and with no initiative and doing nothing to the enemy who had outmanoeuvred us.

I found the house of the Divisional Commander and went in without being challenged. General Holmes was lying on a sofa looking practically all in, which was not surprising. His Division was desperately holding the southern end of the salient to the coast with the French First Army. I reported to him what I knew about the position of my own anti-tank regiment. The General then told me that Colonel Baslow and the CRA were at the church in Le Bizet just north of Armentières. He got up and said: "Go there yourself at once, Captain, and take all the guns you can lay your hands on with you."

This was something definite to work on but I was doubtful how I was to get hold of the guns. Back I went to the house near Verlingen and was delighted to find that Major Stanley had returned there. He had been able to contact the Colonel and was about to set out for Le Bizet himself. I told him of the General's orders and sent a message back with the despatch rider to George Wilcox at Lambersart to bring his guns up to Le Bizet as well as those of any other Batteries that arrived. I then detailed the RSM to remain at Verlingen to direct any Batteries to Le Bizet and then to come on himself.

I and the remainder of Headquarters took to the road again and arrived at Le Bizet just after a damp, leaden dawn had broken. The sky promised rain and soon it came in a steady downpour which did nothing to raise our spirits. Neither the CRA nor the Colonel were in the Church. We searched for them in a deserted school nearby which had suffered from bomb blast and in the miserable morning was even more depressing than an empty classroom usually is.

As there was no further information on the next move we started to look for billets in the town which with the incessant rain seemed a sensible move. However, during the morning, a despatch rider arrived from the Colonel, who was now somewhere to the north of us, with orders to move once more. The billets were abandoned. This time the move was to a farm at a map reference further to the north.

Major Stanley who had been held up, now arrived and we set off again with him leading. After we had been travelling for some time the weather improved and our spirits rose. We were approaching the town of Neuve Église where there was an enormous jam of vehicles in the narrow streets. It would have been a wonderful target to any enemy aircraft and it added nothing to our peace of mind to see that the town had recently been such a target. We proceeded at snail's pace through this logjam of vehicles until we eventually got out of the town. The traffic had thinned out by now and we were able to proceed to our objective which was a farm about two miles north of the town and on the way to Poperinghe.

The farm was a large one and isolated and the owners were still in occupation. They did not take kindly to the arrival of the soldiers. The Mess Sergeant managed to make some sort of a meal after which the Colonel arrived. He had found Divisional HQ and had received orders for a further withdrawal, that night, to a new RV near the town of Bergues. From there a perimeter defence was being put in place with Dunkirk as the centre with the intention of embarking some of the troops from its harbour.

We could see a battle going on in the distance and shells were bursting on a ridge about a mile away. Dennis Timson of 223 Battery appeared with the news that Major Ike Proudlove had been seriously wounded and Paddy Mack, his second-in-command, had taken over.

Our orders were to destroy everything that was not absolutely necessary before starting the withdrawal. It was a sad business destroying one's kit, including my new field boots which I had last worn on that ride on the Downs with Julia. It seemed so long ago. I had thought of her many times and once more I wondered if I would ever see her again.

Now I had to stop thinking of her as I had the job of disposing of the steel filing cabinet which we had carried all the way from England. It contained the files and documents that I had spent so many hours sorting and arranging during my tour as Adjutant. They all had to go and there was not much time. I opened the cabinet and took out the money which had been collected for the RA Benevolent Fund and then threw the cabinet and all the papers into the pond at the back of the farm where it sank and would remain hidden beneath the dark waters, the papers turned to sodden pulp.

Just before dusk, the convoy formed up again. The Colonel led in his car, followed by Major Stanley, my PU and the remainder of the Headquarters. The Batteries with their guns were making their own way to Bergues independently. The convoy got out on to the main road and joined what seemed to be the remnants of the British Army. The speed was pathetically slow and before it got dark it was again an excellent target for enemy aircraft, but none came. The night wore on. We passed guns and tanks of all sizes abandoned on the side of the road. Some were destroyed but others seemed in perfect order, just waiting for the enemy to collect and use. Towards midnight, as we approached Poperinghe, the shelling increased, but the shells were going over our heads and bursting in the town. We passed a mass of vehicles at the side of the road which were blazing merrily. There were many halts, caused mainly by drivers falling asleep with fatigue. Everyone was driving without lights and the night was dark and overcast. I kept myself awake by sharing with Foxley the Cerise en Kirsch which I'd salvaged from the warehouse.

Eventually a T-junction was reached where the mass of vehicles was stationary and the rumour was that Poperinghe, through which we had to pass, was impassable. I took to the motorcycle again and, with the Colonel who had commandeered another machine, reconnoitred a road to the left in the hopes of finding a means of by-passing the town. It was no good. The Colonel returned to the convoy and I decided to see whether the town was really impassable.

Riding round the tightly packed vehicles was not easy in the dark. Everything was very quiet. All the vehicle drivers were fast asleep in their lorries. At last I came to a point where there were no more vehicles. A civilian van, empty and slewed across the street, was the only obstruction. A solitary military policemen said the road was blocked. He sounded unconvincing. Further on there was an enormous crater containing the remains of the better part of two houses. However there was a track between the crater's edge and the houses that were still standing, just wide enough for a lorry to pass. Deciding that it was enough to get the vehicles through, the next thing was to move the civilian van, which might well have been put there by a fifth columnist. The military policeman had gone and there were very few soldiers about, most of them half asleep, but by dint of much cursing and encouragement, the van was shifted and once the drivers had been woken, the column started to move.

It was here that I nearly lost my motorcycle which I had left leaning up against a wall. When I got back to it I found a Frenchman trying vainly to start it. I went up to him, started the machine, just to show him it could be done, and then mounted it and rode away.

The head of my convoy was a long way behind. When I got there I discovered the Colonel had found a narrow lane through which he decided he could get past the town and had taken Peter and my truck with him along it. Major Stanley was still leading the rest of the column through the town, so I stayed on the motorcycle and remained with him, by which time it was getting light.

After Poperinghe I never saw my P.U. or Foxley again during the retreat. And retreat it was, no longer just a withdrawal. By now I was feeling desperately tired, so handed the motorcycle over to one of the fitters and got into Spanners's truck. The road was still jammed and the pace wickedly slow. As the convoy left the town, an aircraft appeared overhead, whether friendly or hostile was not apparent, but it threw the whole column into such a state of panic that bullets were flying in all directions.

Later we made fairly good speed but as we approached our objective the same old jam occurred, but now more and more vehicles were abandoned at the side of the road and less and less attempts were being made to destroy them.

Just outside Bergues our convoy halted and Major Stanley went forward to set up a Headquarters near, but not at the crossroads. After all crossroads were not the best places to be, as they were generally singled out for attack.

We waited for some time at the side of the road while Major Stanley was gone and watched the Army in headlong retreat - vehicles of all descriptions, moving along the roads towards the coast. It was a sight not to be forgotten. There appeared to be no leadership and little discipline, just a mass of men and machines moving in one direction. We realised now, if we had not done so before, the true position.

Suddenly I heard myself hailed by name from someone in a passing truck. The truck stopped and, to my great surprise, I saw driving it the Sergeant in the

Cheshires who had come to my home when I had joined the T.A. *to show me the ropes.* For a moment the years rolled back and I remembered how young I had been. I asked him how he was getting on. He seemed in good form but was trying to find his unit and, like everyone else, was lost. He drove on with a cheery wave and gave me a left handed salute. I drew myself to attention and returned the salute smartly with my right hand.

Shortly after this one of our Officers appeared with the news that Phil East had been killed on the canal at Lille. This was bitter news and hard to accept. He was such a popular young officer and it was difficult to realise that he would no longer be with us in the Mess. How many of us would be like him was another thought which crossed my mind.

Major Stanley now returned and explained where he had set up the Headquarters in a farm - as usual. Why was it he always picked a farm? Perhaps because there was some chance of food. The Colonel had meanwhile left a message saying he was at a crossroads at Haagedoorne.

I had been told that there was a report centre at Krommelhoek, so I decided to go there to see if I could get any news of the Batteries which I had lost touch with south of Le Bizet. I took a motorcycle and one of the despatch riders, Bombardier Dixon, with me. The weather was fine and it should not have been difficult to find the report centre.

In this part of France, close to the Belgian frontier, there are numerous canals which have to be crossed by bridges, and there are also many smaller canals or dykes between the fields in which motor transport would be bogged down if they tried to cross. The bridges were by no means numerous and I found that many of them shown on my map did not exist. Eventually we reached the town of Hondschoote which was too far to the south of our objective. The town was being bombed and vehicles were burning, the ammunition in them exploding.

At the main bridge over the canal we were turned back by the Military Police. No one was allowed across. From the map it appeared that there should be another bridge further to the west, so Dixon and I set out to find it. After spending nearly two hours in a maze of little roads, we were forced to the conclusion that that bridge did not exist either and we could not get across the canal, so I decided to return to the farm.

On reaching it, Major Stanley wasn't there. Taking Dixon with me, I decided to try to see if he had gone to the crossroads at Haagedoorn to meet up with the Colonel. Again the map bore little relation to the ground and we became lost several times. During our wanderings we came across a Staff Officer in his car.

Dixon, speaking to the Staff Officer's motorcycle escort, discovered they were just as lost as we were. There was a good deal of activity going on both from the air and the ground. French soldiers were hurrying across the fields shouting: "Où est la route Dunkerque?".

At last we came to the place given by the Colonel as his RV at Haagedoorne but neither he nor Major Stanley were there. We waited for a little while in the hopes that they would turn up and, while doing so, the Brigade Major suddenly appeared in his car, looking tired and very harassed.

"There's a tank attack coming in from the west," he shouted. "Major Wilcox and Shannon are down there." He pointed to a place on the map about a mile away and then said to me: "Captain Clayton get to them as quickly as you can and warn them. You can get there on a motor cycle where a car would be stuck in the traffic."

Leaving Dixon behind, I set off as fast as I could, with the bike roaring at full throttle and weaving in and out of the traffic and riding across country when the road was blocked. I managed to get to the point which the Brigade Major had indicated.

Neither Wilcox nor Shannon were there but Reggie James was, with two guns and their detachments. He had no definite orders and was wondering what he should do next.

"There's supposed to be a tank attack coming in any moment from the direction of that village," I told him.

"How kind of you to let me know," said Reggie rather sarcastically.

"Pleased to help," I replied amiably, "I'll give you a hand to get the guns in position."

Between us we got the guns sited, by which time shells were falling in the village nearby. The noise of vehicles which might have been tanks could be heard in the distance. We waited for some time but no tanks appeared and the shelling ceased. As everything now seemed to be quiet, I told Reggie that I was once again going to try to find the Colonel and get some orders from him.

The road I had just come through was now blocked, so making a detour I reached a position close to where I had seen the Brigade Major. There were soldiers and civilians running in all directions and, from what I could make out, the enemy were now in possession of the Colonel's RV near the Haagedoorne crossroads. I decided to make for the farm in the hopes that someone would still be there. It was now the only remaining location of the Regiment that I knew of.

On approaching the farm I was met by the Quartermaster in his truck and the remainder of the Headquarter's party coming from it at high speed. Stopping them I was told that the Brigadier - it was not clear whether it was the CRA or one of the Infantry Brigade commanders - had told them "to get out and make for Dunkirk", which they were now doing in great haste.

It seemed to me that there was not much use in trying to get to the farm which was probably now occupied by the enemy, so I decided that the best thing to do was also to make for Dunkirk. I returned the way I had come and arrived at a village where there was a pretty hefty state of panic. The village square was packed with a seething mass of men and vehicles. By now my motorcycle had lost its silencer and was making a most fiendish din. I abandoned it.

While I was wondering what I should do next, one of our officers, Tim Bowden, appeared, driving a truck with some of his troop. He had also received orders to make for Dunkirk, so I got in and told him to drive on, keeping in the flow of traffic which was heading for the coast.

The column was of mixed nationality, French, English and a few Belgians. If an aircraft appeared there was a mad rush from the vehicles to the fields on either side of the road with the result that the column came to a rapid halt, only to move on again when the aircraft had gone and the drivers returned to their vehicles.

Eventually we arrived at a point where a Staff Officer ordered us to abandon and destroy all vehicles, apart from any towing a gun. Tim and I, having found some heavy stones, opened the bonnets, smashed plugs, distributors and carburettors on several trucks. One of the trucks was a cook's, and stocked with all the things a good cook will hoard for a rainy day. As soon as it was clear that this truck was being abandoned, soldiers appeared, apparently from nowhere, and in a moment a horde of shouting, clutching men were ripping and pulling out the contents, cigarettes, chocolate, bully beef. It was impossible to stop them, short of shooting. The cook was in tears.

I assembled the little party we had collected which consisted of myself, Tim and about twenty men from different Regiments, and distributed what food and ammunition we had and moved off on foot. I decided that we would avoid Dunkirk which looked very unhealthy in the distance and strike further east. We crossed a canal. This was the navigable canal from Dunkirk to Furnes which runs parallel to the coast and we were lucky to find a bridge.

We had not gone very far before Tim, who didn't much like walking, decided that with all the abandoned trucks about, it seemed a shame to have to march.

He selected a three tonner which had not been too badly damaged and, being a bit of a mechanic, had it running in no time. We all climbed aboard and drove on.

It was soon dark and we came up behind a troop of 25-pounders making for the coast. Next we passed through a lane of burning trucks, scores of them. It was so hot that we had to keep well down inside our own truck to avoid being scorched. About midnight we came to a village which was totally blocked with vehicles and we could go no further.

We tried to sleep in the truck, but the noise of a heavy bombardment kept us awake. We could see terrific fires in the west which must have been Dunkirk. I was glad I had decided not to make for it but to lead my party further up the coast.

When dawn came it was obvious we would have to abandon our newly found truck and set out once again on foot. Even this was not easy, so great was the accumulation of abandoned vehicles that it was difficult to find a way past them. By degrees, as it got lighter, more and more soldiers joined us and we reached what looked like the street of a seaside resort going down to the beach. There were colourful little kiosks, restaurants and souvenir shops, all empty, but still with a kind of holiday atmosphere. We might well have been some enormous holiday excursion party walking down towards the beach for a swim or a picnic on the dunes. At the end of the street, we came in sight of the sea and the most wonderful and moving sight - The Royal Navy. Destroyers and ships of all sorts and sizes standing off shore as far as the eye could see. It seemed to me that we had come to the journey's end and were now safe in the hands of the Navy.

CHAPTER 16

The beach was long and narrow, typical of many on the north coast of France. Behind us were the sand dunes covered with grasses and some sea holly, easy to dig shallow holes to shelter from bomb splinters. There seemed to be no hurry to take anyone off and we lay on the beach all day. There was not a lot of bombing and I soon fell asleep.

Meanwhile the Colonel who had arrived further along the beach, together with Major Stanley and what was left of their HQ, including my batman Foxley, decided they would try to get to Dunkirk. They were joined shortly by George Wilcox and Shannon with their Battery HQs, and by Peter who had arrived still further up the beach. Leaving Peter behind to contact any of the Regiment who might turn up, they set off with the RSM and marched along, taking cover in the sand dunes whenever a dive-bomber approached. The sand was so soft that the bombs, sinking in deeply before exploding, sent most of their blast and fragments upwards and did little harm to the men on the ground. Against the machine guns their only escape was to get into the dunes as fast as possible, where a little hole, hurriedly scraped, behind a dune might give some protection.

After several narrow escapes, the Colonel and his party entered the town, or what was left of it. It had been completely flattened. As they picked their way through the rubble and burning houses, the town was dive-bombed again and they took refuge in cellars.

"Where's this blasted harbour?" exclaimed the Colonel who had run out of some of his more lurid Indian expressions.

George Wilcox had been to Dunkirk in peacetime with his family on a summer holiday. The holiday had not been a success as, while swimming, he had been stung several times by jellyfishes in awkward places which had caused him and Mrs Wilcox extreme discomfort.

"It's on the far side of the town to the west and some distance from it," he replied gloomily.

"Well I hope we can make it," said Shannon who was getting fed up with the slow pace they were making.

They marched on and on and at last came to the harbour with the long mole stretching out into the sea. The harbour was full of wrecks but lying alongside the mole was the destroyer *HMS Boarhound*. The mole was a long breakwater with a walkway on the top along which were moving troops from many regiments, battle stained, weary, with bloodstained bandages, some limping, but still with their weapons. Someone had found a mouth organ and to the tune of "Blue Bonnets over the Border" the soldiers marched along and boarded the destroyer. The Colonel and his party joined the column and had just reached the ship when a German dive-bomber arrived. The destroyer opened up with all her guns and the troops fired their rifles and Lewis guns at the bomber. The noise was terrific. The scream of the bombs as they fell hitting the water and throwing up clouds of spray, the staccato rattle of the multiple anti-aircraft guns of the destroyer and the deep boom of its 4-inch gun, added to the pandemonium. One bomb hit the forecastle of the ship killing some of the crew and some soldiers who had escaped this far only to be killed on their last lap. After what seemed an age the bombers departed and the ship was still afloat. The wounded were taken below to be cared for and the *Boarhound* was able to steam out of the harbour. She limped across the Channel, shepherded by other warships and reached Dover safely with the Colonel and his party very relieved that they were still alive.

While I slept, Tim decided it was no time for hanging about. He found Reggie who had now arrived in the dunes with his Troop Sergeant and six men and together they set off. They had not gone far when Tim saw, close to the shore, what appeared to be a pleasure boat which would have been more at home on a peaceful river than off the beaches at Bray Dunes.

It turned out to be one of the hundreds of small boats whose owners, at the call of Admiral Ramsay, had volunteered to cross the Channel to help with the evacuation of the troops. Its owner, a retired civil servant, had spent many happy hours cruising on the Blackwater river to Mersea Island and up the river Colne to those lovely little villages along its banks, during last years splendid summer. Mr Williams, who was the proud owner, had purchased the boat second-hand or maybe third or even fourth - it was very old, but in the spring he had given it a fresh coat of paint, polished all the brasswork and overhauled the engine. He had decided that he would have to lay it up due to the shortage of petrol when the call came on the grapevine that any boat that could float was wanted to save the troops stranded on the beaches by Dunkirk.

Mr Williams had never sailed *Bluebird Belle* further than Colne Point. Now he would be faced with a sea voyage of 70 sea miles across the hazardous Thames

Estuary, single-handed, in a boat powered by a not too reliable Ford car engine. He made some last minute adjustments to the engine and set out for West Mersea where he had been told the Royal Navy would take charge. Arriving, he was issued with charts and instructions on the route he was to take along with all the other vessels. Mr Williams was very hazy as to how to use the charts and his compass which he had purchased second-hand was none too reliable but he was determined he would make it.

The flotilla of vessels large and small sailed down the Blackwater river and made for Brightlingsea where they were marshalled by the Navy for the sea crossing. Mr Williams had never seen so many ships. He kept a weather eye open for those German dive-bombers he had read so much about. Although the sea was reasonably calm, it was enough to toss *Bluebird Belle* about and spray came over the sides as the skipper crouched behind the little wheel. He was glad he had brought some oilskins. As they neared the French coast he saw a pall of black smoke spreading over Dunkirk from its burning oil tanks, but they were directed away from Dunkirk, further east towards the beaches at Bray Dunes. *Bluebird Belle* being a river boat was of shallow draught and able to come well inshore and as the tide was rising was in no danger of grounding.

She was about a hundred yards out. Tim with Reggie followed by his men waded out and scrambled aboard, making rather a mess of *Bluebird Belle's* new paint work. Mr Williams turned his boat round and was making for one of the larger vessels which was in deeper water and would take his passengers to England, when the engine spluttered and stopped. Tim being a mechanic quickly removed the engine cowling and decided that the trouble was in the petrol filter. Removing it whilst the boat was rolling and they were receiving the attentions of a Heinkel HE111 was not easy but he accomplished it. The engine burst back into life and they reached the ship. His cargo of men unloaded, Mr Williams returned to the beach for more. Several times he made the journey, bringing back loads of weary men, until on the last one a German dive-bomber singled him out. The third bomb scored a direct hit and Mr Williams and *Bluebird Belle* paid the supreme penalty, a penalty that was paid by so many of those brave ordinary people who, in barely seaworthy craft, crossed the sea to save the British Army from an ignominious defeat.

Tim and Reggie watching from the ship vowed that when the time came, Mr Williams and all the other brave men from the little ships would be avenged. Going below they slept the sleep of utter exhaustion until their ship reached Dover.

Back on the beach at Bray Dunes, I had woken and been joined by Peter. During the day the numbers on the beach had increased by thousands and there was an unending column of French and Belgian soldiers marching along it towards Dunkirk.

It had been rumoured that destroyers would be taking us off that night. On the sand in front of us the Royal Engineers had built an improvised jetty extending a quarter of a mile into the sea, composed of abandoned vehicles with boards running along their canopies. When the tide came in, it was intended to enable boats to be loaded from this jetty.

A sailor appeared on the beach in sea boots, a blue duffle coat and steel helmet. He had two wicked looking guns tucked into his belt and looked every inch a pirate. He was to supervise the loading from the jetty and as he represented the Royal Navy we all felt very confident.

When it began to get dark, the sailor gave orders to form a line of men who would move along the improvised jetty in single file. The time to start was to be midnight. About half an hour before we were due to start an enemy aircraft came over, possibly to try to destroy the jetty. Every gun on land and sea opened up, forming a cone of tracers, the apex of which was directly above us and around the aircraft. The noise was terrific and everyone cheered. It seemed impossible for anything to live in that inferno up there but whether the aircraft was hit or got away we never found out.

It was about this time that some guns were put into position on the beach as an attack coming in from the east was expected. Although I did not know it at the time, the Belgians had capitulated and our east flank was now open. Not long after this three enemy shells came over and burst on the beach unpleasantly close.

At midnight we formed up and started along the jetty, Peter leading. Some Cheshires had appeared, so I shepherded them along with us and brought up the rear. Progress was incredibly slow. It was very dark and we appeared to be poised in mid-air, seeing only the man in front and the boards we were walking on. The sea had an unearthly phosphorescence, every ripple throwing out a light which danced up and down below our feet. A battle in the area behind the dunes was going on and star shells kept bursting. It was comparatively quiet on the beach but nevertheless it was not likely to stay so for long.

The wait on the jetty was interminable. We had been moving at a snail's pace, one foot at a time for two hours or more, when eventually all movement ceased. I sat down on the boards and Sgt Catto, one of the Cheshires, who was in front of me, offered me a drink from his water bottle. I took it thankfully and, putting it to my lips, I took a mouthful but nearly fell off the jetty. The water bottle contained brandy which was stimulating if not refreshing.

It was now getting light and looking down, I saw that instead of water which had been below us all the time, there was just sand! I jumped down and found we were within six feet of the end of the jetty and there were no boats. I swore. The tide had been going out at the same pace as we had been proceeding along the jetty. All that long wait for nothing. There were only about a dozen of us left so we climbed down and I went to look for a boat. I could see through the morning mist which hung over the water some boats floating some distance out. I felt sure that those that had already taken troops to the ships would return. How wrong I was. Boats had been rowed out to the ships by the soldiers who had clambered aboard, but no one was willing to row them back again once they had gained the comparative safety of the ship.

A boat did come in but a Staff Officer on the beach said it was for a party of senior officers. This was not popular with the men on the beach, especially when a party of red-tabbed officers arrived, got into the boat and were rowed away. That boat didn't return either.

About 3 p.m. the enemy started to shell the beach again and some shells burst nearby, rather too close.

One of the Padres, who must have been a good swimmer, took off his uniform and boots and started to swim towards the boats. Although the sea was calm, it was a long swim and when he reached the boats he was so exhausted that he could hardly pull himself into one of them. He rowed the boat to within wading distance of the beach, and we waded out to it.

I was surprised that, even at this juncture, I was loath to get myself wet and it was no easy matter to pull myself into the boat in my wet clothing. Half way across we had to get out and push the boat off a sandbank. At last we arrived at the ship which we could just see through the mist and which turned out to be the Minesweeper *HMS Halcyon*. Very tired and wet we clambered up scrambling nets and came aboard.

The Padre rowed the boat back to the beach and just as he reached it an enemy fighter appeared strafing the waterline. The boat was reduced to matchwood and the Padre died.

I took off my wet clothes and sat on the floor of the wardroom in my underpants. I was given a shot of whisky which did much to restore my morale as well as warming my limbs.

Our troubles were not yet over. We had not been on board for very long before the ship was attacked by an aircraft. The minesweeper replied with her 4-inch gun and multiple pom-poms.

The noise of the former inside the wardroom was enough to fray anyone's nerves. I had to admit I was scared and also furious that I had got so far and was just as likely to be knocked out now as at any time.

However at last the attack was beaten off and I must have dozed. When I awoke it was daylight. I put on my still damp clothes and borrowing a razor had some sort of a shave. I went on deck just as we were coming into Dover harbour.

It was a memorable sight. England again, very peaceful, gulls wheeling overhead, a Spitfire in the distance, and the harbour just as it was when Reggie and I had set out on that summer holiday less than a year ago.

The ship tied up and we disembarked; a crowd of tired and weary, dirty and unkempt men, seething over the quay where I ran into Peter.

"Peter!" I exclaimed, clapping him on the shoulder, "how did you get on?"

"Eh?" he replied jumping nervously and then seeing it was me, he grabbed my hand and shook it hard. "You got off alright then," he said with relief. "I was in front of you on that jetty and you never got to the ship so I didn't know...."

I told him briefly how I'd got out to the *Halcyon* ending lightly with: "Well there doesn't seem to be any customs about, so let's go and find some breakfast."

Later Peter told me his story. From the improvised jetty he'd been rowed out to a destroyer on which, as he scrambled up, he could make out the name *Shikari*. It was the smallest and the oldest, destroyer in the Fleet and, in the end, the last one out of Dunkirk. "I was directed to the wardroom which was full of sleeping bodies. A very cheerful steward brought me a splendid mug of what he called KY and what I've always thought was *gunfire*, anyway it was two thirds thick cocoa and one third navy rum. I fell asleep and then woke to hear the 4-inch gun blasting off. Going up on deck I found it was broad daylight and we were alongside the mole at Dunkirk. The last place I wanted to be! The Luftwaffe was busily trying to bomb us. Charging madly along the mole was a half colonel in his best khaki drill with about 300 army types following, heading for the *Shikari*."

"There wasn't much I could do. Everyone was shouting to the colonel to hurry but he was going as fast as he could, very upright, running like hell and all the others after him. The Navy was firing every gun it could to cover him and soldiers were firing rifles and Lewis guns, quite uselessly mind you, up into the sky against the aircraft."

" I went back to the wardroom and was given another mug of KY but this time fifty percent rum. It did the trick. I fell asleep as we left the mole under yet another attack."

"Later I woke and went up on deck again to find we were tearing along on a mill-pond calm sea. I asked the Number One what speed we were doing and he said: "32 knots - she's never done it before and she'll never do it again!" The poor old ship was shaking all over. I thought we'd miss the harbour and plough straight into the cliffs but she slowed down and docked perfectly. Still panting though!" Peter laughed.

And it was glorious, the relief immense. We went to the Lord Warden Hotel just outside the docks where we bumped into Reggie and Tim and had the best breakfast we had ever eaten. After that we were bundled into trains standing in the dock station and went sound asleep, only to be awakened at the first stop, to be given cakes, tea and cigarettes by a mass of willing helpers.

I remember little else of the journey until we arrived at a rest camp near Shrivenham where we remained while decisions were being taken as to how the Regiment was going to be reorganised.

So ended the retreat - not something to be very proud of, I felt. True some 220,000 British troops had been saved from the beaches and from Dunkirk, as well as over 120,000 French and Belgians, but all our guns and vehicles had been lost. Apart from those soldiers evacuated from the Dunkirk area in the operation which had the code name *Dynamo*, approximately a further 190,000 Allied troops were evacuated from ports in Brittany and around the Bay of Biscay before the end of the fighting and the final fall of France on June 22nd. What many called a defeat, and a defeat it was by any standards, was also a deliverance in that so many troops had been saved to fight again another day.

When the campaign started the Germans had 2,250,000 troops on her western borders. Against them, the French had 2,000,000 plus about 800,000 from her British, Dutch and Belgian allies. The British Expeditionary Force under Lord Gort had 9 divisions consisting of a little under 400,000 men.

In the air the Germans had, available to support their ground forces, 3,500 aircraft including the infamous but effective Stuka dive-bombers. The French had a total of 1,700 aircraft while the British contribution at the opening of the campaign was a mere 450 of all types, although this was later increased to some 1,240 including 600 fighters. In the later stages of the battle, as the airfields in France were overrun, many of our aircraft had to operate from their home bases in England. On paper it appeared that the Allies were not far short of parity with the enemy but many of our aircraft were obsolete types such as the Battle. Both in the air and on the ground the Allies had no recent battle experience while the German pilots and armoured formations were fresh from their fighting in Poland. The French cried out for more squadrons to be sent from Britain, a plea which could not be fulfilled for it would have left England undefended against the German aerial bombardment which was bound to come.

Looking back it seemed to me that there had been such a lot of faulty intelligence about the enemy and no clear orders, with the result that no one knew what to do. The Territorial Army had not been on active service since the last war but somehow there seemed to have been a lack of initiative. I had been at a Headquarters which had not been in contact with the enemy, while our guns had been dispersed to infantry brigades. Some of the guns had been in action and had performed well but too frequently it had been "pull out and get back to the coast". At times discipline was sadly lacking.

It was not until some time later that a different story emerged of those troops who by their dedication and valour had made the evacuation possible.

There were many examples. An outstanding one was that of General Prioux commanding the 1st French Army holding the line Bethune-Arras, who decided to *stand and die* on that position. A decision which made it possible for three British Divisions in the central sector, including the one I was in, to withdraw to the coast.

Then there was the Rifle Brigade who defended Calais; and the Guards at Boulogne who were ordered to hold out to the last man, with no hope of relief. Both held off the Germans from Dunkirk until all the BEF had gone.

When the Belgians capitulated, the eastern end of the perimeter was open, with the result that the beaches and Dunkirk would have been overrun by the enemy but for the heroic action of the 12th Lancers who plugged the gap and few survived.

After the troops had been evacuated from around Dunkirk, fighting continued in the west, supporting the remains of the French army until their capitulation. The 51st Highland Division who had only recently been sent from Britain, were trapped at St Valéry-en-Caux where, after a heroic battle and no hope of succour from the sea, they were forced to surrender.

One intriguing question arose after the campaign. Why, as the Nazi armour was closing in on the beleaguered British and the French, did Hitler order his Panzers to halt for two days? Some say that it was due to Hermann Goering who wanted the glory for his Luftwaffe to carry out the final knock-out blow, others that General Rundstedt did indeed need a respite to overhaul his armour after their long dash to the coast. Another suggestion put forward, was that Hitler expected a French counterattack from the south, which was something that in practice the French were totally unable, both physically and psychologically, to do. In their words they said "il faut en finir" meaning not so much "we must finish it" but "it is finished for us".

The most severe criticism was levelled at the RAF because so few of their aircraft were visible over the battlefields or the beaches, a criticism which was totally unjustified.

Although the RAF were at first equipped with obsolete aircraft, they carried out continuous attacks behind the lines, destroying bridges, airfields and lines of communication and, in the process, suffered heavy losses. I heard that my friend Jonathan from the works in Runcorn had been lost on one of these sorties.

The fighter squadrons of Hurricanes which appeared later, although hopelessly outnumbered, held the Luftwaffe at bay until the British were able to escape. In all 1300 enemy planes were shot down by the Allied Air Force.

During the whole of the retreat and evacuation the British losses on the ground of killed, wounded or missing was estimated to be around 65,000 which was approximately equal to that of the Germans.

Shortly after we returned to Britain I heard Mr Churchill make his famous broadcast in which he promised us "blood, toil, tears and sweat" before the final victory. So ended the first phase of a war which was to last another five years.

CHAPTER 17

We had been at the rest camp for four days when I was granted three days leave. For the first day I went home to see my family. My father, now 77 years old and normally strong and fit, was beginning to show his age. I knew, since he was prone to worrying, that not only the anxiety of war but having one son in the army and with his youngest son soon to join, was not helping his health. It was an example of how those at home, waiting for news, suffered. My parents were not demonstrative, my mother less so than my father, and we tended to skirt round topics that I, too, did not want to go into deeply. My feelings were of wonderment that I was home and yet the strangeness of it all. It was a bitter blow to realise that we had lost the first battle. If I felt fear, I brushed it aside quickly for there was little I could do about it. There seemed to be a protective fatalism to being in the forces, orders came from above and one obeyed. I looked at my workshop but, for the moment, it seemed to belong to someone else.

I had telephoned Julia as soon as I got back to England to tell her I was safe and to arrange to see her. I said goodbye to my mother and father, explaining that I was going to see a girl who I had become very fond of.

I took the train to Wantage and Julia was on the station to meet me. As I kissed her, it seemed to me that she had never looked so beautiful with her long blonde hair so clean and warm smelling, shining in the sunlight, soft between my fingers. She was dressed in a dark blue jacket and slacks, and she had a small open sports car outside the station. We got in and she said: "Where shall we go?"

"Anywhere with you," I replied fervently.

In the end we decided we would drive to Hereford and then to Symonds Yat near Ross on Wye, where Reggie had told me there was a good hotel.

Leaving Wantage we passed convoys of troops and guns but as we got further west the military traffic gradually eased and then disappeared and we were almost alone. It was midsummer, the sun was hot and the English countryside looking at its best. We passed through villages, seemingly untouched by war and so different from those I had so recently left.

The hotel was difficult to find but when we got there it was in an idyllic spot high up on the side of a hill overlooking the river.

We went in and asked for a room. There was no question of *Mr and Mrs Smith*. It was wartime and everyone had identity cards which had to be shown and registered. I was doubtful how Julia would react to a double room as when we had slept together at Wantage she might just have been sorry for me. However it was no problem. Julia asked for a room with a double bed and the proprietor, an understanding gentleman, raised neither eyebrows nor questions in arranging it.

We went up to the room. It was furnished in pink with pink chintzes on the easy chairs and round the bed. All the furniture fittings were in gleaming brass as were the taps in the bathroom. There was a soft carpet and window seats where you could sit and look out through the trees to the river flowing below. And it was so quiet.

We unpacked the few things we had and I started to get out of my uniform. Julia said she was going to have a shower. I heard the shower go on and shortly afterwards she came out, draped in a voluminous bath towel. She came over to me, kissed me full on the lips and let the bath towel fall to the floor. I pressed her close to me and felt her nipples harden as I caressed her breasts. As we made love, I seemed to see all the colours of the rainbow flashing through my mind.

Afterwards we lay on the bed in a tranquillity that I had never known before. After a while Julia suggested we should get dressed and go down to supper. We were given a table in the corner of the restaurant which, apart from another couple, was deserted.

Julia talked of her family in Oxfordshire and how she would like to live on a farm and keep horses.

"Perhaps we should try to find somewhere away from both our families," she said. "Where would you like to live?"

"I think Scotland would be nice," I replied, "I could get some shooting and you could try fishing."

"We must get this war over first," she said sombrely.

We finished the meal and after a brandy, went to bed.

I only had two days left of my leave and it seemed to go in a flash. It was so quiet and peaceful, so far away from the war. We walked in the woods and by the river, watched the anglers and went back to the hotel and made love.

I was realising that Julia was different from all the other girls in my life. I wanted to stay with her forever. On the last day I took her in my arms and asked her if she would marry me.

Julia knew that this was coming but she was careful. She pushed me away gently and taking my hands in hers she looked at me and said, "Thomas, darling, I do love you but I don't want to get married yet. The war.... things are changing so quickly. We haven't known each other very long," she ended simply, "I don't want to be a war widow."

It was sensible, I knew it was sensible and I had to be satisfied with that. The time came for us to go and we drove back to Wantage.

Julia had given up her job and was about to join the WAAF. It was perhaps another reason for her not wanting to marry me. The war was very close to both of us and with it came the desire for security and to hurry forward to a promise of happiness. I knew what I wanted but, for Julia, her world was opening out with new responsibilities and experiences.

She drove me to the station where we said an emotional goodbye and promised to meet again as soon as our leaves could be made to coincide. As the train took me back to Shrivenham I could think of nothing but the girl with the long blonde hair that I had left behind.

On my return to the rest camp, I was ordered to report to Darlington in County Durham where the Regiment was reforming. Colonel Baslow was still in command and George Wilcox was still commanding 222.

Major Shannon had been posted away and there were some other changes. Ike Proudlove, who had been badly wounded, was still in hospital and as there had been a number of other casualties among the officers, I found when I arrived I had been promoted to Major and given command of 223 Battery.

Ike's second-in-command, Paddy Mack, had been given the job of Adjutant in my place. I had no difficulty in handing over to him since all the Regiment's papers and files were at the bottom of that pond in France. I was pleased that I was able to pay over the money I had salvaged for the R.A. Benevolent Fund, although the notes, having been immersed in the waters of the Channel, had to be ironed before the bank would accept them.

Shortly afterwards Peter became an Intelligence Officer with an Armoured Regiment in the Middle East where he was wounded and I didn't see him again until he was repatriated. I asked him how his experiences in a Regular unit compared with the Territorials. "Not exactly an improvement," he told me. "They were very brave but seemed to have been trained for some earlier war."

Dennis Timson of 223 Battery was still in charge of I Troop which had done sterling work in France, knocking out several tanks and armoured vehicles with its guns. Both Dennis and his troop sergeant should have been recommended for decorations but as Ike had been wounded he had not put the citations forward. This question of gallantry awards could go very wrong as I was to find out later.

My Battery, 223, was now moved to Simonston in the Pendle Forest, I had arranged for Reggie to be transferred from 221 to my Battery as my second in command and to be promoted to Captain. John Foxley was still my batman and driver. John was a stalwart fellow. He had worked in the Blue Works at Backbarrow which I remembered well. Everything in the village was covered in a blue powder. The *blue* was used in whitening clothes in the wash - using a *blue bag* as it was called. Why blue should make clothes white was a bit of a mystery.

From Simonston we moved to Askrigg in the Pennines. It was not far from Sedbergh which I had visited from Barrow where Robert, who had been on the same staircase with me at Oxford, was a master. Sadly Robert lost his life early on in the war whilst serving on a destroyer in the Battle of the Atlantic. He left Liz, a widow, and was the second of my pre-war friends to die.

At Askrigg we met the local Home Guard unit which was commanded by a retired colonel who had fought in the last war and was also the local squire.

At the beginning of May when the German *blitzkrieg* started and the possibility of invasion was being taken seriously, public demand to arm the population was so great that the Government had to take some action, albeit reluctantly. They saw difficulties with a body of armed civilians who might interfere with the actions of the Regulars and who would be considered as *franc tireurs* by the Germans.

Arguments between the War Office, Home Office and the Treasury had to be swept aside and on the 14th May Anthony Eden, the Secretary of State for War, spoke to the nation on the B.B.C. announcing that a new force to be named the Local Defence Volunteers was being formed. Even before he had finished speaking police stations throughout the country were being besieged by eager applicants.

They were an unpaid voluntary force to be recruited solely for home defence and used for harassing the enemy if he were to land by sea or from the air. No thought had yet been given as to how they were to be armed or administered. Their uniform at first was solely a brassard on their civilian clothes with the letters *LDV* on it. Later at Mr Churchill's instigation this was changed to *HG* as he considered Home Guard to be a more inspiring title. They soon numbered some one and a half million men and later had a Director General of their own.

Operationally they came under the Regional Army Command and could be called out by the ringing of church bells.

In 1939, before the LDV or the Home Guard had been thought of, men had been asked to volunteer to deal with enemy parachutists who were expected to land and act as fifth columnists. These volunteers were known as *Parashots*. Philip Lansdown who, like the retired Colonel, owned a lot of the land in the district was one, and was also a member of the Colonel's platoon in the Home Guard. He was elderly, older than the Colonel, a keen sportsman but a bit vague. Since it kept being mentioned I suspected the Colonel was envious of Philip's voluntary status of being a Parashot. I asked Philip why he had become one and he replied, "Oh I'm a pretty good shot and know the country well - I heard these German parachutists have collapsible bicycles. I could do with a bicycle now my car is off the road through petrol rationing - that would be quite a prize - better than shooting pheasants."

The Colonel's unit consisted of farm labourers, tradesmen, shopkeepers and anyone too old or too unfit for active service. They were armed with *pikes* which were 1914 type bayonets fixed to wooden poles. They had six rifles between them and a rather dilapidated Lewis Gun. Transport, apart from bicycles was the local baker's delivery van. What they lacked in equipment they made up for in enthusiasm.

Just outside the village, there was a small reservoir with hills on either side. The Colonel was convinced the Germans would land on the reservoir in a seaplane which would then disgorge its troops who would take over the village and harass the countryside. I did my best to persuade him of the futility of this idea, as a seaplane would never be able to land on the reservoir or take off again on account of the surrounding high hills. The Colonel would have none of it and asked for my Battery to join with him in an exercise to repel the supposed enemy after they had landed. He was delighted to think he would have Artillery support. Sadly, I had to tell him that the 2-pdr anti-tank shell was armour-piercing and not explosive and, if it was lucky enough to hit the seaplane, would go straight through and do little damage. I remember saying the same thing to the Divisional Staff in France!

The great day of the exercise arrived.

The briefing was to take place in the School Hall which, much to the annoyance of the schoolmaster, had been requisitioned by the Colonel. I had been invited and came with my four Troop Commanders.

The Home Guard arrived with their assortment of weapons and in a variety of dress. The Colonel, dressed in his old army uniform and sporting the medal ribbons of the last war, strode in and his sergeant, the local greengrocer, called the men to attention which they achieved with varying degrees of success which made my heart sink even deeper. The Colonel, who had been a regular soldier himself, also looked disappointed.

He began: "Stand easy, not that easy Jenkins. Now pay attention. This is a very important exercise and we have the support of Major Clayton and the Royal Artillery. We want to impress them with what we can do. What Philip? Yes, of course, sit down. We have just been informed by Private Green, who has been scouting on his bicycle, that a German seaplane has landed on the reservoir. We are to move up at once and attack it. Corporal Withenshaw - you will mount the Lewis gun in a position to open fire on the seaplane and the rest of your section will engage the crew with rifles.

"Sergeant Slightly. You will take the rest of the platoon and attack the enemy with your pikes, giving no quarter."

"Philip," he continued, turning to the now seated Lansdown who was dressed in a tweed jacket and breeches and had begun to nod sleepily over a double barrelled shot gun he was cradling in his arms. "Philip," the Colonel repeated sharply so that Philip's head jerked up with a mild look of surprise. "You will take your section and prevent the enemy, if there are any survivors, from leaving the area of the reservoir. Major Clayton, you will use your artillery to support us. Any questions?"

I had many but thought it better to keep my mouth shut.

"We've only got one drum of ammunition for the Lewis Gun, Sir," said Corporal Withenshaw. "What do we do after that?"

"You will have to use your initiative," announced the Colonel triumphantly after a small pause for thought.

Whilst the Colonel continued with more lengthy instructions on the route, of which there was only one, and the timing, which had to be instant or the seaplane's troops would be outside the door, Philip nodded off completely. A sighing snore escaped from the elderly Parashot who must have been dreaming of how he could have been out on the moors bagging the odd grouse, or even a parachutist with a collapsible bicycle instead of listening to the Colonel drooling on. I would have been happy to have joined him.

When the order to move was given Philip woke with a start. His gun which was loaded in readiness for the enemy fell on the floor and as he had forgotten to put on the safety catch, went off with a loud bang narrowly missing Corporal

Withenshaw and making us all jump. I was not amused and reversed my thoughts of joining him on the grouse moor.

The Home Guard, intending to move up to the reservoir, all got into the baker's van. Sadly it failed to start in spite of all the platoon's efforts at pushing it down the road. I decided that I had better assist and lent them two of my 15 cwt trucks.

The Home Guard arrived at the reservoir and got to their respective positions where they sat in the sun and consumed their haversack rations which had been provided by their families and thought *what a lovely war.* I had provided two gun teams who mounted their guns to cover the reservoir. The Colonel then went round the positions, decided the enemy had been eliminated and the exercise was over.

We returned to the local pub which, fortunately, was still well supplied with beer, and where a good many reminiscences were told and many lines shot by my gunners.

I felt rather depressed. After what I had seen in France, if this was the best the Home Guard could do, in spite of their undoubted enthusiasm, they would need a great deal of training and proper weapons to withstand and defeat an invading German army, even if they did have the advantage of fighting on their home ground. However the spirit of resistance that arose throughout the populace after the defeat at Dunkirk was something that was going to show itself in many other ways.

We had been at Askrigg for a few weeks when I was called to Wolsingham which was now the Regimental HQ. Here I learned that my Battery was to leave the Regiment and become an independent unit in a Brigade which was part of a Group stationed in the South of England. This Brigade was one of two, formed after Dunkirk, to act as mobile reserves in the event of the expected invasion by the enemy. Having lost in France and Belgium during the retreat, all our weapons, transport and equipment, the result of so much sweat and toil in the factories, there was very little left in Britain. But what there was and what was being produced at breakneck speed, was allocated to the two Brigades.

The one to which I was sent consisted of three regular Infantry Battalions. These had just returned from service in India, keeping the peace on the North West Frontier, and now had to retrain to fight a modern sophisticated enemy. In the Brigade there were also: a Royal Artillery Regiment of Light Artillery, armed with 75mm gun-howitzers, a Reconnaissance Squadron, Royal Engineers, Medical Corps, Signallers and supporting services, to which was now added my

Battery of anti-tank guns which was renamed the 223 Independent Anti-Tank Battery R.A.

I found that commanding a small independent unit was much more fulfilling than being an Adjutant, where I had been more of a staff officer carrying out the administration of the Regiment.

We moved to Oxford where we were accommodated in tents on Port Meadow, the low lying and rather damp fields bordering the river Thames. The Infantry Battalions were also under canvas but in Shotover Park, just outside the city.

As August approached, the likelihood of invasion increased. Hitler, having subjugated all Europe and with Russia apparently friendly to him, had put out peace feelers to Britain. Having convinced himself that he had won the war he was astounded when he was roundly rebuffed. He now decided that he must invade and occupy England at once, before turning his spite on his old enemy Russia who, despite their offers of solidarity, he did not trust.

His Generals were strongly against an invasion until they had obtained air superiority and built up their Navy. The Germans are inherently not a seafaring nation and that little stretch of water that separated Britain from the Continent and had protected us for nearly a millenium, filled the Germans with dismay. Admiral Raeder, in charge of the Navy, wanted to postpone the operation, known as *Sealion*, to the spring of the following year. The Führer insisted - and who was there to contradict him for fear of his own life? - that it must go ahead.

The bombastic Reichsmarschall Goering, head of the German Air Force, told his master that he could remove all British aircraft from the skies in a few days combat. How wrong he was. But only just! So started the Battle of Britain.

My Battery was moved to Ashford in Kent from where I placed my 16 guns to cover the roads and tracks leading from the beaches over which the German tanks were expected to advance. The Infantry Battalions were deployed behind us to act as a mobile reserve to strike at the enemy after he had landed. At the time the shortage of ammunition was such that I had no more than 2 rounds per gun, so there could have been little opposition to the Panzers from my guns had the Germans landed.

All through that hot August and September gunners and infantrymen watched the aerial battle taking place over our heads. Waves of German bombers accompanied by swarms of Messerschmitts swept in, to be met by the Spitfires and Hurricanes with their heroic pilots. August 15 saw one of the major air battles of the war, the Luftwaffe flying 2000 sorties and the R.A.F 1000, over a front of 500 miles.

The superiority of the British, apart from the dedication of its pilots, was in great measure due to the use of radar to warn us of the incoming enemy planes. This meant that our planes did not have to be in the air continuously in order to intercept them. The Germans, at this time, did not have such technology and it was a bitter surprise for them when they found out what we had. However they then identified and set out to destroy our radar installations. Had this gone on it might well have influenced the result of the battle. After that major air battle on August 15, Goering made the first of his fatal mistakes - he called off the attacks on the radar stations, perhaps not realising their importance, giving the RAF a much needed reprieve and time to rebuild them.

The aerial battle continued to rage both along the south and also the east coasts until, when he had almost got the RAF reeling from their losses, Goering switched his air assault to night bombing of London on September 7th. No doubt in retaliation for the bombing of Berlin on August 25th, something which he had promised the German people could never happen. I was to see the results of this when I visited London - vast areas of the Docks and East End destroyed. It went on for night after night, but far from destroying the morale of the populace it strengthened their resolve to carry the war into the enemy's territory and to defeat him. That the bombing of cities did not help either side to destroy their opponents' morale, was something which became apparent as the war progressed.

The Germans had perfected a method of directing their bombers to the target by flying along a radio beam, code name *Knickebein*. This meant they could direct their aircraft to a specific target. In the case of London they could hardly miss, but in blacked out Britain it was not easy to locate targets even as large as Liverpool, Birmingham or Coventry. Two beams were sent from two separate stations which intersected over the target. If we could find the frequency of the beams they were using for that night's bombing we could take countermeasures.

The German armed forces encoded all their secret messages, including the frequencies of the beams, which were changed daily, on a machine known as ENIGMA. It was not until long after the war that the work of the dedicated team of code-breakers, sworn to lifetime secrecy, at GC&CS Bletchley Park, became known. They included Alan Turing, the mathematician who designed and built the first true electronic computer - COLOSSUS - which was used by them. The decrypted and translated signals from the machine-generated ENIGMA codes were known as ULTRA and enabled us to interpret the German instructions as to where the beams were directed and the bombs would fall. Our ability to break their code had to be kept secret at all costs as it enabled us to monitor other German operations, and discovery would have meant that they changed the code.

There were two countermeasures. We could jam the beams with strong radio signals on the same wavelength but that would tell the Germans that we had broken their ENIGMA code. A better method was to distort the beams so that the pilot, thinking he was flying along the correct beam, was fooled to the extent that when he dropped his bombs they missed the target.

The credit for this method of deception must go to a young British physicist - Dr R.V. Jones - who had studied physics at Oxford while I was there. Unlike me, he had obtained a first class honours degree, later a doctorate, and had gone on to study infra-red radiation and short wave radio. Although, at one time in the Grenadier Guards, he had decided, backed by Professor Lindemann, that there was a role for physicists as well as soldiers to defeat Hitler and this he carried out with great success.

In spite of these measures, night bombing, although less accurate, continued. At that time it was very difficult for our night fighters to find the opposing bombers and it was not until a satisfactory form of airborne radar, also developed by Dr Jones, was installed in their aircraft, that they were better able to locate and shoot down the night bombers.

Goering, under orders from Hitler, now made his second mistake. He was so confident that he had the RAF at his mercy that he switched to daylight bombing of the city. September 15th was the decisive battle. 200 German bombers escorted by 600 fighters headed for London. They were picked up on our radar screens and intercepted before they could reach the capital, succeeding waves suffering the same fate. The Battle of Britain was won but night bombing of London and other cities continued.

At the same time the RAF was attacking the invasion barges which the Germans were assembling on the Channel coast. They were so successful in this that by September 17th, a date which four years later was to be etched indelibly on my memory, operation *Sealion* was postponed indefinitely.

For nearly a thousand years Britain had been defended from invasion by sea power. Now it had been saved by airpower and had it not been for Mr Churchill and a few others who supported the build-up of our air force in the early thirties, this would not have happened and we might have succumbed.

I remembered vividly in 1931 seeing in the cinema the race for the Schneider Trophy. Flight Lieutenant Stainforth in his beautiful Supermarine seaplane, the forerunner of the Spitfire, gained the world air speed record of 408 m.p.h. This superb effort was sponsored not by a forward-looking Government as it should have been, but by the generosity of Lady Houston, a private philanthropist.

Now the air battle had been won and I heard on the wireless, Mr Churchill make his historic statement - "Never in the field of human conflict was so much owed by so many to so few".

Whilst this had been going on my Battery was still guarding the area of the South Coast allotted to them, waiting for the expected invasion.

The threat that the Germans would use gas, as the Italians had done in Abyssinia, was being taken very seriously and the population had already been issued with civilian gas masks and an anti-gas cape. The Services had a general service (GS) type respirator. Although, when I was at Runcorn, I knew of the secret poison gas factory which was being constructed at Astmoor, I did not know until much later of the preparations that were being made to use the chemical weapon, nor that Mr Churchill had approved an order that, in the event of an invasion, the beaches, including those in front of my position, were to be sprayed with mustard gas to deter the enemy as they landed. What would have happened to our own troops or the civilian population was not considered. It also came to light that, prior to Dunkirk, both the Germans and the British had large stocks of gas in France which providentially were not used.

CHAPTER 18

By the middle of September the threat of invasion had receded and the Brigade was withdrawn from the coast. My Battery was moved to Kings Langley, a village near Hemel Hempstead north-west of London. Here we stayed for several weeks and while we were there the bombing of London continued.

Julia, in her new unit in the Womens Auxiliary Air Force, was stationed at High Wycombe which was not far away. I wrote and asked her if she could get a 48 hour pass so that we could go up to London and perhaps see a show. I had been told that the theatres were still functioning. I arranged with Reggie to take over the Battery while I was away and waited impatiently for her reply. It came eventually.

"See you Paddington 1900 hours Friday."

I instructed Foxley to drive me up to London in one of the 15 cwt. trucks.

We arrived at Paddington in good time and I went to the barrier on platform 4 where I knew the train from High Wycombe was due to arrive. I scanned the passengers but did not at first see Julia. Suddenly a young WAAF officer approached me and saluted.

"Pilot Officer Julia Jackson reporting for duty Sir," she said with an impish smile.

I forgot to return the salute but instead put my arms round her and gave her a very unmilitary embrace.

I had decided that, whatever the cost, we would stay at a West End hotel. Returning to the station entrance, I got into the 15 cwt truck and Julia got in beside me. There was only one passenger seat in the truck with the box holding the accumulator between it and the driver's seat, so Julia had to sit on my knee to which I didn't object as long as no Military Policemen saw us. Foxley got into the driver's seat.

"Where do you want to go Sir?" he asked deferentially.

"Drop us at the Hyde Park Hotel. It's just off Piccadilly." There were many diversions but Foxley eventually got us to the hotel.

We got out and I asked Foxley to take the truck back to camp and I would let him know when to pick us up on Sunday.

"I hope you have a good time Sir," said Foxley who thought that Julia was a smashing WAAF, and drove off.

Julia and I entered the hotel and booked a double room. The hall porter took our bags and showed us to the room. I tipped him but thought he looked strangely embarrassed as he left.

We looked round. First there was no double bed only two singles. It smelt musty, probably not properly aired because of the blackout. Julia turned down the covers on the beds.

"There are no sheets darling, only blankets!" she exclaimed in horror.

"We're not sleeping here," I said emphatically. "This is supposed to be a first class hotel, the chambermaid must have forgotten to do the room."

I went to the telephone. It wasn't working so I had to go down to the reception. The clerk was half expecting me.

"There are no sheets on the beds. Perhaps you would have that rectified or put us in another room," I said rather pompously, feeling annoyed that I should have had to ask him in the first place.

"I'm very sorry Sir," said the clerk, "our laundry has been bombed and all our sheets have been destroyed - there *is* a war on you know Sir."

His heavy irony irritated me even further. I wanted my time with Julia to be perfect and I decided that under no circumstances was I going to stay in that hotel, war or no war. I got on the telephone and tried several others but they were all full. Finally I tried the Savoy which had a room but it was twice as expensive as the amount I had budgeted for. However to hell with the expense. I booked it and told the clerk we were leaving. The hall porter brought down our bags and managed to get us a taxi.

We found that driving through London in a taxi in the blackout was quite an experience. The taxi started down Piccadilly but did not get very far before it was diverted due to bomb damage and unexploded bombs. The driver had to skirt Piccadilly Circus by Lower Regent Street in order to enter the Haymarket and then down to Charing Cross when the sirens sounded. He managed to get us into the Savoy just as the bombs started to fall on the East End.

In the hotel all was calm and efficient. The room with a large double bed was clean, warm and welcoming. It was now too late to go to a show so we had a quiet meal in the restaurant and then went to bed.

It was October and at the height of the *blitz*. First came the incendiaries. I turned out the light and took down the blackout. We were near the top of the building and looking out we saw a fantastic sight. It was a full moon and there before us was a panoramic view of London in the moonlight, with all its domes, spires and famous buildings silhouetted in the pale bluish light of the incendiaries with here and there an orange glow from a fire that had broken out.

We went back to bed and then the bombing started. The Hall Porter had said that when a raid was on we could go down to the shelter in the cellars if we wished. Julia said she would rather stay in our room and I agreed.

"We could always get under the bed," she remarked practically.

"There wouldn't be much room, but I suppose we could squeeze in," I replied. But it was impracticable and uncomfortable so we stayed on top of the bed.

Next came the whistle of the bombs falling, a fiendish noise rising to a crescendo, followed by the explosions. The building rocked and we clung to each other in bed expecting any moment that the ceiling would collapse and we would be buried in tons of debris. I thought that at least, if we were to be killed, we would be together. Then there were the Ack Ack guns. The noise was deafening.

It was very different from my experiences in France. There the bombs had been lighter and most of the projectiles had been shells whose whine gave you some idea where they would fall. Here the bombs were much heavier and I felt so helpless and defenceless, at the top of a building, with Julia by my side. By about six the raids ended and we fell asleep.

It was late before we woke, dressed and went down to breakfast. The hotel had not been hit but some of the bombs had been very close. The restaurant with the blackout removed was light and airy and our table looked out over the Embankment towards the Thames.

"I'm looking forward to a proper breakfast like we had at home before the war," said Julia. "You know, coffee, bacon and eggs and marmalade."

Rationing was in force and such things as eggs and marmalade were on *points*. You had so many points allocated each month and you could spend them on various things like that. At hotels and restaurants however, you did not have to give up any of your valuable points, but meals had to be limited in price to five shillings. We ordered bacon and eggs, toast and marmalade and coffee. It came eventually but alas, the eggs were a reconstituted powder made into some sort of a scramble and the coffee was very weak with powdered milk. Still, as we had been reminded last night, "there was a war on", so we didn't complain.

After breakfast we went out to look at the bomb damage. It was a bright October morning. Walking along the Embankment we could see large fires burning in the direction of the City and the East End. St Pauls was still standing - at least we could see the dome - but it was surrounded by fires and smoke and the remains of large buildings which had been hit. It had been a very heavy raid.

We turned left into the Strand but were stopped several times by signs - *Unexploded Bomb* - where workers with diggers and heavy lifting tackle were trying to get to the bomb to defuse it, a job which called for skill, patience and defiance of danger of the highest order. At last, entering St Martin's Lane, we found that some of the theatres were still functioning and were able to get two tickets for one of Noel Coward's plays that evening.

At Charing Cross Julia turned to me and said, "Shall we see if the Palace has been hit?"

"We may be able to get there," I replied but when we tried to get into the Mall we were stopped by barriers. Turning right we entered Pall Mall but here the destruction was at its worst. The Carlton Club in St James was totally destroyed and rubble and smoking craters were everywhere. It was a scene of destruction worse than any I had seen in France or Belgium.

Returning to the hotel it seemed incongruous to have afternoon tea with all this going on around us but no one seemed to be taking any notice of it. At half past six we walked to the theatre. In spite of the Blitz it was crowded, mostly with servicemen and women but there were civilians as well.

When the Blitz started, the Government had decreed that there were to be two stages of the Air Raid warning - the Alert and the Alarm. The Alert would indicate that an Air Raid was in progress but that normal life as far as possible could continue. The Alarm indicated that an attack was imminent and everyone should take cover and go to an air raid shelter.

The curtain went up and we began to enjoy the play which was a light comedy designed to take the audience's mind off the war. After the first act we went down to the bar. I ordered a gin and tonic for Julia and a whisky for myself.

"Isn't it wonderful that in spite of the bombing everyone is trying to carry on as normal. Last night I was jolly scared," she admitted.

"I don't mind telling you so was I," I replied. "Hitler's trying to destroy the morale of the people by bombing so we'll agree to a peace. But he won't succeed and that's why we are in a theatre during the blitz."

"I think we had better have another drink," said Julia, "in case we don't have a chance after the second act and it will be good for our morale."

We quickly drank our second drink and went back to our seats. During the second act the sirens sounded the Alert but the play continued. However just after the last act had started, bells were sounded and 'Alarm' was flashed on the curtain which had been lowered. Everyone left the theatre very quickly but without any panic and took cover in the shelters erected in the street or in the Tubes.

I put my arm round Julia and we hurried along, through Trafalgar Square until we got to Charing Cross from where we had hoped to reach the hotel. There an Air Raid Warden stopped us and instructed us to go down to the underground Tube station. Here we spent the rest of the night lying on the platform on my greatcoat, which luckily I had with me, and Julia's coat which covered us. It was an extraordinary sight. Scores of people were camping out on the platforms, their homes and houses destroyed or made uninhabitable, and this was where they slept night after night before returning to work each morning.

We did not get back to the hotel until the *All Clear* had sounded and then slept until well into the morning. I telephoned the Orderly Room but it was some time before they found Foxley by which time the three minutes, which was the maximum time allowed for a call, was nearly up. I told him to be at the Hotel at 1400 hrs.

We got up, dressed, and had lunch. After that we packed and went down to the foyer. Foxley arrived in the 15 cwt truck. He remarked dryly that he hoped we had had a good night as he had heard there had been some bombing. "Perhaps you didn't notice Sir!" he continued with a knowing smile.

I replied calmly, "It was a bit noisy," and told him to get on and drive us to High Wycombe.

We arrived at the Guard Room at the gate to Julia's camp. She got out and I kissed her goodbye. "Until next time," I whispered and she squeezed my hand, smiling.

Foxley drove me back to camp and Reggie met me. He asked me if the hotel had been alright. I gave a wry smile.

"A little unusual," I replied. Yes, it had been an unusual weekend, I thought to myself.

After we had been at Kings Langley for some time, the news came that we were to move to South Wales. This meant that I would be further from Julia. I telephoned her, told her I was moving and said I would write.

We were used to convoys by now and the journey across the south of England to Wales went without incident. Our destination was the village of Crickhowell, outside Abergavenny, not far from the route I had taken with the Regiment's guns from Swansea back to Ulverston when war was declared.

Battery Headquarters was in a workhouse which no longer housed its former occupants who, unless physically ill and admitted to hospital, had been dispersed to do useful war work. With its tower, it stood out against the hillside and was soon christened *The Spike*. There were good kitchens which the Battery cook took over and rooms for the Officers' and Sergeants' messes.

I was talking to Reggie, who was the Battery Captain.

"Well at least we should be getting away from the bombing."

"Don't be too sure," replied Reggie, "you never know, Hitler may take over Ireland and decide to start an offensive from there."

This was precisely the eventuality that the Government had been considering and the Brigade had been sent to South Wales to be ready to counter it.

We had been reinforced by a number of Indian soldiers with mules who were from a unit of the Royal Indian Army Service Corps. It was intended that they should be used in another attempt at the invasion of Norway, now occupied by the Germans. The mountains of Wales were an ideal training ground for the pack-carrying mules with their masters who, when we met them, always seemed to be smiling, their teeth gleaming white against the darker brown of their faces. It must have been strange for them to be so far from home.

Since the expected invasion of Britain by the enemy appeared to have been put off, the Government now decided that the Army should take on a more aggressive role with a view to carrying the war into the enemy's territory. The War Office decreed that training should take place for an offensive in North Africa and eventually a re-entry into Europe.

However life in Crickhowell continued uneventfully for the next few months with exercises taking place in the Black Mountains and firing on the ranges at Sennybridge.

I was keen to try out an idea that I had thought of and one day I said to Reggie: "Suppose we wanted to get a gun across a dyke like those we saw in France. We couldn't use the towing vehicle so we would have to ferry it across with whatever we could get hold of."

"We could try swimming," said Reggie unenthusiastically, hoping that I wasn't going to have one of my bright ideas.

"I don't think you would get very far towing a 2-pdr," I replied caustically.

I was still thinking of the problem when a solution came into my mind.

"I know! We could get some bales of straw and see if they would float."

"What happens if they don't?" said Reg gloomily.

I sent for Dennis who was still commanding I Troop.

"I want you to take one of your guns down to the canal which is by the back road to Crickhowell, and ferry it across."

"How do you want me to do it Sir?" asked Dennis.

"You will have to use your initiative but I suggest you might try using bales of straw if you can get hold of some."

Dennis thought his CO was slightly barmy but, as it was an order, went down to the canal to survey the crossing. Next day he requisitioned six bales of straw from a local farmer, wrapped them in the canvas cover from a 30 cwt truck and pushed them into the canal where, rather to his surprise, they floated. Next he got one of his gun teams to manhandle the gun onto the straw raft and slowly pushed it towards the other bank. Halfway across the straw bales and the gun sank. Luckily the canal was not very deep but the gun crew were not too pleased at having to get up to their necks in water to recover the gun and then spend a lot of time drying and cleaning it. I was watching the unsuccessful operation and had the feeling that I was not very popular with the gun team. I was glad the CRA had not been present.

Towards the end of the summer, the Battery moved to Velindre, a village northwest of the Black Mountains. Here we found ourselves rather isolated, the only amusement being visits to the local pub, where the language was mostly Welsh but to our surprise also included some Polish. The reason, we found out, was that survivors from the Polish Army were quartered in the village. They were brave men who had escaped from the German onslaught and were straining to get back and take their revenge on the enemy who had raped their country. Some of them were to take part in that fateful operation in Holland some time later.

Our 2-pdr anti-tank gun was no longer towed by a 15 cwt truck as it had been in France but was now carried in a much larger truck known as a Portee. The reason given by the powers that be was that it could travel much faster than a truck towing the gun. This was true. However the disadvantages were obvious in that it took a long time to dismount the gun and bring it into action. By which time the enemy would have either departed or, more likely, knocked the gun out.

I had an idea. Why not fire the gun from the Portee?

I selected Dennis again for the experiment.

"Dennis, I want you to take one of your guns down to the range and try firing it from the Portee."

Dennis thought for a moment and then said," I don't think you will be able to traverse the gun, Sir."

"Why?"

"The shield will get in the way."

"Then take it off," I said impatiently, seeing difficulties being put in the way of my experiment.

The shield was a piece of armourplate mounted in front of the gun-layer to protect him and the gun crew from small arms fire.

We proceeded to the ranges.

"I think you will find there is a very loud crack when you fire the gun without its shield, Sir," said the No. 1 on the gun.

"Nevermind I'll fire the first round myself," I replied getting into the layer's seat. No. 2 loaded a round into the breech and tapped me on the shoulder. I trained the gun on the target and pressed the trigger.

There was an almighty flash and a deafening crack which affected my eardrums and left me deaf for several days. I decided the experiment had better be called off.

Later that day, Reggie came up to me in the bar. "I hope you're not going to try any more of your crackpot experiments. You're not in the Steelworks now," he shouted since I hadn't heard him the first time.

I smiled. "Well you know," I said thoughtfully, "we are Territorials and not really professional soldiers so we don't have to do everything by the book. I've got some more ideas." Reggie groaned and I tapped the side of my head to see if I could knock some of the deafness out.

I wanted to improve our anti-aircraft role. In France we had not been very successful at it as our only suitable weapon was the Bren gun. In order to train Bren gunners in this role it was normally arranged for them to practise firing at a moving target, known as a drogue, and towed by a light aircraft if one could be made available.

I arranged for a small party with the Bren Gunners from the Battery to move to a temporary camp on the west coast of Wales where this could be carried out. The firing party went down to the beach near their camp and mounted their guns so that they fired out to sea over Cardigan Bay. We then waited for the drogue to appear. Unfortunately the light aircraft used for towing the drogues were few and far between and much of the time was spent doing nothing.

"This is no good," I said. "We'll make our own drogue."

I instructed the armament artificer to fix up a wire rope between the two cliffs to either side of our deserted beach. Running along the wire was the target and, to simulate an aircraft, it could be pulled rapidly from one side to the other.

Having made sure there was no shipping in the area on which the shots might fall, I then instructed one of the Bren gunners to load and be ready to fire. The artificer then pulled the target as fast as he could along the wire and the gunner fired, the tracer indicating were his shots were going.

It was not bad even though the target could not simulate the speed of an aircraft nor its height but it did at least give the gunner a chance of firing at a target moving through the air.

Although late autumn, the weather was mild and the sea still warm so, having brought some bathing trunks, I plunged into the sea and encouraged the others to follow.

Reggie remarked: "What a pity we didn't bring a 2-pdr. We could have tried your idea of floating it in the sea."

Dennis murmured feelingly that he didn't think it would have been a good idea.

However we spent the rest of the afternoon swimming and lying on the beach in the sun before returning to camp. We all agreed it had been a pleasant interlude and the following day we returned to Velindre.

CHAPTER 19

It was towards the end of 1941, shortly after the anti-aircraft experiment, that I was called to Brigade Headquarters together with the commanding officers of the Infantry Battalions and of the other supporting units. The Brigade was commanded by Brigadier Smythe. When we were all assembled the Brigadier announced that an Airborne Division was being formed. It would consist of two parachute brigades and an airlanding brigade. The latter would be carried in gliders. His Brigade had been selected as the 1st Air Landing Brigade and would be commanded by his successor, Brigadier Hopkinson, who would be taking over in December.

This announcement, as might be expected, was met with varying degrees of enthusiasm and, in some cases, alarm by his audience. There were those who did not relish the idea of being transported by glider. Only recently we had heard the news, which had filtered through, of the heavy losses in the use of gliders by the Germans in the invasion of Crete in the Spring.

I felt rather elated. I had sometimes regretted I had not joined the RAF but now fate was giving me a chance to get into the air. I was not sure if I would appreciate being carried in a glider piloted by someone else but at least I would be flying. Members of the Airborne Division were to be volunteers. That is to say personnel in the new Air Landing Brigade could volunteer *out* if they wished. Very few did, in fact, decide to leave but, more significant, was the decision that only the most efficient soldiers would be transported by air. It was obvious that there was no point in using this expensive form of transport for anyone who was second-best. This caused a problem for commanding officers. We had to weed out the least efficient of our officers and men and replace them with volunteers from other units in the army.

Some of the volunteers we were sent were, in many cases, only too pleased to leave their old units for various reasons and their Commanding Officers, although they had been ordered to send their best, were only too glad to see them go. Many were worse than those they came to replace.

I had a lot of problems, especially in replacing officers I had become attached to. Eventually I built the 1st Air Landing Anti-Tank Battery, as it was now designated, into an efficient unit, but I still had doubts as to whether all the replacement officers would match up to the high standards required.

No one had seen an army glider yet, which was not surprising as, so far, none had been produced. Training had to consist of simulating landing in enemy territory and the tactics to be employed.

At the beginning of 1942 the 1st Air Landing Brigade moved to the area of Salisbury Plain where the rest of the Airborne Division was situated. The first gliders had arrived. They were the Hotspur, a mid-wing monoplane of all-wood construction. Two pilots sat in tandem at the front under a perspex canopy which was hinged for access, whilst six fully armed troops could be accommodated in the tubular fuselage. This was fitted with a number of minute portholes and a door on one side for entrance and exit. It was very claustrophobic and they were soon designated as *flying coffins*.

I was given a flight in one which I didn't think much of. I could see nothing and therefore felt violently air sick. Perhaps fortunately, the Hotspur was never used operationally although it continued to be the standard glider for pilot training.

In order to give the glider pilots training in carrying troops, and the troops experience in being transported by air, members of the 1st Air Landing Brigade were asked to volunteer as *live loads*. Although not always popular, it was a change from military training and Dennis, who was always willing to try something new, volunteered.

The Battery had now moved to Stocks Cross near Newbury and the Officers Mess was in Strawberry Farm. It was all very rural. Our nearest pub was the Dundas Arms where the local character was the *watercress man* who regaled us with stories on how he grew watercress and other subjects.

We had not been there very long when a conference was called for all the commanding officers of the Airborne Division. The Divisional Commander, in the immaculate uniform of the Brigade of Guards, expounded on our role as a *corps d'élite*. He announced that we would wear a distinctive headdress and that our badge would be the Pegasus or winged horse. He then issued everyone with a signed drawing of the badge and a maroon beret - later to be known as the *red beret*. He gave instructions that the berets should now be worn. I noticed how embarrassed some of the Regular officers were when they were told to don this brightly coloured headdress. It didn't bother me as I was used to wearing the Artillery red forage hat.

The conference was just breaking up when a message was handed to the Divisional Commander. He read it and in very grave tones announced that there had been an accident to a glider while flying a live load at the airfield at Ringway. Everyone including the pilots had been killed. My heart missed a beat. I knew that Dennis would probably have volunteered for that flight. I returned quickly to my Headquarters where Reggie met me with a grave face and the news that it was only too true - Dennis had been killed.

What a waste of a young life. He had done so well in France and was popular with his men. A dapper officer in his uniform. Always smartly turned out and smoking a cigarette in a long holder. He was not married but I would have to write to his mother and father.

Amongst his clothing and effects which were returned to us was Dennis's silver cigarette case. It was bent into a grotesque shape. I hoped fervently that Dennis had been killed instantly. I went with Reggie to the funeral in Barrow where he was buried with full military honours supplied by a party from the Battery.

The inquiry into the accident was not conclusive but it appeared that neither of the pilots were properly strapped in. This could have been lethal if the pilot had started to make a steep dive - possibly a *dive approach* which was later forbidden. If the pilot, not being strapped in, had slipped forward in the dive he would have fallen against the control column, increasing the angle of the dive, and would have been jammed against it with all his weight, and no way could he recover control. The glider would have flown straight into the ground at high speed.

After Dennis's death, I thought again that I would be better using my experience as a pilot to fly the glider rather than to be a passenger.

Meanwhile an opportunity to increase my flying hours occurred rather fortuitously. Not far from us there was a small RAF airfield at Shrewton equipped with light aircraft. It was not long before I had made friends with the CO I told him I had been a member of the Oxford University Air Squadron and showed him my log book. He gave me a solo check and then authorised me to fly their Tiger Moths.

The Tiger was a great little aircraft which was used for initial flying training. It was similar to the famous Gypsy Moth in which in 1930 Amy Johnson had made her record breaking flight to Australia, crossing, amongst other hazards, the shark-infested Timor Sea. It resulted in my spending much of my time flying members of my Battery in the passenger seat, giving them, what I considered, useful instruction in map reading from the air and showing them what the land looked like from up above.

On one occasion when I was flying one of the bombardiers, we strayed rather close to the English Channel. My passenger, being somewhat alarmed, shouted through the intercom.

"What do we do if an enemy aircraft appears, Sir?"

I lent out of the cockpit and, handing him my revolver, said laconically," Shoot it down!"

While the Battery was at Stocks Cross, for some reason which I could never understand apart from the fact that the Royal Artillery was a mounted Regiment, we were issued with two horses. Someone in the War Department must have forgotten that our guns were now drawn by mechanical vehicles and would shortly be airborne, so that horses would be even more redundant. Perhaps it was the winged horse they were trying to emulate.

Although I was rather allergic to horses I realised that this might be an opportunity to invite Julia to come for a ride. I had appointed a Bombardier, known as *Pop* to be head groom as he had originally been one in the peacetime artillery and knew a lot about horses.

Julia was still stationed at High Wycombe. One day, breaking all regulations, I sent Foxley off in a 15 cwt to fetch her. She arrived in uniform and I took her to my quarters where she changed into riding kit. Pop had saddled up the two horses which he told me were quite reasonable animals and might even have done some hunting. Being near Newbury racecourse there were plenty of training stables and therefore gallops on the Downs.

Walking the horses at first, Julia broke into a trot as we neared the open country. The weather was fine but there was a threatening cloud which might mean rain. We urged our horses into a canter and with Julia leading galloped over the grass.

We soon had to stop as the horses were not as fit as they might have been. Julia was looking radiant, the wind having brought colour to her cheeks. I was feeling confident now that I had survived the gallop.

"That was wonderful," she said, "we must do it again."

"Yes," I replied enthusiastically, though that depends on how long we are allowed to keep the horses," I added more cautiously.

Julia laughed. I could never fool her for long about being a horse enthusiast.

"I think a Pegasus Brigade should always have horses," she said emphatically and squeezing her heels into the sides of her horse, she turned smartly which made my horse turn with a sickening swerve so that I dropped the reins and had to grab hold of the mane.

"Sorry," she said, waiting for me. "You know, if it was an aeroplane you wouldn't have a problem at all."

We returned to camp and handed the horses over to Pop who unsaddled them, took them back to the stable and rubbed them down with a wisp of straw.

Julia, back in her uniform, had tea with me in the Officers' Mess, after which I instructed Foxley to take her back to High Wycombe and if he was stopped by any Military Police to say that she had been to a secret conference with his CO!

Up to now we had only seen the Hotspur but it was not long before there was news of another military glider. This was the Horsa, a high wing machine capable of carrying 28 fully armed troops. The two pilots were housed side by side in a perspex canopy at the front with an excellent all-round view. There were no machines to fly as yet. The prototype had been constructed in the record time of ten months from the design stage to the first proving flight in September 1941. The Horsa was made of timber in order that its manufacture, mainly by furniture firms, did not conflict with the production of other service aircraft. However a mock-up of the fuselage had been made and was sent to Ringway (later to become Manchester Airport), the airfield where poor Dennis had been killed.

At this time the army had no experience as to how they were to use their airborne troops. They assumed that all the airborne army could do was to deliver troops into the battle either by parachute or by glider. It then occurred to them that the troops, after landing, would be very vulnerable without any heavy weapons, particularly anti-tank guns to support them. The CRA had been thinking about this. He sent for me and ordered me to take a gun and crew up to Ringway to see if the gun could be loaded into the new glider which we knew had been designed only to carry troops. When I got there I had to consider how this could be done. We managed to get a wooden ramp and with a good deal of pushing and heaving and a few uncomplimentary remarks from the gun crew, the gun was got up to the level of the glider's floor. As the door was on the side of the glider, the gun then had to be turned through ninety degrees to get it into the fuselage. The timber floor bowed and groaned ominously under the weight of the gun, which it had not been designed to carry. I was able to get some steel channels which were pushed under the wheels and so spread the load. The next problem was to prevent the gun from moving when the glider was in the air, something which would be disastrous, to say the least. To overcome this the aircraft designers were asked to provide strong points and shackles to which the gun could be lashed.

So far so good. But how was the gun to be towed into battle after landing? The portee was obviously too large to be carried in the glider, as was the 15 cwt truck. However I had heard rumours that the Americans had a small general purpose vehicle called a Jeep or Blitz-buggy which was small enough to be loaded into a Horsa.

But could it pull a gun?

Shortly after I returned to Stocks Cross, the first Jeep arrived from America and was delivered to Brigade H.Q.

The supply of these vehicles was an example of the Lend-Lease Act which, thrashed out between Mr Churchill and the American President, Franklin D. Roosevelt, was to have such a far reaching effect on the prosecution of the war. By now Britain had almost exhausted her gold and dollar reserves and was in effect bankrupt. This Act allowed Britain to be supplied with food and war material from the USA without payment; the supplies being *lent* or *leased* for the duration of the war. It had not been easy to persuade the hard-headed American businessmen, living in comparative ease away from the war, that giving to the Limeys, as they called the British, would eventually be of help to themselves by preventing the dictators overrunning the Western World. This was before Pearl Harbour which changed their views drastically.

The Jeep was so small that, although it was powered by a 60 horse-power four-cylinder petrol engine, it was impossible to believe it could tow a gun. It did however have a four wheel drive - something uncommon in Britain at that time.

I was instructed to try it out to see whether it could tow the gun. This it did successfully on the parade ground but I was then ordered to take it to Divisional Headquarters and demonstrate it in front of the *top brass*, by driving it over a ploughed field. I was very doubtful as to the result, although the four wheel drive should help.

With Foxley sitting beside me I drove into the field and, much to my surprise and unfeigned delight, the little vehicle bounced over the furrows at great speed with the gun cavorting behind it. The demonstration was considered to be a success and from then on the Jeep was the ubiquitous vehicle used by the Airborne Army on all its operations.

In the spring of 1942 I was told there was to be an inspection of all airborne units by the Divisional Commander. It was not to be an ordinary inspection and I was not told what my Battery was to do until the big man arrived. Each troop was then given a different task which the General and his staff officers watched with eagle eyes. I was not very happy with the result, one gun team did not even get to the correct RV. The General left with no comment beyond that a report would be sent in due course.

"What do you think the old boy is up to?" asked Reggie after the inspection. "He didn't seem so keen on *bull* as I expected."

"I don't think we put up a very good show," I replied. "We shall soon know when we get the report."

The report was long and detailed but not very complimentary. The General considered the standard of the NCOs and men was satisfactory but this could not be said of the officers and, with the pick of the army at the Division's disposal, this should not be tolerated.

I was despondent. I knew that some of my officers had their failings but I was loath to see them go. It was all very well to talk about "the pick of the Army at my disposal" but I knew from bitter experience that in practice, that just did not happen. Commanding officers were not going to let their best officers leave. If I had been in their position I would have done the same. Perhaps I wasn't a very good soldier myself. I would much rather be an airman. So, I thought again, why not be a glider pilot?

George Chatterton was at that time Commander of the Glider Pilot Regiment. He was an airman himself, having been in the RAF, and knew of my own flying experience. I arranged an interview with him and the result was that he told me I could transfer to the Glider Pilot Regiment, retaining my rank.

Back in the mess, I told Reggie what I had done. I would be sorry to leave the Battery and all the friends I had made among the officers and men. They would get a new Battery Commander, who might be a Regular Artillery Officer, and would lead them into the coming battles.

Reggie was very thoughtful: "We've been a long way together since those Barrow days. I don't think I would want to be in the Battery if you're not commanding. Do you think they would take me as a glider pilot as well?"

"There's nothing I would like better than for you to be with me. I'll see if I can pull some strings."

It took a bit of doing but Reggie's transfer was accepted and we both left the Battery and transferred to the Glider Pilot Regiment.

CHAPTER 20

For most people a change in their life comes either by chance or design. For me the change to the Glider Pilot Regiment was by design, but none the less dramatic. Although I had as many flying hours as the qualified glider pilots, I still had to go through the whole flying training programme as if I had never flown before. Wonderful, three months flying with no responsibilities, at the country's expense.

In November 1942 I was sent to the Elementary Flying Training School at an airfield near London where, amongst other advantages, there would be no difficulty in meeting Julia. Reggie had been sent to a different school in Wiltshire.

We were taught on Tiger Moths which was no problem for me as I had been flying them at Shrewton and I was sent off solo after a couple of checks. After that it was on to Magisters - a monoplane in which you could pretend you were flying a Hurricane or a Spitfire, albeit at a rather slower speed, but fun all the same.

At the same time there was instrument flying on a machine called the Link Trainer set up in a hangar. It was the forerunner of the sophisticated flight simulators used today to train airline pilots and astronauts on their hazardous missions.

In order to practise flying blind on instruments in the air, the aircraft was fitted with a canvas hood which could be pulled over the pupil's cockpit so that he could see nothing but the instruments. This was done by the instructor when they were at a safe height and the pupil then had to carry on flying the aircraft by the instruments alone. The most alarming manoeuvre was doing a spin *under the hood* and recovering from it. My stomach seemed to be going round inside me with every turn of the spin until I pulled out from it. I was thankful when the hood was raised and I could carry on flying normally.

Part of the syllabus was night flying which I had not done before. My first solo at night was an unnerving experience. The take off along the flare path was straightforward but, once airborne, I climbed into complete darkness and panic seized me as I suddenly realised there was no horizon. In darkness you have to rely on the instruments. It was no good your body and mind telling you that you were turning or climbing when the instruments said you weren't. Now you must use the experience you had gained on the Link trainer and 'under the hood' and force yourself to believe them. It was not all that easy. I climbed to 1000 feet and did a 90 degree turn to port. The airfield lights come into view and the initial panic was over. Fly on the downwind leg, they said, then another 90 degree turn across wind, line up with the runway and another turn and start your approach. It is all supposed to be made easy for you. There are coloured lights - green if you are too high, amber if you are on the correct glidepath and red if you are too low (and about to crash!). Keep in the amber by controlling your height and speed and when you reach the start of the flare path you should be ready for touch down probably with a bit of a bump or a bounce but, never mind, you are down and have completed your first night solo.

The following weeks were pure heaven: flying every day except when the weather clamped; aerobatics, low flying and cross countries; and, at the weekends, slipping over to see Julia who seemed to have no difficulty in getting passes. However all good things come to an end and I finally passed out with an *above average* in my log book.

The next move was to Glider Training School near Oxford. Flying Hotspurs was straightforward. In free flight and unloaded they were almost like a sailplane and if the weather conditions were right, could even gain height in a thermal. There was however one exhilarating exercise, known as the *dive approach*. It was the one in which Dennis had been killed and was later discontinued due to the number of fatalities. The routine was as follows. Release at 2000 feet. Put the glider into a steep dive some distance from the airfield. When it had reached maximum speed and almost at zero feet, pull out of the dive and, with the speed which had built up, fly at ground level, hopping over hedges and other obstructions, and hope that you will make the airfield before the aircraft's speed has dropped and it is about to stall. The idea behind this manoeuvre was that it would take the enemy by surprise with a silent machine suddenly appearing from behind a hedge. No doubt it might have put the fear of God in them, but sadly too many pilots failed to pull out soon enough and ended flying straight into the ground.

After eight weeks at the Glider Training School, I went on to the Heavy Glider Conversion Unit which was at Brize Norton, a station with which I was to have close connections later in my career. Here the pupils were introduced to flying the Horsa. In spite of its size it was easier to handle than the Hotspur and with enormous flaps was able to descend at a steep angle without building up too much speed. With a light wind and unloaded, one could pull off at 1000 feet over the downwind edge of the aerodrome and land plumb in the centre. This sort of landing could be disconcerting for those who were not used to it. I was told the story of a famous fighter pilot who was taken up for a flight in a Horsa, which he enjoyed immensely until they came to the landing. Then his face assumed the colour of chalk and he began to shake like a leaf. After they had come to rest the glider pilot asked him what was the matter. The fighter pilot remarked feelingly: "When I saw, through the nose of the glider, the grass coming up like that, I knew I was about to die. No aircraft I have ever flown could have pulled out from that. Why didn't someone warn me?"

The Horsa was fitted with a device which made it possible to fly in cloud or at night when you could not see the tug. Its correct title was Cable Angle Indicator but it was known colloquially and rudely as the *Angle of Dangle*. It had to be used in the *Low Tow* position when the glider was flying below the level of the tug, a position not always popular as it involved pushing the glider down through the buffetting slip-stream. If fitted correctly, it enabled the glider pilot to keep position when flying in cloud or darkness. Sadly it was not always reliable as the rubber cord connecting it to the tow rope frequently broke.

All too soon flying training came to an end and I found myself returned to the Glider Pilot Depôt on Salisbury Plain where for a short time I was the Senior Officer. As such, one of my duties was to take the defaulters parade.

The Orderly Room was in a typical wooden hut, and I sat at a somewhat rickety trestle table. The RSM, who had been posted from the Brigade of Guards, entered the hut, halted, made a right turn and facing me said in stentorian tones:

"Defaulters. Sah!"

Each time the RSM made a move he brought his foot down with an almighty bang which shook the hut, almost collapsed the table, and, as I was not expecting this, nearly caused me to fall off my unstable and collapsible chair.

The unfortunate defaulter was brought in.

"Hat off. Quick march. Left right. Left right. Halt. Right turn. Private Snodgrass Sah!" said the RSM.

The unfortunate Snodgrass was up for a minor misdemeanour. He had not blancoed his equipment properly and his brasses were not polished adequately. I felt sorry for Snodgrass who I knew was a good pilot, and inflicted a penalty which I hoped would not be seen as too lenient by the RSM.

I had been told that when the Glider Pilot Regiment had been formed, Colonel Rock who was appointed to command it, considered the flying ability of the members of the Regiment to be of paramount importance. His Second-in-Command at the time, Major Chatterton, took a slightly different view. Whilst agreeing that he wanted the men to be exceptional airmen, he also wanted them to be 'total soldiers' with exemplary discipline, drill and turnout. To this end, when he later took command of the Regiment, he appointed two Regimental Sergeant-Majors who had been seconded from the Brigade of Guards. One of whom I had already met at the defaulters parade. They were first-class but, as a result, it was inevitable that some recruits, who might have made excellent pilots, were sent back to their units as unsuitable because they did not measure up to the standard of turnout and discipline required. This caused some resentment amongst the Squadron Commanders who were losing some of their best pilots but, by degrees, the necessary standards were achieved.

The flying schools were by now turning out pilots in larger numbers and they were arriving at the Depôt. I was asked to form a Squadron. The original glider pilots who formed the 1st Battalion were serving in North Africa and it was now intended to form a second battalion of which my squadron would be a part. There was some controversy over whether glider pilots were to be in battalions or wings (like the RAF). The outcome was that the 1st Battalion became No 2 Wing and we would now be in No 1 Wing which was to be commanded by Lt Colonel Iain Murray. Why we should be No 1 and the originals No 2 was not clear.

Reggie had returned from his flying training and was now at the Depôt with me. We were discussing the new squadron when he turned to me and said:

"There were some jolly good chaps on my flying course. Do you think we could use them as a nucleus of our Squadron?"

"Not a bad idea. Let's see if we can arrange it," I replied.

As a result "B" Squadron in No.1 Wing was formed. Reggie was my Second-in-Command and it had two Flights. One was commanded by Captain Douglas Cameron, a cheerful Scot from the Lowlands, and the other by Captain Hamish Macpherson, an Ulsterman.

Douglas had two officers - Paddy O'Leary, a Southern Irishman who had been in the Irish Guards in that abortive campaign in central Norway, and had been evacuated from Harstad back to the UK; and James Broxton another Scot who came from Glasgow.

Hamish had in his flight a rather wild Scotsman - Rory Macdonald - a wonderful character who always wore a kilt, drank vast quantities of beer and was crewed up with a Sergeant *Spud* Simmonds, from whom he was inseparable.

The other ranks, who were all sergeants or staff-sergeants were a grand lot, full of initiative and humour. I felt I was very lucky to have such a bunch of men who I knew I could mould into an efficient and happy unit.

Life at the Depôt, however, was not very pleasant and as soon as possible I arranged for my squadron to be moved to an airfield in the New Forest where the crews of the tugs, who were to tow us, were stationed. This was an important move which helped to build up a firm relationship between the tug crews and the glider pilots.

It was unfortunate that there was still much inter-service rivalry. The RAF called the Army types *pongoes* and the Army referred to the RAF, derogatively, as the *Brylcream Boys*. This had to go. The lives of the tug crews and the glider pilots were intertwined. If the glider kept too high on take off the tug would never get off the ground and, if too low, the tug might well stall and crash. The glider pilot, for his part, had to trust the tug to tow him safely through cloud and enemy flak until they separated over the landing zone. There was no room for inter-service rivalry, only co-operation.

At Stoney Cross, which was the name of the airfield that "B" Squadron moved to, the crewing up of tug and glider pilots came into being and continued throughout all their training and operations. The Tug pilots were from 296 and 297 Squadrons of the RAF and it was a happy marriage. Airforce and Glider pilots struck up many lasting friendships.

We were shortly joined by another two flights to make "B" Squadron up to operational strength. One of these was commanded by Captain Julian Westlake who was a tall, very smart and serious officer, also in the T.A., who had been studying geology at Cambridge. The other was commanded by Captain Jeremy Jackson, a cheerful, outgoing type who had been brought up in Canada and was an all-round sportsman. One of his officers, Howard Hemingway, was later to fall in love with one of the WAAF Officers on the station.

Julia was now an Intelligence Officer (I.O.) and somehow had managed to arrange a posting to Stoney Cross where there were two other administrative WAAF Officers. It was agreed by the squadron that Julia was the Major's girl but the others were open to advances.

As well as the Officers, all the pilots in the squadron were great individualists with considerable initiative and, as such, not always easy to control. I took the view that if they did not blatantly overstep the rules and were smart and disciplined on parade, I would overlook any minor misdemeanours.

Although all glider pilots were to be trained as 'total soldiers', and were taught to operate all the weapons and equipment they might be called upon to carry, I insisted that they must also perfect their flying ability. After all, what was the use of them being highly trained as soldiers if they did not get their glider down safely with its contents? The RAF Station Commander, Group Captain Max Attercliffe, took the same view and, as a result, my Squadron had no shortage of flying training.

There were two classes of glider pilots. The First Pilot who had completed the full flying course, was a staff-sergeant and wore the Army flying badge -The Lion with Blue Wings. The second pilot, who had done a shortened course, was a sergeant and wore a smaller type of wing. He could land the glider in an emergency supposing the first pilot became a casualty, which happened on more than one occasion, but he was also able to take turns at the controls on a long tow which could be a very exhausting task with a loaded glider in rough weather.

We had our personal weapons - rifles and sten guns for the NCOs and automatic pistols for the officers - but the flights which in some cases might have to fight as an infantry platoon were issued with bren guns, 2" mortars, Piats (an anti-tank weapon) and Thompson sub-machine guns, but we had no transport apart from my personal P.U. truck.

Since Dunkirk, the factories had been frantically making up the loss of guns, tanks and aircraft but little priority was being given to transport. Shortly after we arrived at Stoney Cross I was informed that we were to have two civilian impressed vehicles. I detailed Paddy and Sergeant Trog, who was my M.T. sergeant, to go to Southampton to collect them. When they arrived at Southampton, they were somewhat surprised to find the *Requisitioned Civilian Vehicle Depot* was a dilapidated garage with about half a dozen vehicles. They were told that they were to collect two very ancient 1914 Albion furniture vans. Today those vehicles would command a premium in the vintage market, with their vertical steering columns having the steering wheel and the throttle control on top, and the heavy gear change lever and brake on the right of the driver. Having signed for them, they brought them back to Stoney Cross. Top speed was 20 m.p.h. What we were to use them for officially was not clear but our Sergeant-Major, Willy Watson, soon found a use for them.

The local pub, the *Sir Walter Tyrell,* was a little distance from the camp and Willy quickly organised outings in the Black Marias, as they were called, to the pub on Saturday nights. Very popular and quite illegal, I knew of it but turned a blind eye.

Reggie and I were discussing the crewing up of the Squadron, the first pilot with the second pilot and then with the tug crews.

"I think you'd better have a first pilot as your second dicky," said Reg. "You may have too much on your mind when the operation gets under way."

"It seems a shame to take a first pilot who would make up a crew. But maybe you're right. Who do you suggest?" I asked.

"I've just the man in mind," replied Reg immediately. "Arthur Singleton - he's an excellent N.C.O. with lots of initiative and common sense. He'll look after you well."

So I sent for Arthur and asked him if he would like to crew up with me.

"You realise that this would mean you would not be in charge of your own glider on the operation?"

Arthur thought for a minute and then said. "Yes Sir, I would be honoured."

And so it was, and a bond of friendship was forged between us that saw us through many difficulties and dangers.

Rumours of the very first glider operation which had taken place in November of the previous year had filtered through. Some said two gliders had been sent on an operation to Norway to destroy a secret installation, but both gliders had been lost and the Glider Pilots and the Royal Engineers who were being carried had been killed. It was not a very encouraging outcome.

It was August 1943 and the war seemed to have receded and was being fought in far off places. We read in the papers of the fighting in North Africa and knew that Glider Pilots were there. We heard privately, as it was still secret, of the ferrying of Horsas to Africa across the Bay of Biscay, at the mercy of the German Condors waiting to pounce on their unwary victims. One glider had been shot down and one of the pilots survived for two days on a raft before being picked up. On his return he volunteered for another flight and was shot down a second time. This time it was eleven days before he was rescued, by which time he was all but dead. We were all proud of his courage but privately hoped we would not be put to such a test.

News was now coming through of the invasion of Sicily the previous month. It was reported that many of the gliders had been cast off too far from the shore and landed in the sea, Colonel Chatterton amongst them. Then there was the part played by the Regiment in capturing the vital bridge leading to Syracuse. There had been many casualties and General Hopkinson, commanding the Division had later been killed in Italy.

Here at Stoney Cross it all seemed so remote.

We knew that the next stage of the war must be the invasion of Europe and that the airborne divisions would be in the forefront. The 1st Airborne Division was in Africa and later in Italy but now a second division was being formed, the 6th Airborne. It was called the 6th in order to confuse the enemy into thinking we had six airborne divisions when we had only two. General Gale, a charismatic character and one who was a strong supporter of Airborne operations, commanded the 6th while 1st Airborne was now commanded by General Urquhart, a quiet and unassuming Scot.

In order to train the Air Landing Brigades for the coming battles, numerous exercises with paratroops and gliders were carried out. Whoever produced the codenames for them must have had a sense of humour - Flap, Travesty, Chaos - to name a few.

Flap was one of the first and took place in October 1943. I was instructed to produce six crews. The gliders were to carry a company of the Royal Ulster Rifles and land them in a field near Cheltenham. This was the first exercise to be carried out where the gliders landed away from an aerodrome which meant, in order to retrieve them, the gliders would have to be dismantled and returned by road.

I decided I would fly one of the gliders myself as the Brigadier commanding the 1st Air Landing Brigade wanted to fly on the exercise as well. He was a tall man, later to become Governor of the Bank of England and who, as a pilot, already wore Army Wings. He wished to fly in the second pilot's seat, so Arthur had to stay in the back.

The weather was appalling with low mist and cloud and, although normally flying would have been cancelled, it was decided the exercise must go ahead. Because of the cloud, it was difficult to map-read, and the navigators of the tugs had to rely on DR (Dead Reckoning). Two gliders landed safely but one of the combinations could not find the field and returned to base. Another glider released in cloud and by good luck landed a few hundred yards from the objective. No.5 overshot and landed in the next field, narrowly missing a quarry.

I had to fly my glider the whole way as it was too rough to let the Brigadier take over and at times the tug disappeared into cloud. Eventually we arrived over the field and I pulled off and made a normal approach. I had decided that as it was a small field and the glider was fully loaded I would apply the brakes as soon as we touched down. This proved to be a bad decision. The glider landed perfectly at the edge of the field and ran on. It seemed to be going too fast. Little did we know at the time that the Met forecast was wrong. The wind direction was 180 degrees out and we were all landing down wind. My glider was not responding to the differential brakes, the wheels sliding on the wet grass. It was impossible to steer. I saw, to my horror, the one and only tree in the hedge rapidly approaching and shouted:

"We're going to hit that bloody tree. I can't steer the damn machine away from it. The brakes are not working."

Although we were now travelling pretty slowly we hit the oak tree squarely in front of the first pilot's seat, leaving me spreadeagled round the tree, whilst to the sound of smashing timber, the glider sailed on for a few yards. The second pilot's seat was untouched and the Brigadier stepped out unscathed. The Ulsters in the back, disobeying orders, had unstrapped themselves before the landing with the result that 25 men were projected at 10 miles an hour on to the unfortunate Company Commander, Major Napier Crookenden, at the front who found himself being used as a door mat by 25 pairs of army boots.

I was pulled from the wreckage with nothing worse than a broken ankle and my crash helmet, which all glider pilots were issued with, bent into a peculiar shape with bits of the oak tree imbedded in it. I was strapped up and taken to hospital at Cheltenham. I learned later that British Movietone News had recorded the whole incident for posterity! I have to admit that I had my leg pulled unmercifully about hitting that tree.

CHAPTER 21

My stay in hospital was not unpleasant. The nurses were attractive, and attentive to my every need. I was visited by Julia and various of the senior officers who had watched the exercise and the Brigadier who commiserated with me and remarked:

"We would have been alright if that damned tree hadn't suddenly grown up in front of us!"

After a few days I left the hospital and was sent on sick leave which I spent at home. Julia was able to get some leave and came up to Cheshire where she met my parents for the first time. They liked her and she liked them.

I could only hobble on my plaster and could not drive so Julia had to take me round in her car. We went to the meet of the local Foxhounds. Julia said it looked like good hunting country with big open fields, hedges, jumpable ditches and many good covers to hold the foxes. The field with the huntsmen in their pink coats and the hounds streaming across the fields made a romantic picture.

As we drove back in the car I was thinking about Julia. I saw her riding to hounds on a mare which would jump anything. Always up in front. Popular with the Hunt. Perhaps one day she would be Lady Patronness. Then at the Hunt Ball in a low cut dress. All the young men crowding round her and then I would take her in my arms and dance away in an old fashioned waltz - all day dreams.

I turned to her. "Would you like to live here? I think it would be better than Scotland and perhaps we could have a farm that we could work together, and you could have some horses."

"Yes that would be wonderful. I should like it very much and perhaps we could do some breeding."

I wasn't sure if she meant horses or babies! But it sounded hopeful. "I couldn't afford it at first and would have to go back to work but I could always work on the farm in the evenings and at weekends, and I still hope you will marry me."

"We must get this war over first," she replied again.

Leave was soon over and I was able to walk with a stick. I went back to the Squadron.

Arthur greeted me. "The oak tree is none the worse, Sir, except for some bits of glider sticking in the bark," he said with a smile.

Reggie reported training had been going well and flying hours and number of landings were going up.

Shortly after my return, night flying was taking place. There was a half moon and it was intended to carry out landings without the use of the flare path. After all there wouldn't be many landing aids on night operations in enemy territory. One of the gliders was being flown by Rory Macdonald with Spud as his second pilot.

I was in Flying Control watching the exercise and talking to the FCO (Flying Control Officer) Harry Summerton. One of the duties of the FCO was to control the landing and take off of aircraft on the airfield. At first they had been rather nonplussed when it came to gliders. It was no good shining a Red Aldis lamp at them if they were in free flight, telling them not to land. They could hardly go round again.

On this particular night the weather was rather dicey. There was some cloud about which the Met had not forecast and suddenly it started to snow. I realised that Rory was on the circuit and it was now pitch dark. He would never be able to land safely without any lights. I shouted to Harry to turn the Flare Path lights on.

"I'm not allowed to. There's an air raid warning on," said Harry.

"To hell with that. Rory is bound to crash," I said and at the same time turned the switch which put on the lights.

It was too late. We saw the glider disappearing over some trees at the far side of the aerodrome.

Arthur was outside the control room in one of the Black Marias. I got in and he drove as rapidly as the old furniture van would go to where I felt Rory must have come down. We found the glider, rather battered but in one piece, lying across the road. Rory and Spud were unhurt but they had been very lucky to land on the road and not in the trees.

Rory turned to me and said rather pointedly, "I thought you said you were laying on a moon for this exercise, Sir. Someone must have turned it out. I couldn't see a bloody thing."

We called at the Walter Tyrell where Rory had more than one large whisky although Spud still had his usual four pints. I returned to the Mess where I saw Reggie and discussed the crash. Rory had certainly done a good job getting down on the road and it could well have been much worse.

Not long after this incident we received orders to leave Stoney Cross. It had been a happy station and we were sorry to have to leave. However "B" Squadron with it's RAF tug crews were now to move to their operational station which was Brize Norton in Oxfordshire.

For the move, although Brize was only some 70 miles away, someone suggested that as much as possible of the stores and equipment should be transported by glider. The Horsas were loaded, and in some cases overloaded, with all the paraphernalia which makes up an Air Force Station in wartime, and the move was to be carried out as if it were a mass landing exercise.

I was still not flying on account of my ankle, so Arthur drove me over to the new station in one of the new 15 cwt trucks we had just received, to await the arrival of the gliders. They soon appeared over the horizon, some eighty in all. A very impressive sight as they cast off and commenced to land, like a flock of geese alighting on a lake. All went well until one glider overshot and landed on the roof of a hanger on the edge of the aerodrome. No one was hurt but it did no good to the hanger and the glider was a write-off with its contents scattered all over the hanger.

The pilot, Howard Hemingway, was unhurt but I tore him off a strip, telling him that he had not made a very good impression on the new Station, and he would have to improve his flying in the future.

Brize was a peacetime RAF Station with permanent buildings. The pilots were housed in greater comfort and with an excellent sergeants' mess. The officers were in what would have been the married quarters and I was in the Headquarters building which was an imposing edifice. The bedrooms were luxurious with bathrooms just down the corridor. There was a palatial Officers' Mess downstairs with a bar and lounges with easy chairs and the morning's papers. All very different from the spartan accommodation we had been used to.

Flying commenced almost immediately. The Station Commander, who had moved with us, continued to insist that the glider pilots must get the maximum amount of flying training and the tug pilots co-operated to the full.

There were two Tiger Moths on the station. As I was now flying again, I obtained permission to use them for visiting the other squadrons and our Regimental Headquarters which was at Harwell. Later the Station Commander passed me out to fly the twin-engined Oxford aircraft which was used for communications. This gave me great satisfaction to be able to fly a twin.

One day Julia asked me if she could have a flight in a Tiger. Of course it was against the rules to take a WAAF joy-riding but I took a chance and next day arranged for a flight.

Julia was rigged out, a bit bulky in a flying suit with parachute and goggles, but as beautiful as ever, and got into the rear seat. I took off, climbed to 2000 feet and made sure we were out of sight of the aerodrome. I asked Julia if she would like to do some aerobatics and did some steep turns and then shouted through the intercom: "Make sure your straps are tight. We are going to do a loop." After that I did a slow roll, a roll off the top, and some stall turns and landed back at the aerodrome.

"How did you like it?" I asked.

"It was wonderful," she replied, her face pink with elation. "It's as exciting as hunting. Do take me up again."

Somehow the war still seemed to be far away. Everyone knew that we were training for the 'Big One' - the invasion of Europe - which must come soon. Then there would be plenty of excitement and danger, but meanwhile flying gliders was not as dangerous as some would make out. That is except at night.

Flying at night in a glider could cause some apprehension and the adrenalin to flow, as Rory had found out. Night flying took place during the full moon or half moon periods, when it was just possible to see the ground and the ghostly outline of the tug with its dim wingtip lights. When these were extinguished the glow from the engine exhausts was all the glider pilot could see to keep in station behind the tug.

The tow rope, like an umbilical cord supplying his life blood, was all he had to get him to his destination safely. If it broke he was on his own, and forced to land in the dim landscape with trees and obstacles no longer obvious as in daytime.

One night the squadron was on a night flying cross-country exercise. It was a half moon period and the Met had forecast a clear night. But the Met's forecast was so often not quite right.

The tugs and gliders all took off safely and I went up to Flying Control waiting for their return. They came in one by one and made good landings in the moonlight, but one was missing. I waited with growing apprehension. I had a feeling that something was wrong. What had happened? The tug pilot of the missing glider landed and reported that he had run into cloud and his glider had released.

Suddenly the telephone rang. A glider had been seen to crash near the town of Faringdon about 6 miles away.

I got into a 15 cwt truck, and taking Julian Westlake with me, drove as fast as I could to the map reference I had been given. Arriving, I found the local Home Guard in charge and they directed me to a large haystack in the corner of a field. There was no sign of the glider which was completely embedded within it.

The Home Guard Commander told us that they had pulled both pilots out but they had been killed instantly by the impact.

Julian, whose pilots they were, was very quiet as we returned to Brize.

"The war seems to have arrived on our doorstep, even if it was only training," he remarked gloomily.

It was the Squadron's first casualties. I would have to write to their next of kin as I had done for poor Dennis. It would not be the last time. I hated composing those letters. They always seemed so formal and inadequate.

Training continued and although the date of the invasion was still a secret it was obvious that it could not be far away. At the beginning of May a most ambitious exercise was mounted. It was intended to land 90 gliders by night on an aerodrome without any landing aids or lights.

Netheravon was selected as it was a grass airfield with no concrete runways and had the advantage that the gliders could be towed off after the exercise.

Arthur and I were flying and Colonel Chatterton, who had commanded the Regiment since Colonel Rock had been killed, decided to come with us. He did not occupy the second pilot's seat but sat on an empty beer crate in the doorway between the two pilots. It was a moonlit night and clear. As there were to be no landing lights on the ground the briefing had been for all gliders to land from East to West. The flight was without incident until we approached the airfield. Looking down we saw that some one had put out an illuminated landing Tee which we had not expected, but to our consternation we saw that it had been put out West to East, indicating the opposite direction to which we had been briefed to land. Someone had blundered.

The Colonel was livid. He jumped up and down in the glider shouting that all 90 gliders would collide and the airborne invasion would be a failure and, at the same time, telling me at the top of his voice what I should do. I had already made up my mind what to do and turning to the Colonel said calmly, "You know very well Sir, that as Captain of Aircraft, it is my duty to get the aircraft down safely and that is what I intend to do. Please will you keep quiet."

This seemed to have a calming effect on the Colonel and picking what was an unoccupied corner of the airfield we landed safely.

About half of the glider pilots carried out their orders and landed as briefed but the other half, relying on the instructions from the ground landed in the opposite direction. Although gliders had landed in all directions, only a small proportion of them suffered more than superficial damage and no one was hurt. It was a good omen for the operations to come and was considered by the senior officers watching it, to be a success.

Shortly after this exercise I was called to a conference at Divisional HQ. My P.U. was temporarily off the road and all the rest of our new transport was in use but a brand new water truck had just been issued to us. Why a Glider Pilot Squadron should need a water truck was not clear but the 'Q' Department did curious things and it was better not to ask why but to accept what was given. Arthur was going to drive me and decided that we should use the water truck and drove me in it to the conference.

We arrived to find a number of very smart Humber Staff Cars parked, driven by soldiers or women of the ATS (Auxiliary Territorial Service), none above the rank of lance-corporal. Arthur stopped the water truck some distance from the other vehicles, told me to stay put, got out, moved round to the passenger door which he opened for me, standing rigidly to attention, and gave me a very smart salute. I was somewhat mystified by this exemplary treatment but returned the salute and went into the building.

Arthur stayed by the vehicle which was being eyed by the other drivers and the military police with considerable interest. Presently one of the drivers came over and said to Arthur: "We are wondering why you have driven your officer in a water truck and why is he being driven by a staff-sergeant?"

"Ah!" said Arthur, looking round to see if anyone else was listening. "My Major is a very important person on a very secret mission. Our Unit only has Officers and staff-sergeants and we don't drive about in staff cars which would attract attention. So keep it quiet."

This seemed to satisfy the driver who returned to his mates who all gathered round him. He was obviously not "keeping it quiet".

Shortly afterwards I emerged from the building talking to General Gale, the 6th Airborne Division Commander. It couldn't have been better for Arthur who drove up after we had finished talking, gave me another very smart salute and opened the door for me. He then moved round to the driver's side and giving the assembled drivers a knowing wink, as much as to say "What did I tell you?", got into the truck.

We drove off and I remarked, "What was all that charade about, Staff?"

Arthur smiled and explained that it had been a bit of a leg pull on his part and laughing we drove back to Brize.

When I got back to my office I found a message from Wing Headquarters instructing me to provide three of my best crews for a very special operation. I was told they would have to release their gliders at 6000 feet and land by moonlight in a small field. As it had to be a surprise attack on an objective which had not yet been disclosed, no landing aids would be provided. I selected six staff sergeants whom I considered from their flying records to be the best pilots. Each glider would have two first pilots. One would be designated as captain of aircraft but they would work as a team. Training began immediately but it was soon found that the Albermarle tug was not sufficiently powerful to tow a fully laden glider to 6000 feet in the time allowed. Regretfully, I had to transfer my crews to another squadron at Tarrant Rushton, an airfield which had Halifax tugs with boosted engines capable of towing the massive tank-carrying Hamilcar glider. Here they were joined by three other crews and became known as the *deadstick* boys. They trained night after night until they were so proficient that they were able to land all six gliders on an area marked out on the aerodrome to simulate the two fields in which they would eventually have to land. A seventh crew was also trained in case of any casualties before the operation but they were not used.

A little later Colonel Chatterton flew into Brize and took me into the office. Everyone else was told to go outside. When he was sure no one was listening he said: "I have been asked to supply three glider crews for another special operation. It will be very hazardous. I have picked your Squadron for it. I think you should call for volunteers but I cannot spare any officers to go on it. Also it is very secret and whoever is on it must keep their mouths shut."

I sent for the Sergeant-Major and told him to get the pilots on parade. The Colonel then explained that he wanted three crews to volunteer for what was likely to be a very hazardous mission.

Somewhat to his surprise almost all the pilots stepped forward. They must have forgotten the old Service maxim - Never Volunteer! This left me with a problem. I now had to select another three crews. This I did, once again from those I considered had the best flying ability.

The pilots who had been selected were told their gliders would be released near the objective which was a heavy gun emplacement and which would be strongly defended. They would have to land on top of the objective, so that the troops they carried could blast their way in and destroy the guns. It would be, in many ways, similar to the operation the Germans carried out at Eben Emael at the commencement of the war in 1940.

The gliders would be fitted with REBECCA, an instrument which would respond to EUREKA, a radio beacon set up on the ground by the *pathfinders* - the paratroops who would land shortly before them. The signals from EUREKA, picked up by REBECCA, should then lead the pilot to his objective. I had tried this equipment myself on the aerodrome and it worked very well. The gliders would also have arrester parachutes which could be streamed just before landing to reduce the landing run. Everyone was sworn to secrecy and their flying training was stepped up using the tug crews they were crewed up with, and who would tow them on the operation.

At the end of May the objective was disclosed but not its location. It was a battery of heavy guns commanding the landing beaches, whose location again was not disclosed. The guns must be destroyed before the seaborne landings could take place. The attack was to be carried out by one of the parachute battalions, some of whose assault troops would be carried in the gliders. The battalion had produced a full size model of the gun battery and its environs on fortyfive acres of good agricultural land near Newbury. In spite of financial compensation, the farmers who were dispossessed were somewhat annoyed. I arranged for the glider pilots to be sent over to the model to familiarise themselves with what they and the troops they were carrying would have to do. I drove over one day to see how they were getting on and was nearly shot by a sentry guarding the site. Security was extremely tight!

A few days later Colonel Murray who commanded No 1 Wing of the Glider Pilot Regiment came over to see me. He too sent everyone out of the office.

"So, at last we know where it will be," he said, unfolding a map.

We both looked at the map which was of the coast of Normandy near the town of Caen, and the Colonel said suddenly, "I hope to God they've moved the Bayeux Tapestry to a place of safety." He drummed his fingers on the table as though he was going to say something else and then continued quickly.

"It's come at last, Thomas. The second front is about to start. The date is the 5th of June."

He then started to give me the plan.

"All the squadrons of both Wings will take part but one half of each squadron will go on the first day carrying the 6th Airborne. The other half will carry the 1st Airborne Division which, as you know, is now back in this country, to reinforce the bridgehead within the following fortyeight hours. I want you to stay with the second half of your squadron and send your second-in-command on the first day."

"Very well Sir," I replied, "I will organise the flights at once. I'm sorry you aren't sending me on the first lift but I suppose it won't be long before the second lift is called for."

I admit I was disappointed, especially when I heard later that the Major in charge of "A" Squadron was going on the first lift. "A" were stationed at Harwell which also housed Wing Headquarters so I often felt they got special treatment.

Everyone now had to be briefed after which the camp was sealed. No one was allowed out. Armed guards were on the gates and patrolling the perimeter. Everyone knew the need for secrecy. Our lives would depend on it. The date had still not been revealed except to me and the Station Commander.

I called Reggie in and explained the plan. 17 crews under Captain Hamish Macpherson would land behind the beaches in the early hours of D Day. It's code name was *Tonga*. The remainder of the two flights which would be under Reggie's command, code name *Mallard*, would land later on D Day. They would include Captain Julian Westlake's flight.

I spent the next 48 hours dashing round the various Headquarters, obtaining last minute instructions and briefing my pilots. Towards the end, Foxley who was driving me said:

"You really must get some sleep Sir. You look all in."

"No. I must give the lads all the *gen* they need. I can't leave anything to chance," I replied.

Then the news came: "D Day postponed 24 hours". It was a terribly difficult decision for the Supreme Allied Commander to make, depending as it did so much on the fickle forecasts of the weathermen.

On the 5th of June there was no postponement. D-Day was to be the 6th of June.

The first gliders to take off from Brize would be the 17 on *Tonga* at twenty past one on the early morning of the 6th of June.

I went down to the tow path and spoke to Hamish. "Sorry about the anti-landing poles that we hear Rommel has put up. The sappers will do their best to blow them down."

"Don't worry we'll knock them down," said Hamish confidently.

"How are your lads?"

"All fine and raring to go."

It was pretty dark. The half moon was only just rising. The engines of the tugs were running. The first one taxied on to the runway and the airmen ran to connect the tow rope between tug and glider. The Towmaster, having looked at Hamish who gave the *thumbs up*, waved his baton to signal to the tug to take up the slack of the tow rope. As soon as the glider started to move he waved both batons. The tug pilot opened his throttles and the combination started to move down the runway with ever increasing speed. The glider took off first and the pilot held it down until the tug was airborne when they both climbed away as the second tug and glider came on to the runway. They took off at 1 minute intervals. I turned to Reggie who was flying later in the day.

"Thank goodness they've all got off safely. The second front really has started. Let's hope it will see the end of this rotten war. Now let's go and see how the Battery boys are getting on."

The three gliders on the battery mission were due to take off at 0230 hrs, one hour and ten minutes after the others. Three days before there had been a drama over these gliders. On account of it being a very special operation we had been promised new gliders, fitted with REBECCA and arrester parachutes. The gliders duly arrived but there were SIX - three with REBECCAS and the other three with parachutes! Someone had blundered yet again. Panic all round. I was furious and played hell with the engineering department who had made such a cock-up.

Replacement gliders had to be found and fitted with the special equipment, but time was short. They arrived on the afternoon before the take off and there was no time or tugs available, to flight-test them. The most serious thing was that whilst two of them were obviously new gliders, the third was far from new. I explained the situation to the pilots and rather than allocate them, I decided that the only fair thing was to draw lots for them. Arnold Bradshaw drew the old glider with results which were to become apparent later.

As Reggie was not due to take off until the early evening, he and I went down to the Mess for breakfast. On the way we met Julia. She was very quiet and seemed preoccupied with something. I did not question her as my mind was also occupied with the coming operation. As soon as I had finished breakfast, I went back to the runway to check that all was well for Mallard.

The Horsa glider had wheels which could be jettisoned in flight by the pilot if he wished. We had been told that in the event of ditching in the sea with the wheels still in place, the glider would overturn on hitting the water. Unfortunately the release mechanism was not always very secure and the wheels had been known to release themselves prematurely. The Engineer Officer had decided that the catch on the release mechanism should be wired up so that it could not be activated accidentally. This meant the pilot would not be able to jettison the wheels if the need should arise. I had only just been told of this decision and after a heated discussion with the engineer, the wires were removed and I hoped that the catches would survive the take off. If the wheels came off afterwards it would not matter very much as the glider could land on its skid without its wheels quite safely.

As the time for *Mallard* approached, I was on the tow path talking to the pilots. I went up to Reggie who had checked his glider and was about to get aboard.

"Best of luck. Hope you miss all the anti-landing poles. We'll come and get you out of trouble as soon as the 1st Division gets the word to go."

Little did I know at the time how long this would be.

At two minutes to seven the first glider started to take off followed by the others at one minute intervals. All went well until the twentyfifth glider was just about to lift off when the one thing I had prayed would not occur, happened. One of the wheels of the glider came off, bounced, smashed into the wing, causing the glider to crash on the end of the runway. The tug pilot, realising what was happening released the tow rope and took off safely but the runway was blocked until the wreckage of the glider could be removed.

I foresaw the whole of the operation being a fiasco with half the gliders from my station failing to arrive. I was to blame over those blasted catches. However by the superhuman efforts of the ground crews the runway was cleared and the rest of the gliders were got away without further incident and by cutting corners on the flight plan the tugs got them into position by the time they were to cross the Channel. The pilot of the crashed glider was badly injured and was taken to hospital but thankfully survived. I felt I was justified in ordering the locking wires to be removed for the sake of my pilots, but for future operations the catches were modified so this accident could not happen again.

In the Operations Room, reports by the tug pilots who had been on the night operation were coming in. *Tonga* had been a success although one tug had been shot down after its glider had cast off but the crew had escaped. On the Battery operation two gliders had been released over the target area but the third - the ropey one - had force-landed before crossing the Channel. It was not until some time later that Staff Sgt. Arnold Bradshaw reported to me.

He came into my office saluted and I told him to sit down.

"Now tell me what happened, Staff," I said.

Arnold started his story: "As soon as I commenced my takeoff, I knew something was wrong with the glider. It wouldn't lift off the runway. The tug pilot shouted to me over the intercom that a hedge was coming up and he would have to release but at that moment I managed to get the glider into the air and the hedge passed a bit too close for comfort just below. The port wing of the glider started to drop and I had to apply full rudder and aileron just to fly straight and level. I realised I would now have to fly the whole way to the target with a glider I could not fully control and which was agony to fly with my whole weight on the rudder bar. It was obvious that the glider had been badly rigged.

"Next the intercom failed, as it so often does Sir, and I couldn't tell the tug pilot of my predicament. Even so we might have reached the target with my co-pilot taking some of the weight off the rudder, but some clouds appeared. I was unable to tell the tug pilot that I couldn't go into the low tow position where the blind flying instrument would be effective, and I couldn't ask him to avoid the cloud which we then entered. There was no way Sir, with that badly rigged glider that I could keep station with the tug who didn't know what was happening behind him. Finally the tow rope parted and lashed back across the glider. You can imagine my feelings Sir. I was devastated."

"However the glider could still fly although the air speed indicator wasn't functioning. By good luck my co-pilot saw the lights of an aerodrome below and I was able to make a safe landing but Sir, it was a rotten way to end, not getting to the target at all."

"When daylight came, I inspected the glider and saw how the tow rope had coiled back, removed the airspeed indicator and had cut into the wings. Luckily it missed the elevator or I wouldn't be here."

It was a great shame. Arnold was one of my best pilots. When he had finished I got up and said: "Staff, you did a dammed good job. You got the glider down in one piece and no one was hurt. It was not your fault that the glider was in that state. I know you are bitterly disappointed but there'll be other battles to fight."

Meanwhile the *deadstick* operation had been a resounding success. The six gliders carrying the Oxford and Buckinghamshire Light Infantry under the command of Major Howard, who were to capture the canal and river bridges, had been released at 6000 feet. From there they had to follow a predetermined flight path in darkness with the co-pilot calling out the heights and headings and the first pilot flying the machine and applying flap as required.

Three of the gliders landed in the field by the canal bridge as briefed, the leading glider placing Major Howard through the wire on to his objective. One of my pilots lost an arm through machine gun fire just after landing but otherwise casualties were relatively light. The canal bridge was captured It is now known as *Pegasus Bridge* and remains as a memorial, commemorating the first part of France to be liberated.

Of the three gliders briefed to capture the river bridge, one glider had been taken to the wrong release point by the tug. They captured this bridge and then, realising it was the wrong one, marched 17 miles to join up with the other two crews who had already taken the river bridge without loss. This bridge, about 500 yards from the canal bridge is now known as *Horsa Bridge*.

I felt that now that the D Day operations had been launched I could relax. I wondered why I had not seen Julia on the tow path along with the other Intelligence Officers and WAAFs but, for the moment, I was so tired that I went to my room and told Foxley not to wake me until reports of the operations on the ground were coming in.

CHAPTER 22

Of the three WAAF Officers at Brize, Mary and Ingrid were *Admin* while Julia was an Intelligence Officer (IO), of which there were three, the other two being Ivor and Jack. The duties of the IOs were to obtain all the relevant information for the pilots before an operation. This involved such things as navigational aids, enemy opposition which included flak and fighters, issue of maps and routes to navigators and to see that all this was passed on to the crews at the briefings. On return from the operation they had to debrief the crews and collate the reports and enter up the war diary. Occasionally an IO was sent on an operational flight to give him experience of the action. It was decided that for operation *Mallard* one IO would fly in one of the tugs. All three wanted to go and although a WAAF had never been allowed to go on an operation, Julia was excited and saw no reason why a woman should not go. However the Station Commander decreed that they should draw lots and, privately, told his Adjutant to fix it so that the WAAF did not fly. The Adjutant was not sure how he was going to do this without it being obvious. He produced three match sticks and broke the heads off two and concealed them in his hand. In spite of trying to offer one of the headless matches to Julia he was unsuccessful and to his frustration and her great excitement she drew the match which still retained its head.

They all said that, as she was a woman, she could not go. Julia thought differently.

"I've drawn the match with the head and I'm going," she said defiantly.

She knew she would be the first woman to fly on such an operation and would incur the wrath of both the Station Commander and the *Queen Bee*, Squadron Leader Millicent Muggeridge, although the latter would probably be jealous. All the women wanted to fly, they wanted to be there with the men. It was hard waiting. Julia must have decided not to mention it to me because she felt sure I would have tried to dissuade her from going. However the Squadron Leader in charge of the tug squadron realised that she was determined to fly and allocated Ron, one of his most experienced pilots, to take her. His aircraft was *F* for Fox which Julia thought very appropriate.

Kitted out with flying suit, boots, flying helmet and a parachute, she was driven down to the tow path with the crew. Although the other tug crews knew she was flying she was worried in case I or the Station Commander should see her.

However all was well and they clambered into *F* for Fox. Ron started the engines and they taxied on to the runway and the glider was hooked up. The moment for take off came and Julia would have realised that this was the point of no return.

She was sitting behind Ron and his navigator and could see the shapes of the other tugs and gliders as they approached the French coast. There, flashes of light and puffs of black smoke appeared which were anti-aircraft shells bursting around the leading aircraft. A short time later they passed over the coastline and she could see in front, gliders casting off and swooping down to the ground. Suddenly Ron said, "We're there", and the glider pilot released his tow rope. They felt the drag of the glider lessen and then Ron did a quick turn, released the now trailing tow rope, and dived to avoid the aircraft behind him. They set course for home looking forward to a meal and some drinks in the mess. As they again approached the French coast, the Ack Ack opened up and it seemed that *F* for Fox was being singled out, for shells were bursting all around it.

Suddenly there was an enormous explosion inside the aircraft and flames engulfed them. Ron was killed instantly but Julia, my poor Julia, may have known she was going to die. She had only a few more seconds to live when another shell burst in the aircraft killing the rest of the crew. *F* for Fox, now a flaming mass of metal plunged into the Channel.

News of the loss of *F* for Fox was brought back by the returning crews who knew there could be no survivors.

I was sleeping in my room when Foxley came in to tell me the tug crews had returned. I went down to my office where I heard that *F* for Fox was missing. It had been flown by Ron, a pilot I knew well. He was one of those great pilots of the Royal Australian Air Force who had come over to fly with the RAF in the fight for freedom. As I was sitting in my chair, I noticed that the flight record chart which recorded all the flights of the pilots would have to be made up with the operational flights in green. Mervyn, the squadron clerk, was in the office and I told him to get on with it and to clear up my desk which was covered with all the paperwork of the operations.

As I was leaving the office, Ingrid came up to me and, stretching her arms up, pulled me down towards her. She said softly, "Thomas, Julia was in *F* For Fox."

I was stunned. I could not believe it. She had not told me anything about it. Why had she done it? I knew how brave and headstrong she was but why throw her life away unnecessarily? Ingrid did her best to comfort me and took me back to her quarters where I wept on her shoulders and kissed her passionately, thinking for a moment that she was Julia.

After a while I recovered a little.

I went over to the Mess which was unusually quiet. The Station Commander explained how he had tried to prevent her going but his orders had not been carried out. Inconsequentially I thought that at least I wouldn't have to write to her parents, the Queen Bee would do that. And I could not face seeing them, not now, one day perhaps, but not now. I tried to remember when I had last taken her in my arms and kissed her. It was no good, nothing could bring her back.

Two days later the glider pilots from *Mallard* returned. Reggie was safe but 3 pilots had been killed and 3 were missing, a number had been wounded, but in general, it was a success. Many stories were told and many lines shot by the returning pilots. Rommel's *asparagus* had not been a problem. Some broke off easily having been weakened by the French labourers whom the Germans had coerced into installing them. The aerial photographs showed how little damage to pilots or passengers was done. Wings were broken off but, so long as the glider did not hit a pole head on, there was no problem.

One pilot came back from *Tonga* saying how he had been looking for his Headquarters when he saw what appeared to be a farmer in a grey mackintosh riding a carthorse. On asking him in halting french where they were, he found the rider was none other than his Divisional Commander, General Gale, who had commandeered the horse as his personal transport.

So D Day was over and I waited for instructions for the follow up operation with 1st Airborne. During the next few days news of the success of the whole invasion kept coming in and although several further landings behind the enemy lines were planned (*Tuxedo* and *Wastage*) they were cancelled at the last minute. A few days later *Reinforcement* was planned to assist the 82nd U.S. Airborne to control the Carentin peninsula and then *Wild Oats* to prevent enemy reinforcements reaching the south of Caen. All were prepared, briefed and then cancelled. We were not required in that promised fortyeight hours and so life continued waiting for the next one.

I was haunted by the loss of Julia. At times I could not believe that she was no longer there, with her happy smile and talking of how we would plan our future.

At other moments I had a deep hatred for the Nazis who had killed her but then I thought of the thousands of civilians who had been killed in Germany by our bombers, and those in our own cities by the enemy. It was war and wars had been fought as long as history had been written but now its pages were the present and for me personal.

At the end of the first World War, which ruined both victor and vanquished, the world, and particularly Europe was in turmoil. Russia had been taken over by the Bolsheviks. The treaty of Versailles, which had been set up between the victor nations, was intended to subjugate Germany by reducing her armed forces, removing her colonies and, by imposing such punitive reparations (which she could not possibly meet) to pay for the cost of the war which she had just lost. On the ratification of the Treaty, the League of Nations came into force. This was intended to settle differences between its members by negotiation rather than war, and the great hope was that it would make another war impossible. In this it signally failed.

Perhaps one of the causes of these failures was that in the middle of the 1920s the world economy plunged into the greatest crisis since the Industrial Revolution. Inflation in Germany reached spectacular heights. Those of us who are used to annual inflation of 3 and 4 per cent, cannot visualise what inflation of 1000 per cent or more can mean. In Germany the value of its currency was reduced daily. As a result the Government printed more and more paper money so that, it was said, workers had to take their earnings home in wheelbarrows. One story is told of a German whose insurance policy matured during the inflation. He was expecting a substantial sum but, when it arrived it was just enough to buy him one drink at his favourite cafe. It meant that in practice the value of money was reduced to zero. The resulting poverty and civil unrest was ripe for the arrival of a man who claimed he could lead Germany out of the abyss.

Many years afterwards, the historian, John Keegan, wrote that in his opinion Hitler's motive for plunging his people into war was simply *revenge*. He had been wounded and gassed in the First World War and had seen thousands of his comrades slaughtered by the Allies. The Germans may have called it the slaughter of the innocents, but Hitler repaid it a thousandfold with the extermination of innocent civilians and the destruction of regimes with which he did not agree. According to many of his followers, Hitler was considered to be something approaching a deity but his intuition, generally contrary to the views of his generals, often failed.

So this was the man we were up against. But apart from Hitler there were other milestones on the road to Armageddon. The Japanese invasion of Manchuria in 1931, the Italian invasion of Ethiopia in 1935, the German and Italian intervention in the Spanish Civil war and the German invasion of Austria in 1938, all led up to the conflagration in 1939. There had been many opportunities for the politicians to step in and stop the escalation but they vacillated and then acted too late. If the Americans and Russians had not come to our aid we ourselves might have been subject to Nazi rule and sufferred the atrocities they practiced on the Jews and others. So we must fight on, until victory is won no matter what the cost in the loss of lives, remembering that every loss is a personal tragedy for someone.

So perhaps Julia had not died in vain. I wondered if I would follow her in this War and, if so, when it would be?

Now that the success of the operation to capture the Orne bridges had been established, the question of awards to the pilots came up. As a Territorial Officer, this was something that I had not considered. I certainly don't remember hearing any lectures on the subject nor about how one should set about making a recommendation. However it did seem to me that the pilots of the bridge and the battery operation deserved some recognition for their outstanding performance. Accordingly I asked the CO of the Wing what I should do?

He replied, "It's all being dealt with by Wing H.Q. You need do nothing."

So with that I felt I could safely leave it in their hands. How wrong can one be? In October when the awards came through there were some glaring mistakes. Two of the battery pilots were awarded DFMs (Distinguished Flying Medals) but of my two pilots who got to the bridges, one received a DFM but the other nothing, whilst the reserve pilot who never flew on the operation got a DFM. Sadly he was killed at Arnhem so never knew he had received a medal. The three pilots from the other squadron were awarded DFMs but in one case it went to the second pilot and not the first pilot which was a terrible error. I was furious and told the Staff at Wing HQ, in no uncertain terms, what I thought of the mess they had made of it. They apologised but said that as the awards had been made they could not be changed in spite of reference to the highest authority. This battle with the authorities went on for a long time but later I was pleased that my pilot on the bridge, who had lost an arm, did receive his DFM but the other first pilot who should have got his, never did.

On this question of awards, a story was told to me about a Brigadier who was seriously wounded at Arnhem and was looked after for several months by a dedicated Dutch family. During this time he carefully wrote out a list of recommendations for awards which the Dutch were able to transmit to the British. Later when the Brigadier was able to escape across the river and was sent home on leave, he called at the War Office and asked what had happened about his recommendations? He was told: "We are very sorry but we could not take any action as the recommendations were not on the correct form"! I don't think I need describe the reaction of the Brigadier.

Towards the end of June and the beginning of July several more operations were planned, mainly to help the Americans. *Beneficiary* was to capture St Malo and establish a bridgehead for the occupation of Brittany. *Swordhilt* was to destroy the Morlaix viaduct to cut off Brest. *Falaise* was to assist in the breakout from the Falaise pocket, and *Handsup* to assist General Patten by cutting off Quiberon Bay and establishing a port. All were cancelled due to the speed of advance by the ground forces. Then there was a lull, as far as the Airborne Division was concerned, until the beginning of August.

In August after the British and Canadian armies had fought the Germans in the bloody battles round Caen and Falaise, 21st Army group were moving towards the Seine. Operation *Axehead* was planned to assist them but before it could be mounted they were across the river. The Americans were also driving on towards Paris. It had been agreed by the Allies that a battle in Paris must be avoided because of the horror and devastation that had been caused by frontal assaults in Warsaw and Stalingrad. The capital would therefore be encircled and forced to surrender. A large airborne operation was now planned - *Transfigure* - involving ourselves, the Poles and the Americans, in order to establish an airstrip at Rambouillet as a forward base for the advance on Paris.

For this operation my squadron was moved to Greenham Common, an airfield occupied by the U.S. Airforce. This was a great change, living on an American base with U.S. rations - scrambled eggs and pineapple for breakfast, and *cawfee* or Coke. I watched some of the Americans gambling. They were using pound notes as we would use pennies!

Transfigure was planned in great detail. Douglas's flight would be the first to land with Rory Macdonald amongst the first three. At the briefing I asked: "Any Questions?"

Rory stood up and said with a little smile, "We wouldn'a be far from Paris, Sir. Couldn'a I land ma gliders on the Champs Élysées? There'd be plenty of room and I know a nice wee café in the Avenue Montaigne. I expect it'll still be working. It had some very nice lassies as well. Without a doot I think I could persuade them to help us, Sir."

The men cheered and I said I thought it a great idea but doubted if the Americans would agree to it! However by the time the operation should have taken place, General Leclerc and the French had already reached Paris and on the 25th August the German Commander surrendered. Then on the 26th, General de Gaulle entered the city amidst tremendous rejoicing.

As was becoming rather too usual, the airborne operation was cancelled.

There had been much talk of Hitler's 'Secret Weapon' with which he was going to deal a devastating blow to the Allies. I wondered if this might be something to do with an atomic bomb. When I was up at Oxford in 1930 I knew of the theoretical possibility of atomic fission which could cause an explosion of devastating power, but it had been considered that the practical achievement of this in the foreseeable future was remote.

Many years later information was released as to what had actually happened about this during the war years. Werner Heisenberg, an eminent German physicist, knew of the research that was being carried out in Germany with the object of making an atomic bomb. He was Jewish but, in spite of the danger, he decided to remain in Germany in order to use his influence as a scientist, clandestinely, to hinder the research, in the interest of the Allies.

It has been recorded that the German nuclear reactor was first active in the autumn of 1942. The American reactor, designed by Enrico Fermi, first went active on the 2nd December 1942 in Chicago, so we have to accept that at that time the Germans were ahead. That they did no proceed as fast as the Americans is partly due to Heisenberg, to whom we should be eternally grateful, but it was also true that Hitler was not enthusiastic about a weapon he did not understand, and about which Heisenberg was careful not to enlighten him except to explain the difficulties in constructing it.

Although Heisenberg was successful in slowing down work on the bomb, the German Post Office Department was also working on a weapon, not an explosive bomb, but one which would deposit radioactive substances over a wide area. Targeted at the big cities of the USA this would have killed thousands of people and caused long term devastation. That such a weapon was not deployed was one of timing. Hitler did not want to be the first to use it but was prepared to let the Japanese have it.

After the war it was reported that the German submarine U 234 was at sea in May 1945 when the war in Europe ended. She surrendered at New Hampshire USA where it was discovered that she was carrying 550kg of enriched uranium which was intended for delivery to the Japanese. This would have been lethal if spread over cities such as New York or Chicago. It has been said that the knowledge of this cargo persuaded President Truman to drop the atomic bomb on Japan.

However, the atomic bomb, which the enemy had not been able to produce, and the radiation bomb, were not Hitler's only secret weapons. In the late 1930s in Germany, Dr Gerhardt Schrader had been carrying out research on possible new insecticides (DDT). During the course of his work he stumbled on a substance which was extremely toxic. He had produced the first nerve gas, *tabun* and later another substance, *sarin*, which was ten times more dangerous.

This was taken up by the Wehrmacht as an offensive weapon and research was stepped up, including lethal tests on some of the unfortunate inmates of the concentration camps. The enemy began to accumulate vast stocks of both tabun and sarin, enough, if used, to alter the outcome of the war. When Germany's position became desperate in 1944 the most fanatical Nazi leaders urged that the gas should be used. Hitler, having been gassed himself in the First World War, had an aversion to using this weapon. His Army Commanders also advised against it although they were under the mistaken impression that we had large stocks of nerve gas which we would use in retaliation. In fact we had none, and it may well have altered the outcome of the war if it had been sprayed on the beaches during the invasion on D Day. Thankfully it was not used.

All this is history of which I knew nothing at the time. The secret weapon that was used turned out to be an unmanned, automatically guided aircraft known as the V1 or 'Doodle Bug' or more colloquially as the 'buzz bomb' due to the strident note of the exhaust from its engine.

The V1 was at first difficult to counter as it was too fast for our fighters. Although anti-aircraft fire might bring it down, these guns were located round the towns so that if they did score a hit but failed to destroy the aircraft in the air, the missile would then fall on the town and explode, causing the damage it was designed to do. Throughout July and early August, London and other cities bore the brunt of these attacks.

As a result it was decided to mount an operation, code name *Boxer*, for the Airborne Division to capture Boulogne and attack the sites from which the flying bombs were being launched. As it turned out, by the time the operation was to take place on the 17th August, our counter measures, including redeploying the ack ack guns further from the targets, the balloon barrages and the advent of a faster fighter, meant that the threat of the V1 had been largely overcome, and *Boxer* was added to the list of cancelled operations.

As things now seemed to have quietened down, the Squadron was sent on short leave and I took a 48 hour pass and went home.

My mother tried to comfort me on the loss of Julia and I found my father again looking less well than when I last saw him. Life in a country house was perhaps easier than for those in towns. Food was not such a problem with vegetables from the garden, eggs from the hens and the occasional gifts from farmers of a bit of pork or mutton, but the war was still not so far away. Bombing raids on Manchester and Liverpool were close by and the flying bomb had also reached that far north. Some of them had missed the industrial centres and had landed haphazardly in the countryside. One had landed in a large field not far from the house.

I spent a quiet night in my own bed. After breakfast I went out on the terrace. It was a warm and balmy summer's day, with a hint of autumn. The leaves were beginning to turn and fruit was ready to be picked - plums and damsons, and blackberries beginning to ripen in the hedgerows. The sky was blue with little fleecy clouds. There was a slight breeze. I found Cuthbert, my old canvas canoe and carried it down to the river below the house and paddled slowly down to the deep part where I swam and then lay on the bank in the sun, musing on the folly of war. As I lay there in peace and solitude, men and women in the forces and innocent civilians were dying. Some were being humiliated and tortured in camps in Germany and the Far East. Man's inhumanity to man had always been so. But now he had made it more intense by new weapons of destruction, the bombers, the submarines and the tanks he had perfected.

A martin flew by to its hole in the sandstone cliff. A wood-pigeon cooed in the clough beyond the bank. I got back into the canoe and paddled further down the river until I was opposite the house where the girl that I had fallen in love with so long ago before the war, used to live. Where was she now? I had heard that she had joined tha ATS. As she spoke both French and Italian, perhaps she was in Africa or the Far East. I did not know. Should I have asked her to marry me? Would it have been better than with Julia, had she lived? Question I could not answer. I paddled slowly back to the house, had supper and went straight to bed.

Next morning, as I was enjoying my breakfast of bacon, eggs and sausages, which my mother had made for me in spite of the rationing, the telephone rang. It was Reggie.

"All leave is cancelled," he said. "There's a flap on. We're sending an aircraft to bring you back. See you later."

Was it just another operation to be added to the list of those planned, mounted and then cancelled? I had a feeling that this one might be different. I said goodbye to my father, and my mother drove me to the aerodrome in the pony trap which they now used in place of the car, due to petrol rationing. I kissed her goodbye and she left to wait for the aircraft. When it arrived it was an ancient Anson, flown by one of our tug pilots, and had an undercarriage which I had to wind down by hand before landing.

I arrived at Brize on the Wednesday to be told that we were to be ready for an operation on the following Sunday, September the 2nd.

Reggie met me.

"Well what's the flap about this time that you've brought me back in such a hurry?" I asked, thinking about the idyllic time I had spend on the river.

"Oh, the usual," replied Reggie. "We're to land ahead of the 2nd Army, but I expect they'll get there before us, like they've done before. We're to land in the Lille-Tournai area where we were in 1940."

"I wonder if we'll go over Camphin en Pevèle? You remember, we were billeted there - a nice little village. If a tow rope happens to break we should be among friends," I said, remembering the cream.

"Come on old chap," said Reggie, "concentrate. Leave doesn't seem to have done you any good at all." He went on," the plan is to land astride the railway at Bersham, north west of Ronse. And, by the way, some of us will be carrying the 1st Air Landing Anti-tank Battery - our old battery. Quite a coincidence."

"Perhaps we shall meet some of our old pals," I said, looking at the file Reggie had been trying to hand me. "I see I'm carrying Lieutenant Colonel McCardie the CO of the South Staffords, a nice chap, and we'll be first off."

"The code name for the Op is Linnet - I don't know who thinks up these names. I can't see much of a song bird in this one," said Reggie wryly.

On Saturday the briefing of crews and loading of gliders was completed and all was ready for take off in the early hours of Sunday morning. It would be a dark take off and since it had rained hard all of the day before, the ground was soft and gliders and tugs could easily get bogged down as they were being moved on to the runway.

I asked Foxley to pack my rucksack for the operation. Foxley was in some doubt as to what to put in. He sought out Arthur Singleton.

"The Major has asked me to pack his rucksack. What do you think I ought to put in?"

"I don't think he'll need his pyjamas! You might put in a couple of pairs of socks and some spare underpants might be useful," said Arthur grinning.

I went up to my room and checked my maps and the details of the briefing. I wrote a letter to my mother. It must have been the fifth or sixth I had written but somehow it seemed this one might get to the post. I had a feeling that operation *Linnet* would take place. It would be the first I had taken part in personally. Thoughts flashed through my mind. What would it feel like flying through enemy flak with nothing but plywood and perspex to protect one? I had no worries about the landing. That depended on me and I was completely confident about it. But what about the opposition on the ground just as we landed and were most vulnerable? It was no good worrying. Just as I had started to take off my clothes before going to bed the Tannoy broke into life - "Night flying for tonight is cancelled". That was the code for postponement. Relief and disappointment surged up together. I went downstairs to find out what was happening. The bar was in an uproar. This must have been the twelfth operation to be put off at the last minute. Drinking carried on well into the early hours but after a few drinks I went back to bed.

The next morning after breakfast, as nothing much seemed to be happening, I took my truck and drove into the country.

It was Sunday, so I thought I would look for a church. After a while I came to a little hamlet nestling in the countryside. Just outside the village was a stone building. From the cross on the gate it seemed that it must be a church. It had no tower nor spire but a single bell hung from a central gable. I went inside. The walls were plain, although here and there the plaster had been removed to disclose ancient paintings and decorations. It was very old - perhaps fifteenth century. Oak beams and pews. No organ but a simple harmonium. No stained glass, just plain glass in the windows to let in the light of Nature. The only flowers were some wild ones from the hedgerows. The congregation was just four souls and the priest, but I thought of the people who must have worshipped here since the church was built. I sat at the back and went forward to take communion. Afterwards the priest spoke to me. He was pleased to have someone from the Services. The war had taken all the young men from the village.

I drove back, thinking how quiet and pleasant it had been - something worth fighting for and even losing one's life for if it meant this way of life could continue.

Arriving back at Brize there was another frantic flap. The station was to move to an aerodrome at Manston in Kent ready to operate from there on the morrow. Julian came up to me.

"Can you believe it? The chaps planning this operation have only just realised that our Albemarle tugs can get us to the objective but then won't have enough fuel to get home! So we've got to move to a base as near to the Continent as possible."

"I'm no longer surprised at anything the planners do," I replied. "I suppose Manston on the S E coast of Kent is about as near to the Continent as you can get without swimming!"

After superhuman efforts at loading and marshalling, all was ready for a take off in the afternoon. Then word came through not to move as *Linnet* was now cancelled completely since the 2nd Army had already reached the area just as Reggie had predicted.

That evening I was called to Wing H.Q. at Harwell for briefing on another operation. Arthur drove me in a 15 cwt. As Colonel Chatterton had not yet arrived, there was time for a meal and a session in the bar. He did not arrive until 10 p.m. by which time a good deal of liquor had been imbibed. However maps were sent for and the briefing commenced. The operation was called *Linnet 2* and we were to land by the Maastricht and Liege bridges. D-Day was the next day and Brize Norton aircraft would have to operate from Manston. All was finally complete when the telephone rang. It was a bad line but eventually the Colonel got the message - "the operation is cancelled" - once again. One of the officers started to laugh. His laugh was infectious and soon the whole bar was in an uproar. It wasn't funny but exasperation and relief need some outlet. Eventually we all dispersed having been told that yet another operation was being planned. Arthur drove me back to Brize.

The following day the move to Manston had to be postponed on account of weather but the next day it cleared up but there was a strong wind.

Arthur and I took off with the rest of the squadron. It was exceedingly bumpy and at one moment it seemed that the rope was about to break. However we hung on and managed to reach the aerodrome.

One of my pilots was not so lucky. Shortly after take off his tug aircraft's engines failed and in the subsequent landing his glider was damaged but with no serious injuries to anyone. The following day he took off again in another glider with another tug but after about twenty minutes the tow rope broke (or came adrift) at the tug end and although the glider pilot released his end of the rope he did not realise that it had caught on the undercarriage of his glider and was trailing behind. As a result, after a perfect approach for a forced landing in a field, the rope caught on some trees causing the glider to make a heavy landing and to break in half, again with no serious injuries. They eventually had to get to Manston by road. In spite of these mishaps, his passengers who were a platoon of the South Staffords insisted that he should fly them on the operation, which he did, landing them safely and fighting with them until he was taken prisoner and survived. As it happened they were No 13 platoon. Perhaps 13 was not so unlucky after all.

Although Manston was an emergency landing airfield used to handling all the *lame ducks* returning from the continent, it had never seen gliders before, although I counted thirtyeight different types of aircraft while we were there. The sudden influx of so many RAF and Army pilots, not to mention the troops they were carrying, stretched the resources of the RAF to the limit

It was a most exciting station. The Tannoy would suddenly burst into life: "Liberator coming in on two engines. Stand by crash party". And shortly afterwards: "Aircraft removal party to end of No.2 runway. Fortress with undercarriage collapsed". Shortly after we arrived, five Typhoons crashed on take off due to a burst tyre on one. Two of the aircraft burst into flames and bombs, rockets and small arms were exploding all round.

At one point Julian was talking to one of the pilots of the new Jet planes - the Meteors - and asked him about their speed.

The pilot, who was very proud of the new aircraft, replied: "There are three throttle settings - very fast, f.....g fast, and Christ Almighty!"

On Wednesday Reggie and the second lift arrived and Hamish brought the maps for the next operation which was called *Comet*. In this one the British 1st Airborne Division was to land at Arnhem, Nijmegen and Grave and to hold the bridges over the rivers at these places until the British Second Army arrived. In each case the bridges had to be captured by *coup de main* parties as for the Orne bridges on D-Day. Although some of the same pilots were being used there had been no preparatory training which was so essential in this type of operation.

My squadron would land at Groesbeek and advance into Nijmegen with the South Staffords to take over the bridge over the Waal which should by then have been captured by the *coup de main* party.

The camp theatre had been taken over for the briefings and one of the dressing rooms served as operations room where Reggie and I worked out the landing and military plan while the RAF worked on the flight plans. It was all very difficult as very few details had been provided by Wing HQ and for some reason telephone communication with Harwell was not working. Then the rain started. The theatre leaked, the tents leaked and everything was wet. The troops had to be moved into the NAAFI, the Church, and all over the place. The ground where the gliders were parked became a bog and it was almost impossible to move them with the tractors. Briefing was completed eventually and take off was scheduled for the following morning. Then a twentyfour hour postponement came through. Probably just as well as it was doubtful if the gliders could have been got on to the runway due to the soft ground.

Then confusion set in. It appeared that the high ground overlooking my landing zone (LZ) was occupied by the enemy; not a very pleasing prospect. Orders arrived that six gliders had to be returned to Brize with their loads. This was done but the following day they were returned with no explanation.

I was next told to expect to receive ten Waco gliders. They arrived under an officer - *Peggy* Clark - a flamboyant character who had flown gliders carrying French SAS and weapons into France to help the Maquis. The Germans had put a pretty high price on his head. He had little information as to what he now had to do and this was further complicated when six of the Wacos were sent back to Harwell, still with no explanation and then returned shortly afterwards. He was later told he was to carry some very secret American radio equipment but it had not arrived, and no mention was made as to where it was to come from. Eventually it did arrive and later he landed it in Holland but it was destroyed before it could be used.

By Friday the rain had dried up and marshalling was complete. The Field Cashier had been round and issued everyone with 5 guilder and 10 mark notes, for use in the event of becoming an evader. This was a distinct possibility if one had to land prematurely in a different part of Holland. Once again everything was ready for a morning take off but just as everyone was going to bed another twentyfour hour postponement came through.

The following day, as there seemed to be so little information, I flew over to Harwell in the Oxford, to see Colonel Chatterton. Wing Headquarters was in a state of chaos and as there was nothing new to be gathered, I returned via Brize, where I collected a few things, and later arrived at Manston to be met by Julian who said the operation had been postponed fortyeight hours. By now everyone had lost interest in it. The security about it must have long since been broken and the next day, as expected, *Comet* was cancelled.

Sunday: one of the glider pilots has crashed on his motorcycle and is in hospital. As nothing much seems to be happening, Reggie, Julian and I take the day off and explore the pubs of Ramsgate.

Monday: tugs and tug crews return to Brize but the glider pilots and their loads remain at Manston. The following day, order and counter order and consequent disorder is the order of the day. It is unbelievable. In the morning orders are received to unload the gliders. The gunners who we are carrying are told by their officer not to unload. Group says continue unloading. Then at 3 o'clock the order is received not to unload. Howard Hemingway arrives shortly afterwards from Brize to say the next operation is postponed ten days and we are to unload. Not long afterwards the Station Commander arrives with orders not to unload. Really this is too much. Everyone sits back and laughs and laughs and then goes to the bar and gets uproariously drunk.

Wednesday: the gliders having by now been unloaded, word comes through that they may have to be loaded by Friday as the next operation may be sooner than expected. Everyone is pretty apathetic by now. It will never come off.

On Thursday I flew over to Brize and spent the night there - very nice to have a bath and change of clothes. The following day I went on to Harwell to get the information about the coming operation. It is code-named *Market Garden*. Market refers to the airborne side of the operation whilst Garden is the land operation by XXX Corps to cover the 64 miles to Arnhem. The Market part is very similar to Comet but this time the American 101st and 82nd Airborne Divisions will be landing at Grave and Nijmegen respectively. The British 1st Airborne and the Polish Brigade are to land at Arnhem to hold a bridgehead over the Rhine for up to fortyeight hours until the 2nd Army, which is now south of Eindhoven, should arrive. The Corps HQ under General Browning will be at Nijmegen, flown in by 36 gliders of 'A' Squadron. Our D-Day is likely to be Sunday 17th September.

CHAPTER 23

Sunday, 17th September:

The great day dawns. My glider will be the first off from Manston. Take off is not till 1040 hrs so there is time for a leisurely *operations* breakfast of bacon and eggs. Little do I realise that this will be the last for some time. I drive down to the tow path. Arthur is already there checking the glider and the load. Arnold, who had that traumatic experience on D-Day is flying No.2 and I tell him, jokingly, he had better keep in formation on landing, which in fact he does.

It is ten minutes before take off. There has been no cancellation. I climb into the glider. Check that the passengers are all strapped in and that my own kit is where I can get it. McCardie the CO of the Staffords is calm and confident. I wonder if he realises that his life and that of the others are now in my hands. I do my cockpit check for what seems the umpteenth time. Wave to Reggie and Julian on the tow path. My tug *V* for Victor, flown by the Wing Commander of 297 Squadron, taxies out. The tow rope is connected. The *angle of dangle* fixed and the intercom checked. I call up the 'Winco' to say all is well. *V* for Victor taxies out. The towmaster switches his lights from amber to green (he now has 'traffic signals' in place of his batons) and we are away gathering speed up the runway. The nose wheel starts a most monumental judder. I heave back on the stick and at last the weight comes off it and the judder ceases. Must ease stick forward now or we shall become airborne too soon and make it difficult for the tug to take off. At last we are off, a trifle nose-heavy but nothing to worry about.

It is a little bumpy on the forming-up course. We see a squadron of Spitfires and Typhoons outward bound, which sends our morale sky high. Coming back on the outward course, we pass over Ramsgate and looking down at Manston there is nothing on the runway so all must have got off. As we start out to sea, we pass behind a formation of Dakotas and hit their slip streams - a most frightful bump which feels as if we had hit something solid - is this the end? Gingerly trying the controls and finding them responding normally, confidence returns.

Flying east from the Channel to the North Sea all is steady and after a short time the rest of the force is seen stretching out as far as the eye can see; little specks in the sky, each of which contains up to thirty men with guns and jeeps and weapons of all kinds. At last the Dutch coast comes into view. There is a bank of cloud which may prove troublesome, and what are those little black smudges in the sky way out in front? It's Flak and it may be for us before very long. This is where the morale pills would come in useful. If we had any! The land over which we are flying is flooded as Intelligence told us it would be. Little red-roofed houses sticking up through a mass of dirty yellowish water. Typhoons and Spitfires are now appearing. A house is burning below us. Probably a flak position. A Dakota bursts into flames on our port side. After a few seconds which seems like ages the troops bale out followed by two white 'chutes which must be the crew. A second later the machine dives into the waters and disappears. A glider towed by a Dakota breaks away on our starboard and goes down to make a forced landing. Cannot see where it lands as I am too busy with map reading, coping with the slipstreams of preceding combinations and cloud which we go into for a couple of minutes. Arthur is flying the glider. He is invaluable and I have every confidence in him so that while he is flying and fighting the slipstreams I can concentrate on reading the map and checking where we are. We are nearing the target. I can see the three rivers. We are running up over the bends in them as arranged. We are right on course. I see the bend in the Lek which is our last pinpoint. There is a lot of smoke coming up from the woods around the LZ. Our bombers must have been busy, which is a good sign. I see my release point. Up into the high tow. A shout of thanks to the Winco. Pull the release lever and we are off. Half flap. Almost up to the LZ. Full flap and nose down. The stick is fully forward and still the speed keeps at 80. Terrific juddering as if we are stalling but we are dropping fast and going straight for the LZ. Aiming a little short of some trees and pull up over them to get rid of some surplus speed. The landing is O.K. and well short of the overshoot boundary. Take off flap and allow the glider to run on to clear the field for the others. Half way across we run into some heavy plough which slows the glider up so that we come to a halt unfortunately in the middle of the field. Arnold, who I watched as he pulled off, landed safely on my right. I undo my straps and follow Arthur out of the glider and lie panting on the ground hugging my stengun.

There appears to be no opposition. It is a fine day and the sun is shining. Gliders are all around us and the field is surrounded by trees. Going round to the rear of the glider, Arthur has already cut the control cables preparatory to removing the tail. I start to slacken the bolts. The bottom one sticks and I am sweating before it is eventually removed. The tail drops off with a crash and is pulled to one side. The driver doesn't wait to get the ramps out but drives the jeep and trailer straight out over a three foot drop, nearly causing disaster.

McCardie asks where we are. Studying the map and the ground I point out we are in our correct field not 50 yards from our RV. We make a dash for the edge of the field in case there are any Germans waiting to pick us off. The Colonel presses the trigger of his sten which makes me run even faster not knowing if he has seen an enemy or if they are firing at us.

The RV is a farm called Reigers Camp where we meet the CO of the Independent Squadron who dropped before us to mark out the LZs. He has captured some prisoners who look a pretty dejected lot. It is altogether too quiet. Ominously so. We start to dig in - rather too enthusiastically and my hands are soon blistered - I don't think I have learned how to use an entrenching tool properly. Now some more gliders are coming in. A Hamilcar goes close overhead. The air a little distance away is thick with paratroops. Enemy flak opens up. Soon everything is quiet once again. We eat our sandwiches. It is like a picnic. Checking up on Douglas's flight, there are two gliders missing. Unfortunately they contained his other two officers and his flight sergeant. One glider has been unlucky and landed within a few feet of an enemy machine gun wounding the pilots. Jeremy Jackson's flight, carrying the anti-tank gunners, has landed successfully on his LZ which is on the other side of the railway.

The Dutch people on the farm are pleased to see us and the farm appears to be prosperous with the farm implements in good condition. We might be on a farm in Cheshire only the barn is full of tobacco leaves laid out to dry. As we are to defend the LZ for the troops arriving next day, I go round to check our positions and have a word with Douglas.

During the night sleep is difficult with the excitements of the day. There is spasmodic rifle and machine gun fire but no bullets come our way. There is the sound of gun fire coming from the direction of Arnhem which is 4 or 5 miles away. We see some Spitfires in the evening and during the night our bombers go over.

Monday, 18th September:

All is quiet, the weather still clear and sunny. I have a complete wash and shave at the tap in the farm. Shirt full of sand from the trench. Breakfast, porridge, meat tablets and biscuits from the twenty-four hour ration pack. Everyone is walking about as if it were an exercise, except that the Padre is burying one of the men who died in the night.

Two of my pilots turn up with a Bren Carrier they have salvaged from a

Hamilcar which had turned over on the soft ground killing all the crew. A Horsa on the LZ has crashed through a line of trees but the fuselage is still intact. Salvage parties are organised to reclaim anything useful from the gliders.

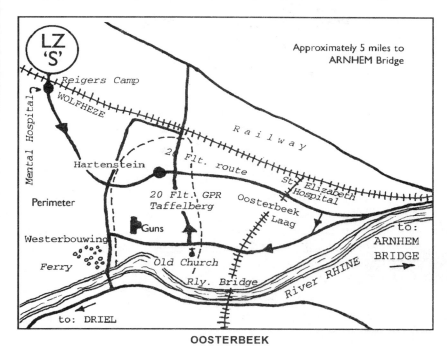

OOSTERBEEK

McCardie now tells me that General Urquhart, commanding the Division, is missing and the plans are changed. The Staffords and my flight of glider pilots are no longer required to guard the LZ for the second lift although who is to do this is not clear. We are to keep with the Staffords for the time being while they move to the area where Division HQ is supposed to be, south of Wolfheze. They will then press on to the bridge. I explain the change of plan to Douglas and get ready to move.

When the time comes to move off we load our kit on to the carrier whose track is tied together with wire and may break at any moment. We move off, cross the railway line at Wolfheze, past the lunatic asylum which has been bombed (unnecessarily as we find out later). We hear aircraft overhead. Perhaps they are Spitfires. Jim Eardly, one of my pilots thinks otherwise. He is right. They are F.W.190s strafing the LZ. We are now moving through the woods on the side of the road. There has been a battle here and bodies of dead Germans and our own troops are lying on the ground. My pilots are salvaging German weapons and ammunition, motorcycles and even a machine gun for future use. McCardie now tells me we are held up by a machine gun position which they are going to attack. My glider pilots are to act as rearguard. We now come out on to the main Utrecht-Arnhem road where at a crossroads there is a German Staff car with two dead Germans hanging out of it. Move cautiously along the road. Column stops. Everyone a little jumpy. Meet a party of 3rd Parachute Battalion who have had a fire fight with the enemy. Spasmodic rifle fire ahead. McCardie sends for me and I roar along the road on the pillion of a motorcycle which he has sent for me. No sign of him but I meet Major Timothy from the 1st Parachute Battalion who is trying to get to the bridge with some of his men. I decide to stay with him. Wait in the woods around a building which is later to become the Medical Dressing Station. It is now 3 o'clock and no sign of the second lift which was due at 10 this morning. Everyone a little anxious. The noise of flak and aircraft is hopeful. Later a report that gliders have been seen cheers everyone up. A Dutch woman in a house holds up the *Stars and Stripes* and a *Union Jack*. We are handed flowers. It is quite fantastic. Here we are walking down a street in Oosterbeek, a small town on the outskirts of Arnhem, with our weapons at the ready, looking for snipers at every turn and the Dutch civilians are moving about quite normally, doing the shopping just as if it were a street in Chester. I go into a house which has been the local Gestapo HQ. It is well stocked with food. I take a tin of asparagus. There is continual firing and sniper hunts. A bullet comes through the window.

Timothy's men now receive orders to move down towards the railway. Douglas and his flight have at last caught up with me. We move off in the rear of the Paras. It must be between five and six. Everyone is feeling tired. More fruit from the Dutch is very welcome. A Dutchman produces a Bren and ammunition, two stens, a rifle and some grenades which we add to our armoury. He must have been hiding them. The advance is very slow and heavy rifle and machine gun fire is coming from the woods on our left, north of the railway. Reconnoitring to the right I see that the railway bridge over the river has been blown. This would have been a second crossing point if the road bridge across the Rhine in Arnhem could not be captured. Resting for a moment by the Oosterbeek Laag railway station, I eat the asparagus which is not very satisfying!

We move on to a house overlooking the road into Arnhem. It is getting dark and everyone is tired. The firing in the direction of Arnhem is increasing, and now includes mortars, shells and a lot of tracer. Fires are burning in the town. Going down the road with Timothy, I meet an RAF Squadron Leader who says he is in charge of a radar unit. He looks incongruous in his smart blue uniform in this unhealthy place. I take him back to the house. His tug, a Stirling, was shot down south of the river. The glider landed safely and the Squadron Leader and his unit crossed the river by going to the ferry which took them across after they paid the usual fare! (If the ferry is still working, why was it not included in the plan?) He is trying to get to Divisional HQ and as this is also our eventual objective I suggest he stays with us although it does not look at the moment as if the opportunity to get to the Headquarters will arise.

All the civilians are now in their cellars or in air raid shelters. One woman is in hysterics. Arthur says she is about to give birth. What a time for it to happen. I suggest he tries to find a doctor.

The Dutch in our house are very helpful and do their best to get us some food. Alas, we have hardly started to eat when an order comes through that we are to advance and put in an attack with the Paras. Arthur and I go forward with the Paras' O group. The darkness helps and the enemy firing is going over our heads. The pace is very slow. We stop in a street with houses on one side and a high wall on the other. Lying on the pavement, in spite of the smell of drains, the tracer passing over head and mortars dropping unpleasantly close, we drop off to sleep spasmodically from sheer exhaustion. The enemy rocket launchers are now added to the din with their devilish *hissing* followed by an almighty *crump*. About 2 o'clock in the morning Timothy arrives and directs me to a certain house near the St Elizabeth Hospital on the road into Arnhem, which is the Stafford's temporary HQ. There is a lot of wrecked transport on the road, both German and British. The house is dark except for a single candle on the table in what must be the sitting room. The furniture is all as the owners had left it; yet this house is in the middle of a battle, the only evidence being a bullet hole in the blind. Seated round the table with the candle are McCardie, looking a lot older than when I last saw him a few hours earlier, Lieut-Colonel Dobie commanding the 1st Parachute Battalion and two other officers. The atmosphere is tense and dramatic. Lieut-Colonel John Frost, commanding the 2nd Parachute Battalion, reduced to about 80 men, is still holding the bridge in Arnhem and must be reinforced at once if the whole object of the operation is not to be lost. Division have decided that it is impossible to hold the bridge without taking the high ground behind us which dominates the river. This so far has not been done.

Division have not heard from Frost and assume he has been wiped out so have ordered the Staffords and the Paras to withdraw. The two Colonels in the house however have been able to hear Frost faintly on their radio and know of his plight. We are told to go out of the room. When we return they have decided that they "cannot let Johnny down" and turning a blind eye to the Divisional Commander's orders, will make for the bridge at all costs.

The Staffords are to advance into the town past the St. Elizabeth Hospital in spite of an 88 mm gun firing down one of the streets along which they have to advance. One of the parachute battalions will advance along the river bank which is also known to be strongly held. Zero hour is 0345 hrs. Shortly before this McCardie calls me in and says that my pilots are not to advance with him but to return to Divisional HQ which was our original objective. I have to admit I am very thankful but feel I'm leaving a body of very brave men on a forlorn mission.

Retracing our steps I meet Douglas who is trying to find our transport. As it is approaching dawn and the road we have to pass along is under enemy observation and fire, we had better start moving fast. The Squadron Leader is still with us but has lost his men. Just as we are moving off a body of Staffords, marching smartly in threes as if on parade, approach us led by Major Cain (later to be awarded a VC) who was flown in by Tom Geary, one of my pilots. The rope broke before crossing the Channel. They force landed safely and then flew in on the second day. I tell Major Cain where I last saw McCardie and we then set off past the station and across the railway. We are going down the road which we used earlier in the evening when a burst of tracer comes straight down the centre. Thank goodness we remembered our training - never move down the centre of a road, always at the side. The tracer is coming over us from the embankment on the right. I decide on a detour. It is rapidly getting light but we manage to get away safely and make our way along the lower road towards where we assume Divisional HQ should be. No casualties so far.

Tuesday, 19th September:

As it gets lighter, people in the neighbouring houses wake up and bring us water and fruit. A Dutchman with a yellow armband tries to help and shows us where he says there is a German sniper. We move off, our Bren Carrier leading but there is no sign of the sniper. Eventually we get back on to the main Utrecht-Arnhem road where we were yesterday. It is a fine, sunny morning again and we have no difficulty in finding the Divisional HQ which is in a hotel called the Hartenstein. Lieut-Colonel Murray, the CO of No 1 Wing, is there and is pleased to see me. Things are going well he says and tells me to rest my men in a house in the hotel grounds. The house is in good order except for blood in the kitchen and a filthy smell - one of our troops has been killed here and there is a hole in the shutters where a cannon shell has come through which is probably what killed him.

We take off our boots, have a shave and general clean up, and cook some food - porridge, meat tablets and tea - from our 24 hour ration packs which are still holding up after 72 hours. Tommy Geary and his co-pilot join us. They are the ones who flew in Major Cain of the Staffords. Reggie now appears and reports that the second lift arrived safely but very late due to fog on the airfields in England. Just as well, as we found out later. The Germans had captured a copy of the operation order and were expecting the lift at 10 a.m. When it didn't arrive the fighters had to return to base to refuel. Reggie, who brought over the guns of the Light Regiment, tells me that he is going to join them at their position by the Old Church which is not far from the river. He says he'd rather be there than near Wing HQ who he has never been very fond of.

There is rifle fire, mortaring and shelling going on in the distance. Aircraft overhead. It is the first re-supply mission. A Dakota is hit and goes down in flames. We do not know at the time that the dropping zone for the supplies is in enemy hands. The owners of the house return and start collecting their things. A canary has disappeared but we eventually find it. Language is a difficulty but Douglas makes a hit with the daughter who is young and attractive and speaks a little English.

Our comparative peace is rudely shaken by the Colonel who tells me to take up defensive positions round the hotel and to hold the area round a house which is to the south-east of the Hartenstein. Arthur and I reconnoitre it and suggest to the owners who are still in residence that they had better leave. We dig our trench in the garden of the house. Arthur and I share this very sandy slit trench and try to get some sleep but in the cramped conditions this is nearly impossible. Every time we move brings a cascade of sand on to us. During the night a mad woman, possibly from the Asylum at Wolfheze that was bombed on the first day, walks past our position. She is singing an unintelligible song in a high-pitched monotonous voice. She continues singing without any intermission until she is out of earshot. Most weird. It seems as if she is afraid to stop singing for fear of her life. It is very eerie as the sounds of battle have stopped for a moment and there is a background of silence.

Wednesday, 20th September:

A fine day again but somewhat cloudy. Water is no longer available in the taps so we shall have to conserve our resources. Feeling very tired. It is an effort to do anything. Make some tea and porridge in the kitchen then move to cellar and clean sten magazine which is jammed with sand - sand everywhere, pistol, grenades, equipment. All have to be cleaned.

Julian arrives. He flew in with the second lift and looks very tired. Borrows one of our jeeps which we had scrounged, to go down to see his pilots who he says are in good heart and with the Artillery near the old church.

I am told by the Adjutant of the Wing that we are too near the Tafelberg Hotel which is the Medical Dressing Station and are to move to positions in the gardens about 100 yards behind us. Rumour has it that the XXX Corps will link up with us tomorrow.

During the morning the Sergeant-Major who has been snooping around, returns with a beautiful BMW coupé which belonged to the local Gestapo. He thinks it would be ideal to drive into Arnhem, the capture of which we are still confident cannot be long delayed when XXX Corps arrive.

The Sergeant-Major, Douglas and I go to look at our new position which is in a vegetable garden, by a line of trees and adjacent to the tennis courts which are being used as a cage for German prisoners. There is a sports pavilion which has a small cellar in which I make my HQ. During the afternoon, Douglas's flight digs in. We are told there is a sniper in some houses across the allotments in front of our position. We organise fire from everything we have including the Piat. Possibly a waste of ammunition but the sniper is silenced. We hear that Major Royle, the second-in-command of the Wing, has been killed when he went out on a patrol. We have had no casualties so far.

There is another supply drop in the evening. The flak is heavier but we are powerless to do anything. We show our yellow identification panels and wave them but to no avail as the supplies still go into German hands. Those Dakota pilots are heroes. They fly on and on and round again to drop their supplies even when they are on fire and with no hope of survival. Many of them go down in flames. It is terrible.

Cleaning my sten gun and automatic pistol for the umpteenth time, I sleep in a slit trench by myself, whilst Arthur is in another.

Thursday, 21st September:
Still fine. Enemy activity less than usual but perhaps we are getting used to it. The flight are well dug in and the transport stowed away in the garden between

a hedge and a row of runner beans. I am sitting in the cellar, cleaning my pistol, when there is a loud explosion just outside. Looking out a mortar bomb has landed a few feet from the entrance and its fin is still there. On brushing off the earth, the inscription shows it was made in Paris! Later on there is a whining whistling noise and a series of sharp explosions, very loud and close. A moment later, as I dash up the steps out of the cellar, I see Douglas staggering towards me exclaiming, "Andrews is killed". Andrews was his co-pilot. They were both in their slit trench when the bomb landed on the lip of it, killing Andrews instantly and wounding Douglas in the hand which is covered in blood and looks a mess. How he wasn't killed is a miracle as he was lying on top of Andrews when the bomb fell. Going round the flight it is obvious our position has been plastered by these *Moaning Minnies*, as we call them. We have several casualties - two pilots killed and three wounded. The Sergeant-Major is wonderful. He gets all the casualties, including Douglas, to the dressing station in our second jeep. Meanwhile I urge everyone to dig deeper and to put top cover on their trenches as lack of this has caused the casualties. It was an expensive lesson to learn.

That afternoon a Military Policeman appears at the entrance to my cellar, escorting a female German prisoner. He says she is the only female in the POW cage and wants to pee but doesn't want to do it in front of all the men in the cage. "Can she use your cellar Sir?" he asks. What a request in the middle of a battle. The woman looks pretty frightful and I am so astounded that, reluctantly, I leave the cellar which quickly becomes a lavatory, with liquid swilling round the floor. The woman must have had a very large bladder.

As the cellar is now uninhabitable, Arthur and I decide to dig a slit trench in the garden. We pick a spot where the ground is soft and cover the trench with a door wrenched off the pavilion. It was perhaps foolish to have picked that spot, in spite of the easier digging.

We have heard that Colonel Frost no longer holds the bridge at Arnhem and the remains of the Division are now holding a defensive position round the Hartenstein and down to the river. We keep hoping that XXX Corps will reach the south bank of the river and get across to help us.

Friday, 22nd September:

Heavy shelling and mortaring all day. During one of the infrequent lulls a loudspeaker from the houses opposite our position crackles into life. The message that comes over is that Colonel McCardie has been captured - the last time I saw him was in that house near the St Elizabeth Hospital before he made his gallant attempt to get to the bridge. The message continues - "If you want to see your wives and sweethearts again there is no point in holding out any longer but give yourselves up and come forward with a white flag". This produces a stream of invective from the flight and a burst of bren gun fire in the direction of the loudspeaker which is effectively silenced.

I am going round our positions with the Sergeant-Major when we hear a shell coming - by now we are experts at judging when it will arrive - and we both jump into an adjacent slit trench.

The Sergeant-Major is underneath me. The trench is not very long and my boots protrude at one end. After the salvo is over I notice that a piece of shrapnel has cut a neat groove in the toe of one boot, missing my foot by a fraction.

Saturday, 23rd September:

Rained in the morning which solves the problem of drinking as we collect as much rainwater as we can. There is still no food but the blackberries on the bushes give one something to chew. Arthur and I are in our trench in the garden when the morning *hate* begins. It seems as if the enemy gunners have decided to wipe out our little burrow. The shells come closer and closer. The concussion in our trench is shattering. We are covered in sand, the sides of the trench are falling in. Arthur says in a rather sepulchral voice: "This is it Sir. I think we've had it". I have never been so frightened in my life. Death seems only a second or two away. However I know that as an officer it is my duty not to show fear so I reply rather shakily, "Don't worry Staff we shall be all right". Just then as I am looking out from what is left of the trench I see an unexploded 88 mm shell lying about a foot away - not a very pleasant bedfellow. Without a word Arthur and I scramble out and run to the line of trees where the rest of the flight are dug in. I jump headfirst into the nearest trench saying to the occupant, Tommy Geary, as I arrive, "You don't mind if I join you?" I must have timed it pretty well as the next salvo arrived just as I was disappearing below ground. I distinctly remember seeing one shell bursting a few feet away, as I was upside down, all yellow and orange stars, splashed in a circle, just like the illustrations in our boyhood comics.

Sunday, 24th September:

Yesterday, just before the bombardment started, I was shaving. The first shell sent my shaving kit for a Burton. I was so tired I really didn't care.

During the afternoon, a soldier arrives with a message that I am to go to the

Divisional HQ in the Hartenstein Hotel. It is only 100 yards away but the route is covered by sniper fire. The ground round the hotel is littered with trenches, shell holes, dead bodies, and the trees immediately surrounding it have been reduced to stumps. The hotel itself is a wreck. It is surprising that it is still standing. Arthur and I enter by a hole in the wall of what was once a bedroom. Lieut-Colonel Iain Murray is there with his Adjutant and Intelligence Officer. Brigadier Shan Hackett, commanding 4th Parachute Brigade, has been severely wounded and is in the MDS at the St. Elizabeth Hospital. Iain Murray is to take over his command and I am to take over what remains of the Glider Pilot Regiment. I make the hazardous journey back to our position to inform the Sergeant-Major what is happening and to tell him to take command of the flight and to find out what other glider pilots there are in the area. The area which we now hold has been reduced to a narrow salient extending from the Hartenstein to the river on the South. There are a variety of troops holding each side of it facing east and west and also to the north of the Hotel. Movement around the area is difficult but I try to locate any glider pilots that are left. Returning to the hotel I am told a sniper is firing at the main entrance and am advised not to go in that way. I decide to try the trick of putting ones helmet on a stick round a corner. I do this and, rather to my surprise, there is a loud crack and a bullet grazes the helmet, but even so I cannot locate the sniper who is too well camouflaged. I therefore take another route into the hotel. There is still no news of XXX Corps coming to relieve us. We have heard that they have got as far as Nijmegen and their medium artillery are now able to give us supporting fire at an extreme range of 11 miles from south of Nijmegan. These shells, which we can hear coming some seconds before they arrive, land with a terrific explosion on the German positions. It is very heartening and makes us realise we are not alone. Now at last the Typhoons are able to attack the enemy gun positions with their rockets. When they come over the Germans keep their heads down and there is comparative peace for a few minutes. Oh why couldn't we have had them sooner?

Arthur and I spend the night at the Hartenstein. It has become very cold at night. In the wardrobe, or what was left of it, there are a number of lady's smart coats and dresses. It seems a shame to make such a mess of the clothes but their owner will certainly never see them again, so Arthur and I wrap ourselves in them and sleep. Meanwhile in the cellar below, General Urquhart and his Staff are directing what is left of the Division, encircled and waiting for relief from the South.

Monday, 25th September:

Very tired, finding it difficult to concentrate and thinking is an effort. Must be the effect of those shells bursting so close and continuously.

At 1200 hrs, Iain Murray tells me that orders for withdrawal of what remains of the Division across the river have been given. It is to start at 2200 hrs. I am unshaven and in my present state could not care less about my appearance. Iain very tactfully suggests that if we are getting out tonight we don't want the rest of the Army to think we are a lot of tramps. I tell him my shaving kit has gone. He offers to lend me his razor with a tiny bit of lather which he has conserved over many shaves. I manage to get the worst off and it is amazing how much better I feel both mentally and physically. Iain is no doubt suffering more than I from fatigue, both mental and physical, but he was in the Guards, and such things matter.

The remaining glider pilots are to act as guides down to the river where the Canadian Engineers will be waiting to ferry us over in boats while XXX Corps put down a hell of a bombardment to cover us and will fire tracer from across the river to mark the crossing points.

Just as I am considering how to organise the guides an officer, who has obviously not been able to shave for some days, comes into the room. I look at him and suddenly recognise one of the officers in my old anti-tank battery who, like Reggie, joined the glider pilots after I had left. I have not seen him since then.

"Robin! what a place to meet," I exclaim. "Not much good asking how you are. Obviously still alive! But you're just the chap I want. How many men have you got?"

"Most of the flight Sir. Luckily not too many casualties. We're dug in on the west of the tennis courts and you're on the east aren't you? Surprising we haven't seen each other before," Robin replies.

"Yes," I say smiling at him, for we both know the danger of wandering about. "Now, for this withdrawal the men furthest from the river will go first. That means those north of the hotel will start to pull out at 2200 hrs. I'll get my Sergeant-Major to give you a hand to collect any glider pilots and put them in position on the route through the woods to the river. It'll mean your men will be the last to pull out at 2300 hrs if Jerry doesn't get wind of what we're doing. The Padres and the doctors will be staying behind with the wounded. Best of luck. See you on the other side." As I say it, thoughts of the Spike at Crickhowell crossed my mind for it was there that I gave him permission to marry his wife.

(Robin did make it and, having guided the survivors to the river, got across himself.)

As the evening draws near there is a feeling of frustration that we have suffered so much and lost so many men and for a task which nearly came off. On the other hand we are relieved that we are getting out and have acquitted ourselves pretty well. We have held out for nine days, holding the bridge for 5 when we were only asked to hold it for 48 hours. There is still the question as to whether we shall live to see the withdrawal.

It starts on time. Lines of men appear with boots muffled, equipment fastened to stop it rattling, holding on to the man in front as it is dark in the woods through which they are passing. The rain helps and so far the enemy has not realised what is happening. The wounded keep up a desultory fire to confuse the Germans, as do the signallers who keep up a signals traffic to make the enemy think we are still there.

About 2300 hrs Arthur and I start out. We pass through the woods without incident and come out on the lower road which we cross. There is a ditch on the other side which I fall into. Arthur says it is a sewer. He is correct and tells me that I smell like a polecat. Then across a field and over a bank. Just as I reach the top of the bank, a star shell bursts out illuminating the whole area. In training we had been told that in such a situation you must not move - freeze - and you will look like a tree. I do just that, not sure as to what sort of tree I am supposed to be, but feeling very naked until the flare burnt out, which seemed an eternity. Then on across another field. We have almost got to the river bank when a barrage of mortar shells starts to fall. Everyone hugs the ground, myself included. I feel something very hot by my neck but think nothing about it at the time. We are now close to the river and can see boats crossing. However the river is being mortared and bullets are flying everywhere. Arthur is hit in the shoulder and I get him into a boat. There are other boats but they are all full. One boat loaded with men is hit by a shell and starts to sink. It is obvious the occupants cannot swim and they start to drown. I get into the water but cannot get to any of them. Now that I am in the water I decide to swim. After all what is a river? I had spent many hours on that river at home. But the Rhine is vast. I cannot see the far side. All is flashing lights, smoke and the noise of the shells and the mortars. I have one advantage. At Brize we were issued with an inflatable belt to be worn under one's shirt, ostensibly for use in the event of ditching. Discussing it at the time, Reggie had said he was going to keep his on in case of having to cross a river. I had agreed I would do the same and now blew the belt up. I had read somewhere that if you have to swim in your clothes, always take off your boots as they will drag you down. I do this, but as they are a good pair of boots from Trickers of

Jermyn Street which I do not want to lose, I tie them together and hang them round my neck. In the water I find I can swim quite well and the belt helps to keep me up, but the mortars are still falling. Remembering the fish which we had stunned on training at battle school by throwing grenades in the water, I decide to risk the concussion and keep myself under water for as long as possible to avoid the shrapnel. When I come up, I find a boat is passing so I hang on but in so doing turn on my back and my boots float away.

Scrambling out on the far side I was told to keep my voice down, as the enemy were very close, and to follow the tapes down to the road, then turn right and continue to Driel which is the Divisional RV.

When I get to the road I realise that I will have to walk the 2 miles to Driel in my socks. The road is rough with sharp stones and soon my feet are bleeding. How I cursed having taken my boots off on the other side. I join up with a party of survivors who are making for the RV. Amongst them is a sergeant who walks with me. He remarks that he didn't know a Major could swear like I am doing! He didn't know I had been tutored in a steelworks!

Eventually we arrive at Driel after the most painful journey I can remember. I realise for the first time that I have a minor shrapnel wound in my right hand which is bleeding. This is perhaps fortuitous as I am directed to the first aid post where I am given a mug of tea liberally laced with rum. Oh how good that is. It makes me forget my wet clothes and my injuries which are in any case very minor. The Medics patch me up but as I am now under the Red Cross I have, regretfully, to give up my automatic pistol and two grenades which I still have on me.

Tuesday, 26th September:

After a while a party of the lightly wounded, including myself, were put into an ambulance to be taken to Nijmegen. Although elements of XXX Corps had got to the south bank of the Waal their hold between it and the Lower Rhine was tenuous to say the least. The ambulance set off, but it was obvious that the driver did not know the way to Nijmegen. We told him to stop and held a council of war. It would have been ironical if, having got so far, we were to drive back into enemy territory and be made prisoners. However we decided on a direction which, as luck would have it, happened to be correct and eventually crossed the bridge over the Waal that had taken so long to capture and arrived safely at Nijmegen.

I am not sure where we slept. It may have been a hospital. My memory fails me on many points but what I do remember was when I undressed for the first time since leaving Brize. Taking off my airborne smock I noticed a cut about six inches long in the collar at the back of the neck. I took off my shirt. Another cut in the same place. Finally my string vest. Another cut - the same. This must have been the cause of that heat I felt on the other side of the river. That was it, I thought, one eighth of an inch from death.

Two days later we moved down the corridor which was very narrow with the enemy close to it on either side. I realised then the difficulties XXX Corps must have had in trying to get through to us. We had several narrow shaves with the enemy but, at last, having passed through Eindhoven, we arrived in Brussels. After a wait of twenty-four hours we were taken to an airfield where there was a fleet of Dakotas to fly us home. In the aircraft with me there were about eighteen of my pilots and my Sergeant-Major, but no officers. The aircraft took off but due to bad weather had to land at Lympne in Kent. The weather cleared and we flew on to Brize.

As soon as I arrived at Brize, I went to my office. It was deserted. I found out that my Adjutant, the clerk and the medical orderly had stowed away in gliders against all regulations and had not returned. My Quartermaster-Sergeant had done the same and I was told had been killed. They had wanted to be in the action. Only one officer had got back - Max Taylor - who had flown in on the second day with the gunners. All the rest were missing. Their quarters were empty. I went round the Sergeant's huts - empty bunks with some of the survivors sitting by them, shocked and silent by the enormity of the losses. I tried to find out what had happened. Reggie was missing. Some said he had got to the river. Hamish, it seemed certain, had been shot, down by the church. Spud Murphy had been killed and Rory had gone out night after night to avenge him but on the last night had not returned. Howard Hemingway, they said had been taken prisoner and shot while trying to escape. The sense of shock at the losses is something that stayed with me for a very long time. I hoped that some had been wounded, taken prisoner, or escaped. I found out that Arthur had been wounded a second time in the leg but got across the river and was in hospital.

All the survivors were sent on fourteen days leave. I was flown to the aerodrome near my home which I had left just three weeks before. Somehow I couldn't take it in that I was home. I couldn't sleep at first. I kept hearing the bursting shells and mortars and seeing the corpses lying on the ground. I tried to lead a normal life. At the end of the fortnight I was able to go back to duty but my memory for the next few months was very confused. I suppose it must have been the result of the concussion from the explosions.

CHAPTER 24

When my leave was over I returned to Brize only to find that my squadron together with the RAF, had moved to Earls Colne, an airfield near Colchester in Essex. We still had the same tug crews from 296 and 297 Squadrons but their Albemarles had been replaced by four-engined Halifax tugs which had more power and range.

It was now apparent that the losses in the Regiment had been so heavy that there would not be enough army pilots to make up the deficiency. There were however a large number of RAF pilots who had finished their training in the Empire Flying Schools and were waiting to be posted to operational squadrons, but here there were many more pilots than vacancies in the squadrons. After a good deal of lobbying by Colonel Chatterton, the Air Ministry agreed, somewhat grudgingly, that these pilots could be asked to volunteer to become glider pilots. This was not at all what the pilots had joined the RAF for but, as it seemed the only way they would see any action before the war ended, a large number did join the Regiment. They then had to learn to fly gliders which many thought would be a *doddle* until they realised they had no engines! What was more, after landing they would have to fight on the ground as soldiers.

In general squadrons were made up of half army and half RAF pilots. It worked very well. I had a Flight Lieutenant as my Second-in-Command. Two flights were commanded by Captains and two by Flight Lieutenants.

I had a new Adjutant - Mackenzie - known of course as Mac.

He was a dapper little Scot from one of the Highland Regiments, a good disciplinarian and able to cope with the paper-work. He had a tremendous capacity for booze which never seemed to do him any harm. I found him a delightful and amusing companion and off duty we had many happy sessions together.

A few weeks after we arrived at Earls Colne, Paddy O'Leary and James Broxton turned up. They had taken off on the Sunday but over Holland had run into cloud and the ensuing turbulence caused the tow rope to part. However they made a successful landing with their load of South Staffs in occupied territory south of the Rhine. Paddy reported to me what had happened:

"Straight after we landed we were surrounded by excited Dutchmen who were sure we had come to liberate them. I quickly told them this was not the idea at all. We were then handed over to the Dutch Underground who took us away whilst the Germans, who had seen the glider land, arrived and set about burning it. We had landed near a village just North of Tilburg. A little later we were joined by a party of Gunners who had also force landed. Then some American parachutists turned up. We were now a party nearly 100 strong. I wanted to fight our way to the Allied lines in the corridor, but some of our party were not too keen on this and I was overruled." Here Paddy looked crestfallen and I knew he'd have been happy to take on the enemy single handed if only his fellow soldiers would have let him. He went on, "The Dutch now hid us in the community centre at Drunen and later moved us to a lunatic asylum in Elshout. This was our home for several weeks. It was a bit dicey. Germans were billeted on the ground floor and were only kept from us by the very brave Brother Superior who told them that there was an outbreak of diptheria in the upper floors where we were housed. This scared them stiff. The Germans were peeling potatoes for their men while the brothers added a few more which were diverted for our use. It was quite amusing Sir, to have the Germans peeling potatoes for us." Paddy's blue eyes twinkled mischievously.

"Finally we made contact with the 51st Highland Division and it was decided that we should break out. This we did, and advancing on the village of Boxtel found the Germans had already fled. The following day the Scots arrived and we were evacuated. Well I'm sorry Sir, we didn't quite make Arnhem but we bumped off a few Jerries and caused a certain amount of mayhem amongst them. You know Sir, those Dutch people, they're very brave. I'll not forget them." It was a sentiment with which I fully agreed.

As soon as I had heard Paddy and James Broxton's story I sent them off on fourteen days leave. It was great to have them back, but I now heard that Reggie had been drowned. His body was found some distance downstream from the crossing point. Whether he tried to use the inflatable belt which had saved my life I shall never know. He was one of my oldest friends from the days in Barrow when we went out on pub crawls and chatted up the girls, that holiday in Europe just before the war, through France, Dunkirk and then D Day - now he was no more. Like Julia he was another victim of this devastating war.

Julian Westlake and Jeremy Jackson were Prisoners of War. Tommy Geary who had brought in Major Cain VC on the second day, was back. In addition it now seemed certain that Hamish, Rory and Howard had been killed as well as a number of my staff-sergeants and sergeants. How many more? Not surprisingly Mac and I spent much time in the bar, trying to drown our sorrows but without much success as thoughts of Julia and Reggie kept flashing back through my mind.

Although no one liked to admit it at the time, it became clear that operation *Market Garden* had failed in its main objective to open a way to the Ruhr, the heartland of the German war industry, and so shorten the war. It was true that holding the north bank of the Lower Rhine for 9 days had helped XXX Corps to reach and cross the Waal, but their hold on the land between the two rivers had to be abandoned as their lines of supply were tenuous and overstretched.

The problem was a logistic one. By September, there were in America many new divisions trained and equipped with heavy weapons and ready to go, but there was no means of landing them in north-west Europe. Although the ports of Boulogne, Calais and Le Havre had been captured by the Canadians in September, the approaches to them had been mined by the Germans and the port installations so damaged by the Allied bombing, as to make them of little immediate value. The prize was Antwerp with its heavy cranes and enormous handling capacity. It had been captured, almost intact, at the beginning of September but was virtually useless as the Germans continued to command the seaward approaches. The Canadians, who had been given the task of opening those approaches via the Scheldt estuary, were denied the forces required, partly because so many troops were tied up on *Market Garden* but also because Antwerp was not given the priority by the Allied command that it merited. As a result it took some 85 days before the approaches through the various islands were cleared and it was the end of November before the first Allied convoy could enter the port.

We now realised that as a result of the failure of our operations in September the Germans, who had been reeling from the Allied onslaught since D Day, gained time to reorganise their defences. Sadly it seemed that many lives had been lost in a gallant operation which, given better planning and reasonable luck, might have succeeded.

Earls Colne airfield, before we arrived, had been occupied by two bomber squadrons of the U.S. Eighth Air Force, and we were able to make use of much of their accommodation. The airfield was situated on the Marks Hall estate which was a traditional estate, mentioned in the Domesday book and owned by the Markshall family for 500 years. The mansion, an imposing building dating from 1609, was used as the Headquarters and housed the officers. The whole area was famous for its woodlands, the trees of which now bordered the aircraft dispersal areas. Altogether it was a very pleasant arboreal setting for an airfield and not too far from the village of Coggeshall and the city of Colchester. These two places gave my pilots plenty of opportunities for R and R (Rest and Relaxation) which generally entailed visiting the pubs and making friends with the locals.

Paddy O'Leary was a born countryman and when off duty patrolled the woods with an American carbine he had come by, in the hope of bagging a rabbit, a hare or even a pheasant to improve our wartime rations. As Christmas was approaching it was essential to replenish the Station's stock of liquor which, being rationed, was in short supply. We had heard that there were liberal stocks in Belfast so the Station Commander agreed that a Halifax should be organised to carry out a training cross country flight to Belfast. When it arrived the crew were instructed to purchase what liquor they could. This they did and when the Halifax returned and the bottles were stacked on the shelves in the bar, they made a goodly show.

Christmas 1944 was cold and frosty. The day before Christmas Eve the freezing fog was down to the ground and flying was cancelled so the station got the 'Stand Down' and three days Christmas leave was granted. Within half an hour everyone had vanished. The place was deserted. I decided that, as Julia had died, I could not face a leave without her so I let the other officers go and I remained as duty officer. Paddy found that it would take too long to get home to Ireland so he also decided to stay. As a result he and I were the only glider pilots left on the station.

After lunch, as I was going to my quarters, I heard the noise of aircraft overhead. Presently a Halifax appeared out of the fog and landed. It was followed by another and then still more. They turned out to be two Canadian squadrons of Bomber Command who were returning from a mission over Germany and, as their home station in Lincolnshire was completely fog bound, they had been diverted to us.

They were nice lads, very young, the eldest a veteran of 21. Having fixed up accommodation for them in vacant bunks, they came down to the mess, had a meal and then started drinking in the now well stocked bar. I was pleased to see them and told them how their engineers had saved our lives by their heroic efforts to ferry us across the Rhine. They were not so interested in this but they were interested in Paddy with his Irish brogue and many drinks were bought for him. Both Paddy and I had a good capacity for beer but knew when to stop. Not so these boys. They went on and on and the noise reached a crescendo as everyone tried to make his neighbour hear what they were saying.

Eventually Paddy and I retired to the anteroom where we stood warming our backsides at a rather poor fire. Suddenly two of our visitors, who must have gone outside to relieve themselves, appeared at the door. They were very drunk but quiet. With an air of deliberation they walked slowly and came to a swaying halt beside us. One of them was carrying a frozen, dead rabbit, from the middle of which dangled a piece of brass wire. It had obviously been caught in a snare and they had picked it up. They placed the rabbit on the mantelpiece behind us where it began to drip, and then went into conference. They were so drunk they were speechless but understood each other perfectly in dumb show. They looked at the fire, they looked at the rabbit, they looked at us and so we moved to one side, they took down the rabbit and tried to remove the snare.

Their hands missed the target each time and it was beginning to make me dizzy when Paddy came to the rescue and loosened the wire. The first young drunk, a downy moustache just beginning to show on his upper lip, nodded his head with great satisfaction. The second drunk, who had left the room, re-appeared with a great shining twelve-inch cook's knife in his hand which he had found in the kitchen. Paddy, alarmed, moved forward but then we saw the young pilot was going to skin the rabbit. This interested us and we stood back to watch the show. The knife made several circles in the air and I thought he was going to cut the rabbit's head off but no, he cut a small piece of skin off one of the legs and held it up.

It upset Paddy to see them so inept. "So much for the Canadian Mounties!" he muttered to me and again went forward to help. In a matter of seconds he had the skin off. Now they had to disembowel the rabbit. Again the knife circled in the air and plunged haphazardly into the rabbit's stomach. Most of the innards and the blood fell on the smoking fire. It smelt terrible and Paddy and I retreated hastily to the bar, laughing and wondering what they would do next. It was both macabre and compulsive.

When we got back a third drunk had appeared and they had put him on a chair in front of the fire with the head of a broom under him. At the other end they'd hung the mangled remains of the rabbit so that it could roast over the fire. The fire having had a dose of rabbit entrails was in no mood for roasting but the young pilots persisted. Again Paddy and I retired to the bar to finish our drinks and returned 10 minutes later. The young drunks now expected the rabbit to be cooked. It was still raw but warm which encouraged them and they were going to eat it, come what may. What warm raw rabbit tastes like I shall never know. They offered us a portion but we pleaded we were not hungry and returned once again to the bar for the rest of the evening.

Late the following morning they appeared at breakfast apparently none the worse for the previous night's diet of raw rabbit and beer.

Christmas Day was frosty. There had been some snow showers in the night and now the trees sparkled in the clear sunlight. Although the station would have been empty had it not been for the Canadians, the cooks made a valiant effort for a Christmas dinner with what trimmings could be obtained in this our sixth year of rationing. Rabbit was served beside the tinned turkey, which both Paddy and I refused.

On Boxing Day, the Canadians returned to Lincolnshire and the day after everyone returned from leave and life at Earls Colne went back to normal.

We now had to convert the RAF pilots on to gliders and to train them to be soldiers. My pilots who had returned were all good soldiers and were able to introduce the RAF boys into the pleasures of P.T., run marches, crawling on their bellies through undergrowth and firing a rifle at a target at the end of it. Although there were some protests most of the RAF made good and became excellent soldiers. Paddy was a good instructor and I put him in charge of the training.

There were other changes afoot. James Broxton was posted away and Paddy and Max Naylor were the only ones of my original officers left. Three new Army Officers were posted in. They had done their flying training but had not been on any operations and were a little diffident when put in charge of my pilots, many of whom had been on two or even three operations.

As we now had Halifax tugs some of us were converted to fly the Hamilcar. I had some flights in this massive glider capable of carrying a light tank and found it remarkably pleasant to fly.

Just before Christmas I had been ordered to send a party of pilots to join the GPR in India. I had picked some of my best N.C.O.s together with my Sergeant-Major. I now heard that a Dakota carrying some of my party had crashed in the Pyrenees, killing, amongst others, the Sergeant-Major who had done so well at Arnhem and earned himself a Military Medal. The death toll seemed never ending.

It was not only the military setback at Arnhem that failed to shorten the war. Around the same time, the politicians were making mistakes.

The American government had made a plan for the future of Germany when she had been defeated by the Allies. It was known as the Morgenthau Plan after its author, the American Secretary to the Treasury. The plan made it clear that after the unconditional surrender which would be demanded, Germany would be reduced to: "a country primarily agricultural and pastoral in its character". Its heavy industries and mines would be destroyed and as an industrial nation it would never be able to rise again to threaten the world. This vindictive plan was supported by Roosevelt and Churchill but was strongly opposed by certain members of the American government as a "plan of blind vengeance" which would entirely wreck the European economy. In the autumn, for some reason, the details of the plan appeared in the American Press, much to the annoyance of the President as it played into the hands of Dr Goebbels who, for once, no longer had to distort the news for the sake of his propaganda. It reinforced what he had always been saying, that defeat would mean the slavery of the German people, and it strengthened their resolve to fight on whatever the cost. It gave Hitler the incentive to have one more *putsch* which his intuition told him would win the war in his favour. As a result, in December he launched an unexpected offensive in the Ardennes which breached the American defences and was aimed at the recapture of the port of Antwerp. If it had not been for General *'Blood and Guts'* Patten and Field-Marshal Montgomery it might well have succeeded.

On the day before Christmas Eve when Paddy and I were roasting rabbits with the Canadian pilots, the 6th Airborne Division, who were looking forward to their Christmas leave, suddenly received the order to move at once to southern Belgium to counter attack the German Ardennes offensive. After severe fighting the German advance was stopped and the position stabilised. The Division was then sent back to Salisbury Plain to train for what was now to be the final assault on the Reich.

At first I was given little information about this operation except that instead of mass landing exercises, our training was to be concentrated on spot landings.

About the middle of March, I was asked to select four gliders and crews for an exercise named *Token*. I was not told anything about it but was to send the crews which were under Captain Max Naylor to Group HQ for briefing. They returned, very secretive, with Max refusing to give me any details of what they were going to do. However Paddy, who was sharing a room with Max, soon found out. Max told him they were to carry sidearms, 50 rounds of ammunition, parachutes and Mae Wests. Obviously no ordinary *exercise*. They took off the following day together with three crews from G Squadron and returned that evening. It later became clear that they had flown over the route to be taken by the coming operation. Why this was necessary was never disclosed, but it must have alerted the Germans to the fact that an airborne operation was being planned and there is no doubt that on the day they certainly expected us.

Details of the operation were now starting to come in and I was called to Wing HQ for briefing on what was to be called *Varsity*. The British 6th Airborne Division, now commanded by Major General Bols, and the 17th U.S. Airborne Division would be taking part. The former would be flying from airfields in East Anglia and the Americans from airfields round Paris. The Glider Pilot Regiment would be fully stretched supplying pilots for the British Airborne Division.

21st Army Group, which was poised on the west bank of the Rhine, would cross the river after a heavy artillery barrage and aerial bombing had obliterated the town of Wesel and, hopefully, the enemy artillery. The following day gliders and paratroops of the XVIII American Airborne Corps which now included the 6th British Airborne Division, would land and drop to the east of the Rhine to clear any remaining opposition on the high ground known as the Diersfordter Wald and secure the bridges over the river Issel and the town of Hamminkeln.

This time we were to avoid some of the mistakes made at Arnhem. We were to land individually on top of our objectives, so there would be no long march from the LZ to the battle ground. The whole airborne army would land in a matter of a couple of hours, with no loss of surprise by landing over several days. This time the ground forces would have crossed the river some hours before we landed - no waiting for them to arrive. All this was fine but it meant it had to be a daylight flight and depended on the ability of the Allied airforces to prevent any interference from the Luftwaffe and, also, we were promised that any anti-aircraft weapons on the LZs and DZs would be liquidated by the time we arrived by the attacks of our rocket-firing Typhoons.

CHAPTER 25

The 14th March 1945 was my birthday. I was 33. Shortly afterwards the camp was sealed and briefing for the operation began. It was a very thorough briefing since each glider was landing on a spot selected acording to the troops being carried and therefore the pilot needed to know what his individual task would be. Excellent air photographs had been provided and we could see exactly where we were to land.

As in Holland I had two flights with me. 20 Flight was commanded by Paddy because Douglas was still listed as missing, though we knew he had been taken prisoner and would not be surprised if he escaped. 4 Flight was commanded by an RAF Flight Lieutenant, who in civilian life was an artist. He had made one or two sketches of me including a caricature with the Irish briar, a long knobbly stick which Paddy had given me and which I used on parade. I put Max Naylor in charge of the other two flights as he was the most experienced and would also be good on the ground after they had landed. One of his flights was commanded by one of the new army Lieutenants and the other by Ken, the Flight Lieutenant who was now my Second-in-Command. Many of the tug crews had been with us since Stoney Cross and where possible towed the same glider pilots. This time we would be carrying the 53rd A/L Light Regiment RA.

Detailed briefing commenced three days before *D-D*ay which was set for Saturday the 24th March. Loading of gliders commenced on the Thursday. The final briefing of tug crews and glider pilots was on Friday evening by which time all the maps and photos had been issued. As my squadron was carrying the gunners, we were given the precise positions where they wanted their guns and command posts to be landed. I was carrying the Battery Captain so had to get him as near to his HQ as possible

At the final briefing I was surprised to see some important VIPs present. These included The Secretary of State for Air, Sir Archibald Sinclair and Air Chief Marshal Sir Arthur Tedder who had been Deputy Supreme Commander under Eisenhower ever since D-Day. Tedder gave us a short talk in which he said that the RAF would have dealt with the light Ack Ack on the LZ before we arrived and that the Luftwaffe would not be present. On the latter point it turned out he was correct but not on the former. Sir Archibald Sinclair then gave us a pep talk on how important the operation was. After that we all returned to the bar and the party became rather merry. It must have been nearly midnight when the Air Chief Marshal approached me and said, rather sternly: "You have work to do tomorrow my boy. You had better go to bed." As reveille was at 0400 hrs I had to agree and went.

I doubt if I had had much sleep before Foxley woke me with the usual cup of tea. Breakfast was at 0430 hrs and at 0530 hrs a final brief to check if there was any change in the plan or the Met forecast and at 0615 hrs I went down to the tow path. Arthur, now returned from hospital, was flying his own glider as first pilot on this operation, so I had an RAF Flying Officer, George Telman, as my co-pilot. I was flying a MkII Horsa which was a modified version of the MkI which I had flown on the Arnhem operation. The nose section was hinged so that after landing it could be swung to one side allowing the load to drive straight out. At least that was the theory!

George closed the door of the glider, the tug took up the slack in the rope and we were off. Forming up over the airfield I was able to see that all my gliders were safely airborne. We crossed the coast of France by Cap Gris Nez where there were tremendous bomb craters caused by our onslaught on the V1 sites and the cross Channel guns. On to Béthune - the country below looking very quiet - then Lille, Tournai and looking down on the little village where we spent a couple of nights before the retreat to Dunkirk in 1940. What a long time ago it seemed.

There was no cloud and we were in brilliant sunshine with visibility of 5 to 8 miles. All around us was the great fleet of aircraft as far as the eye could see in all directions, with squadrons of fighter aircraft weaving about above and below us. It was the largest and greatest Armada of aircraft of all time and a sight always to be remembered.

As we approached the Rhine on which I could see no movement of shipping, a great pall of smoke appeared on the far side covering our objectives. There were several crashed Dakotas on our side of the Rhine and, as my tug pilot told me later: "I saw a lot of very frightened looking Daks streaking out of the smoke like bats out of hell and I said to my crew - this is it chaps."

On my LZ 'P', there was a very prominent small square-shaped wood, code-named *Bunty*, near which I was to land, but it was entirely obscured by the smoke. Luckily our run in and release point was clear and I blessed the pilot of the Mosquito who had taken the oblique photographs which showed me where we were before I had to cast off. When we were over the release point I said cheerio to my tug pilot, thanked him for the tow and hoped he would get home safely, pulled the release and flew towards the railway which I could still just see. After that we were flying completely blind in the smoke and haze. I had worked out previously the flight path from the release point and followed it on the compass, turning through 90 degrees to starboard after the time I had calculated would get me to my objective. Suddenly another glider appeared out of the murk and I had to dive to 140 mph to avoid it. I then cut the speed back to 85 but there was still no sight of the ground. At about 200 feet I saw the tops of some high tension power lines and I knew I was going in the right direction and could just see the ground. However, as I was preparing to land, I saw some low tension cables or telephone wires on posts below me. There was no time to take avoiding action so I ploughed straight into them hoping they would break. They did break but in so doing caused the glider to stall about 20 ft up so that we landed heavily and the front of the glider was damaged, but no one was injured.

The first troops I saw were some U.S. medicals and paratroops and I was sure I had overshot by miles and was in the American Zone. However as the smoke cleared a little I was able to see *Bunty* and realised I had landed very close to my correct position. Considering I had been flying blind from 2000 feet I thought it not a bad show, although perhaps not as good as my pilots on the Orne bridges who had done it from 6000 feet and in the dark.

So far there was no enemy fire. Had we landed 100 yards further on we should have been raked by one of several of the 88mm guns which had NOT been eliminated by the Typhoons. These guns accounted for most of the casualties in the air and on the ground. As the front of the glider was damaged and would not open we had to unload by the tail. George had a terrible time getting the tail off as the bolts were jammed and they had to resort to sawing through the timber to get it off. Bullets had now started to arrive. One of the gunners managed to set up his Bren behind one of the wheels of the glider, and returned the fire whilst George and the rest of us eventually managed to remove the tail. The Battery Captain got the jeep out and drove off with his men.

I now started to look for the farmhouse which I had selected as my Headquarters. I soon found it as it was not far away and was joined there by two of my pilots. I ordered them to put the house in a state of defence against a counterattack which I expected might come at any moment.

Outside the house, on the ground, leaning up against the fence was a soldier. Thinking he was asleep, I went over to him to tell him to rouse himself and not lie about doing nothing. Then I realised he was dead - shot through the head by a bullet, with a smile on his face, frozen as he died.

As I was standing there, looking down at the soldier, a woman emerged from the farmhouse, obviously the *Bauenfrau*, and started to scream at me in German, presumably complaining about the soldiers taking over her house. My knowledge of German was pretty rudimentary but I was furious, shaken by seeing the dead soldier outside her house.

I shouted back at her: "Das ist deine Krieg - this is your bloody war. You started it. If we want to use your house we jolly well will."

The woman calmed down and we continued with taking over the house, knocking out the glass in the windows and moving the furniture to act as cover as we had done in Oosterbeek.

George came up to me. "There are some pigeons in the loft, Sir. I wonder if they are carriers, taking messages. Should we kill them?"

"Yes. Maybe as well," I replied.

Shortly afterwards a small boy aged between 4 or 5 appeared clutching a pigeon and, with tears in his eyes, was obviously trying to say "Please don't kill my pet". I really couldn't believe they could do any harm, so cancelled the order. The relief on that child's face was something to atone for the horrors of war.

We had just settled down in the house when Arnold Bradshaw came to the door.

"I'm very sorry to have to tell you Sir, but Captain Naylor has been killed. He was digging a slit trench when a mortar got him."

"Where is he?" I asked

"Just up the road."

"Very well. I'll come."

Arnold and I went up the road towards Hamminkeln. There was some shelling and small arms fire but it was comparatively quiet.

Max had been laid on his back in a shallow grave. His smock with the glider pilot wings looking as if he had just come off parade. He wore no flying helmet or beret and his blonde hair shone in the sunlight. There wasn't a mark on him

"It must have been the blast what killed him. Like those poor buggers in the slit trenches by the tennis courts at Hartenstein," said Arnold grimly.

I stooped and looked at my friend. He appeared serene and peaceful. Another of my original officers gone. It all seemed so pointless. I would have to write to the family. I had written so many of those letters.

All of us in the T.A. had volunteered for this, Max included. What would have happened if we had not joined? Max would have been....? All supposition. If. If. But now it was real. Max had had a premonition that he would not survive this, his third operation. Paddy had been in the hut when he was writing his last letter to his mother. He had said he doubted whether he would ever see her again. And now it had happened but he was at rest and those of us who were left had to carry on.

I returned to the house with a heavy heart.

There I found we had accumulated a number of prisoners who we accommodated in the pig houses, which seemed the easiest place to keep them under guard. Meanwhile I instructed Paddy, who had just arrived, to collect as much food as he could, and water which we had been so short of at Arnhem. He detailed Percival, one of his men, to look for eggs. Percival was not a countryman and came back shortly in great glee with a bucketful of eggs. Paddy told him sourly he wouldn't get very fat on them. They were *pot* ones.

That night we were dug in round the farm listening for the sounds of an attack. An enemy aircraft flew low over our position and came back. Paddy, ready as always to wipe out the enemy single handed wanted to engage it with his Bren. I told him not to as the chances of damaging the aircraft were minimal and by giving our position away would have brought all hell down on us. I had no desire to lose any more men unless it was really necessary.

Next morning as the opposition seemed to have been eliminated, I went round the LZ. It was a mass of smashed and burnt out gliders. In one which appeared to have made a perfect landing, the pilots and all the troops were dead, still sitting in their seats. The glider had been raked from end to end by a machine gun just after it landed.

Shortly after midday we heard the roar of approaching aircraft and a squadron of Liberators appeared low over the trees, dropping hampers of supplies. They were so low we could see the pilots waving to us. What a difference to those heroic pilots who tried so hard to drop supplies to us at Oosterbeek.

Later Colonel Murray who was now commanding all the British Glider Pilots on the operation, came to our position to tell me that 21st Army Group had crossed the river on the night of 24/25 March, according to plan, and had occupied the Diersdorfer Wald. Their armour was now over the river and was pressing into Germany. Then we heard the unmistakable noise of tanks. Surely we weren't going to be attacked by Panzers? Then they appeared. The Sherman tanks of the Guards Armoured Division. What a wonderful sight. It brought a lump into my throat to see them as they roared past and to realise that they were now advancing into Germany.

So *Varsity* was over. For me it had not involved any fighting. The guns had been delivered and we had guarded the prisoners who we now handed over to the Americans. Then the orders came to withdraw. I collected as many of my pilots as I could and we marched towards the river, through the woods where there was a large party of prisoners in charge of an American, who surely must have been a cowboy. He was stripped to the waist with a carbine cradled in his arm and riding a horse bareback, probably thinking he was herding a bunch of steers back home. Next we crossed the Rhine by a floating bridge constructed by the Engineers and were taken by lorries to a camp where we were supplied with showers, NAAFI and all the luxuries of army life. After that we were taken to Louvain where once again a fleet of Dakotas flew us home.

There have been many arguments as to whether *Varsity* should have taken place. Was it worth landing airborne troops after the river had been crossed to build up the impetus of the advance? Was it taking too much of a risk to land gliders and paratroops on top of the enemy when it could not be guaranteed that their guns had been eliminated? Then there was the smoke and dust from the bombardment, which had not been expected. It made it difficult for the attacking Typhoons and bombers to see their targets but more important was the decision to withdraw them ten minutes before zero hour when the main stream of gliders and parachute aircraft were due to arrive - just long enough to allow the German gunners, who had survived, to recover and cause havoc amongst the slow flying tug aircraft and gliders. I had had a number of casualties amongst my pilots but I still think the smoke and haze which obscured the ground saved many gliders from being shot up when in the air. A well trained pilot should be able to land under those conditions and many did. However the operation, as a whole, did succeed and the march into Germany had begun.

CHAPTER 26

Shortly after we returned from *Varsity* the squadron left Earls Colne and moved to Blakehill Farm, an airfield near Chippenham. Training continued as there was a possibility of another operation. There was talk of one even larger than *Varsity*, code name *Arena*. This was to land troops near Kassel, seize airfields and fly in infantry ahead of the Allied armies who were striking at the heart of Germany from behind the Ruhr. The advance of the British and American forces was so rapid that this operation became redundant. A second one, code named *Eclipse,* was intended to ensure the capture of Berlin before the Russians got there. The Yalta conference which produced the deal between the big powers to split Berlin into three sectors, meant that this operation also had to be cancelled.

There was still action by airborne troops, mostly American, in the Far East and the Pacific. The Regiment had a flight of glider pilots in India including the survivors of those I had sent when my Sergeant Major had been killed.

Douglas Cameron had now rejoined the squadron. After he had been wounded by the mortar bomb in the gardens near the Hartenstein tennis courts, he had been taken to the St. Elizabeth Hospital in Arnhem. As he was classed as walking wounded, he was transferred to a train with hundreds of other prisoners en route to Germany. This didn't suit Douglas at all, and seizing a suitable opportunity he leapt from the train, avoiding being seen by the guard, and landed in a ditch. He hid for a couple of days and was then picked up by the Dutch underground who looked after him for several months until they were able to get him across the river and home. He telephoned Earls Colne the day before *Varsity* which, of course he did not know about, and was rather mystified when told by Mac to take 14 days leave forthwith. However he had now returned and I was very pleased to have him back. He and Paddy were now the only ones of my original officers in the squadron.

From what we heard it seemed that the war in Europe would soon be over. On the 7th of May the news was broadcast that Germany had surrendered unconditionally to Field-Marshal Montgomery on Luneberg Heath. The following day VE-Day commenced. There were tremendous celebrations. The black out came down. The lights went on. The Church bells rang out in joy. There was dancing in the streets and squares, the pubs ran out of beer. Everywhere feelings were euphoric. Mac and I celebrated it in Chippenham where there was a massive party in the Town Hall and everyone was dancing in the town square. I think it is a memory which will stay with me and everyone who experienced it, in contrast to the dark years of war.

But there was still a cloud on the horizon - Japan. The war in Burma and the Pacific was still raging. I knew that with my age and length of service I should be high on the list for demobilization but there was always the chance that I might be sent out East. When the bombs were dropped on Hiroshima and Nagasaki, that problem was solved for me and for many others and many thousands of lives of those fighting the Japs or mouldering in their prison camps were saved.

The celebrations for VJ-Day in August were less exuberant than those for VE-Day. Now, for most of us who were not regular servicemen or women, it was a question of waiting for *Demob*. This was unlikely to be before the end of the year and there was still several months to go. The question for me was how to keep the squadron occupied now that there were no operations in the offing and glider flying was being curtailed. To break the monotony, I hit on the idea of forming a training camp by the sea to which parties of pilots would go for two or three weeks at a time.

I told Paddy to arrange this and he set off for Devon. Not far from Ilfracombe he found an ideal site in the country and set up a tented camp. It was a very suitable area for run marches, swimming and other forms of physical exercise. We called it Watermouth camp.

I flew down in my Tiger Moth to Chivenor which was the nearest airfield. Paddy met me and drove me to the camp. It certainly was a pleasant enough site, surrounded by trees, with a stream for washing and an inlet not far away for swimming. I had arranged for a couple of trucks to be available to take the lads into town. We found that Ilfracombe happened to be the Headquarters of the Army Pay Office and was staffed by a large number of ATS who were delighted at the influx of soldiers with whom they were pleased to fraternise. The camp may not have met with War Office approval but it was certainly popular with the Squadron.

I flew back to Blakehill Farm and after supper and a few drinks in the Mess went to my room.

VJ-Day had come and gone. I sat down to think. Had I failed as a soldier? I hadn't *killed* anyone and surely that was what I had been trained to do. If an enemy had appeared in front of me, would I have fired my pistol or my sten gun or used my fighting knife? If it were a question of survival. Yes, I would. But if it were not? Would I?

I had survived. But was survival what was required? I had not stood out in the open as some of the other officers had. I had thought them foolhardy but realised that their action had been an example to the troops, boosting their morale. I had trained my pilots well and had led them successfully to the battle. But was that enough? I had been afraid. As an officer it was my duty not to show that fear. I had tried not to but we were all afraid. I had obeyed orders when confusion and mistakes seemed to be behind what we were asked to do. I could not agree with blind obedience. Neither could I agree with disobedience for that would not have worked. Perhaps it was Dunkirk which shattered my illusions and made me respect individuality and initiative, to be well trained and alert. These were my men.

But so many of them had died. I had wanted to conserve life, to make the losses less. Was I still too much of a civilian pretending, albeit proudly, to be an officer in the T.A.? I wanted to be a civilian again for I was not a regular soldier and I did not want to be. The war was over.

For those, and they were in the majority, who were not in the Regular Army or did not wish to stay on, the next stage was 'demob' and return to civilian life. The thousands involved could not all go at once although they might have wished to. It had to be done in an orderly fashion and this was based on age and service. I was 33 and had been in the service since 1930 so my number was soon to turn up.

By December I had received my papers and knew where I was to go to get my free 'demob' suit, which included a hat and shoes. I also received a letter from the War Office which released me from active military duty. It read:

"Now that the time has come for your release from active military duty, I am commanded by the Army Council to express to you their thanks for the valuable service which you have rendered in the service of your country at a time of grave national emergency."

"At the end of the emergency a notification will appear in the London Gazette (Supplement), granting you the honorary rank of Major. Meanwhile, you have permission to use that rank with effect from the date of your release."

It was nice to be thanked but it felt like an anti-climax.

The Squadron arranged a farewell party for me at which they made a presentation of a magnificent silver tankard with a horn handle, something which must have been very difficult to obtain but which I suspected had been organised by one of my new officers who had connections in the City. I got rather drunk that night, but not so much that I could not get to my quarters without assistance. Sitting on my bed, I read the inscription on the tankard:

"From a happy and grateful Squadron to a great leader and a good scout".

Tears came into my eyes. I thought of those friends who had helped to mould my squadron into a band of brothers and had not come back - Reggie, Hamish, Rory, Howard, Max and then Julia and so many others. Why them and not me? It seemed so unfair.

In the morning there was a telegram - "Father seriously ill. Come home at once". The Station Commander arranged for an aircraft to fly me home.

John Clayton was sinking fast. He was lying in bed very frail but pleased to see me. We talked for a short while and he then asked me to give him a shave. No one had thought of doing it. I was pleased that I could do that for him. The doctor came later but told me there was little hope.

Next morning I was answering the telephone. One of my father's friends was saying how sorry he was to hear of my father's condition. He went on and on. Sybil, my eldest sister, came running to me and said, "Come at once. Father is dying".

I cut the telephone conversation short and ran upstairs to my father's room. My mother, Marianna, was holding his hand, Sybil and myself were at his side, and a nurse was spooning brandy into his mouth. His breathing was short and laboured and finally with a sudden rattle it stopped.

And so my father, who had wanted me to be trained well enough to withstand the war, my dearest friend, had like the others, gone to another place. I felt a great sense of loss and sadness.

The funeral was in the village. The British Legion had turned out with their Standard. I, dressed in my uniform, marched solemnly behind the coffin, through the village to the cemetery.

After the burial we went home. Several people arrived to convey their condolences, amongst them a smart young ATS Officer with brown hair and sparkling eyes from a house along the river. I recognised the girl I had fallen in love with, oh so long ago and whom I had wanted to marry before the war began. Now we both had changed.

Not long afterwards we were married. The world was still suffering from the aftermath of war. Rationing remained in force, clothing was scarce, building materials were only obtainable under a licence which was well-nigh impossible to get. New motor cars were on several years waiting lists and petrol was still rationed. The world for which we had fought so hard for six long years was not quite what we had hoped it would be.

IAN TOLER was born in Cheshire in 1912 and commissioned into the Territorial Army in 1930. Educated at Macclesfield Grammar School and after studying physics at Christ Church, Oxford, he spent four years working in the blast furnaces and steel works at Barrow-in-Furness and then at a chemical works in Runcorn.

At the outbreak of WWII, he was appointed Adjutant to an Anti-Tank Regiment and joined the BEF in France, subsequently being evacuated from the beaches near Dunkirk. In 1941 he became a Glider Pilot assigned to the newly-formed Airborne Division. He commanded "B" Squadron which took part in D-Day, the Battle of Arnhem and the final crossing of the Rhine in 1945. He was awarded the DFC and, for long service in the T.A., the TD.

After the war he returned to civilian life, working as an engineer in the chemical industry. He has published a book "Is Science a Dirty Word?" explaining scientific theories and their practise, and has written articles on mustard gas and some of his war experiences. He has four daughters and lives in Cheshire with his wife, Joan.

CELIA TOLER is the youngest daughter of Ian Toler and was born in Cheshire in 1950. After studying at art school, she co-scripted with Maria Holt for a live performance group; she received a Greater London Arts' bursary for writing a play for children; and produced and edited the literary and visual magazine 'RAMP' with Ally Raftery. Recently she has published a book of three stories under the title "Francis' Wife" and writes articles on art and gardening for various magazines. Within this book she has worked as editor. She is married and lives in London.